Synthetic Methods of Organic Chemistry

Volume I

1942-1944

Synthetic Methods of Organic Chemistry

A Thesaurus

by W. THEILHEIMER

Volume I · 1942-1944

With a foreword by T. REICHSTEIN
Translated from the German
by HANS WYNBERG

1948

INTERSCIENCE PUBLISHERS, INC., NEW YORK
INTERSCIENCE PUBLISHERS LTD., LONDON

A translation of W. THEILHEIMER,
Synthetische Methoden der Organischen Chemie, Repertorium I

Printed in the United States of America by New York Lithographing Corp., New York, N. Y.
Composition by Graphic Production Corp. (Emil P. Popp & Son Composition Service),
New York, N. Y.

Foreword

A well-organized system is already in operation for the continued recording of new organic compounds. It consists of volumes appearing periodically (*e.g.*, Beilstein's *Handbuch* and abstracting journals such as *Chemical Abstracts*), and the system has now become indispensable for a chemist working in any branch of the subject. On the other hand, barely the beginnings of a similar system exists for the publication of the actual methods of chemistry. Consequently, it is often very tedious for the research worker and industrial chemist to obtain information concerning the procedures for new syntheses and degradation reactions which are most likely to have a good chance of success. Therefore, it often becomes very difficult for the specialist in a particularly narrow field to complete an unusually difficult reaction. Should he happen to venture into a new field of research he may have to spend valuable time in solving problems that may have been solved by others, but are obscured in the tangled mass of literature.

Of the books on methods available, that of Houben is still the best, although somewhat out of date. However, the enormous difficulties encountered in the preparation of an all-embracing and systematic classification of the matter in hand have not been solved, for much time is often wasted in finding the desired reaction, and the same reaction is often described in different places and in different volumes.

Books on methods which really do meet modern needs exist only in strictly circumscribed fields, *e.g.*, *Newer Methods of Preparative Organic Chemistry* (Interscience, New York), and *Organic Reactions* (Wiley, New York) edited by R. Adams. However, there are no comprehensive periodic supplements of the large collective works and current abstracts, so useful for the recording of compounds.

Dr. Theilheimer has undertaken to fill the gap in question in this series of volumes. He has now encountered two main difficulties, first, in making the correct selection of material, and second, in introducing a classification with sufficient coverage of the subject. A new, truly fundamental method of organic chemistry is discovered, at the most, every ten years. In practice, however, real success often follows decisively significant, although small, variations in a procedure. The determination of what should be considered to be new, and therefore to be included in this series, is largely a matter of personal opinion.

Since a recognized, comprehensive method of classification of chemical reactions does not exist, the author has attempted to arrange and characterize the reactions in question on a purely formal basis by means of symbols. Whether or not this system will endure will depend largely upon its success in actual use. Even if our colleagues do not approve of the symbols, and continue to look up particular reactions in the alphabetic index, this collection of methods, which is to be brought up-to-date periodically, will remain of value.

T. Reichstein

Author's Preface

In the series of volumes beginning with this book there are going to be recorded regularly: new methods for the synthesis of organic compounds, improvements of known methods, and also old proved methods that are now scattered about in the specialized journals and in the original published work. The first volume will deal with the literature of 1942–1944. The second volume will include the works of the years 1945–1946 and the foreign work of the earlier war years published in journals not generally available. Further volumes are expected to follow yearly.

The attempt has been made to develop the system of Weygand (*Organisch-chemische Experimentierkunst,* Barth, Leipzig, 1938), which groups reactions on a less simple, but on a more purely formal, basis. This had led to the invention of reaction symbols that can be classified systematically. It contrasts with the current trivial, or author-naming, method using terms such as "Oxidation" or "Friedel-Crafts reaction." By means of these new reaction symbols, the methods can be traced without knowing the common name—a simplification for the foreign reader in particular. The difficulties on hand make it imperative that the system should not receive a final definition in this volume. Since the material was put together step by step many changes had to be made during the writing of the manuscript. In order not to delay the appearance of the first volume the rearrangement of some of the articles which would have required further extensive changes had to be deferred; cross-references are made in such cases. The system will be improved and completed in the following volumes as the result of further experience and ideas; we will always be grateful for new suggestions. The first volume should therefore be considered as being in the nature of a trial.

Readers who are accustomed to the old classification will find this used in the complete alphabetic index. It is thought that the volumes should be used for immediate reference in the laboratory. They should provide a quick survey of the situation at hand, and obviate the necessity of first searching the entire literature. Syntheses are recorded in the alphabetic index by starting materials and end products, along with the systematic indexing of the methods. Another innovation is the indexing of very complex compounds. General terms, such as synthesis, exchange, and heterocyclics, are especially emphasized.

The articles are limited to what is necessary for an appraisal of the applicability of a desired synthesis. This would include, for instance, the number and nature of the reaction steps, the yield, and the importance of the literature in question. In order to carry out a particular synthesis it is therefore still necessary to have recourse to *Chemical Abstracts* * or other abstracting journals, and also, if possible, to the original papers. To avoid repetition where the same method is applied in similar cases, the actual instance chosen is the one most fully described and giving the best yield. Syntheses that are split up into their various steps and are recorded in different places can be followed with the help of the notations "s.m." and "Prepn."

This book is dedicated in the hope that the material will serve as a useful tool for chemists, especially for the younger ones who still have little experience of their own, also in the hope that the first volume may serve to bring returning veterans and war workers up-to-date in their temporarily abandoned fields.

I should like to thank heartily Dr. H. Erlenmeyer for valuable advice and encouragement, and also Dr. T. Reichstein for the introduction.

Basle, November, 1945. *W. Theilheimer*

Method of Classification

The following directions serve to explain the system of indexing.

Reaction Symbols

The first part of the symbol refers to the chemical bonds formed during the reaction. These bonds appear in the reaction symbols as the symbols for the two elements which have been linked together (*e.g.*, the bond between hydrogen and nitrogen, as HN). The order of the elements is the same as in *Chemisches Zentralblatt* and in Beilstein's *Handbuch der organischen Chemie*: H, O, N, S, Hal (Halogen), and other elements. C is always placed last.

* *PUBLISHER'S NOTE:* In translating this book, references to *Chemisches Zentralblatt* have been changed to corresponding *Chemical Abstracts* references where available.

The "principle of the latest position" determines the order of the element symbols, and is used whenever possible.

The methods of obtaining a particular chemical bond are subdivided according to its method of formation. Four types are distinguished: addition ($\Downarrow$), rearrangement ($\curvearrowright$), exchange ($\Uparrow\!\!\Downarrow$), and elimination ($\Uparrow$).

The next part of the symbol refers to the types of bond which are destroyed in the reaction. As a general rule, only one of the elements that forms the bond is mentioned, namely, the one which (according to the "principle") is last in the above order of elements. In addition reactions the destroyed double bond or ring is shown by two element symbols.

The use of the reaction symbols will be made clearer by the following simplifying stipulations. (1) The chemical bond is rigidly classified according to structural formula, with no consideration of the mechanism of the reaction. (2) Double or triple bonds are treated as being equivalent to two or three single bonds, respectively. (3) Generally speaking, only stable compounds are taken into consideration. Intermediary compounds, such as Grignard compounds and sodiomalonic esters, are therefore not expressed in the reaction symbols.

Examples   Addition of hydrogen bromide to a carbon-to-carbon double bond: Hal C$\Downarrow$CC (HC$\Downarrow$CC).
Beckmann rearrangement: OC$\curvearrowright$ON.
Ketone synthesis by the Friedel-Crafts reaction: CC$\Uparrow\!\!\Downarrow$Hal.
Dehydrogenation: CC$\Uparrow$H.

Systematic Review See page x.

Reagents Used in the Methods
A further subdivision, which cannot be expressed by the reaction symbols, is made on the basis of the reagents used to bring about some of the reactions. The order usually follows that of the periodic classification. Reagents made up of many components are indexed according to the element responsible for the reaction, *e.g.*, $KMnO_4$ under Mn, NaClO under Cl. When a constituent of the reagent goes into the product of the reaction, the remainder of the reagent, which acts as a carrier of this constituent, is the criterion for the classification; for example, phosphorus is the carrier in a chlorination with PCl_5 and sodium in a nitrosation with $NaNO_2$.

The material in this subdivision is arranged with the simple examples first and the more complicated ones following. When changes in several chemical bonds occur during one reaction, as in the formation of a new ring, or if the reaction can be carried out in different ways, it will necessarily be indexed in many places. The main entry in such cases will follow according to the "principle of the latest position"; the other entries will be cross-referenced back to it.

Alphabetic Index

The names of the methods, types of compound, reagents, etc. are classified in the alphabetic index at the end of the book. Individual compounds and individual authors (when a method is not named after them) are found, as usual, in the index of the abstract journals. Very complex compounds, as those with several reactive groups, are referred to under the derived simpler compounds, under the term *"see also"* (*e.g.*, aminocarboxylic acids are found under amines and under carboxylic acids). Methods of synthesis for a given substance are indexed under the name of the substance itself, with *"from"* appended, *e.g.*, carboxylic acids *from* alcohols, hydrocarbons. Syntheses which are carried out from a particular starting material are indexed under the starting material, followed by a subentry, *s.m.*, which represents *starting material for the preparation of* (for example, alcohols, *s.m.* ketones, carboxylic acids).

Generally speaking, classes of compounds are designated by reference to the functional group that is changed during the reaction. A reaction in which an amino alcohol is prepared from an aminocarboxylic acid is therefore indexed under "Alcohols *from* carboxylic acids" or "Carboxylic acids, *s.m.* alcohols." Ring signs may also refer to the corresponding hydrogenated rings, unless the latter are also listed specifically. Greek letters and single letters which are separated from the proper word by a hyphen are not considered to take part in the alphabetic arrangement, *e.g.*, "*O*-Acetyl derivatives" are indexed under "A."

Abbreviations

abs.	absolute	Ex	example	N	normality
alc.	alcoholic	F.e.s.	further examples see	Pr	propionic
aq.	aqueous			prepn.	preparation
Ar.	aromatic	F.m.s.	further methods see	satd.	saturated
asym.	asymmetrical			sec.	secondary
atm.	atmosphere(s)	hr(s).	hour(s)	soln.	solution
Bz	benzene	liq.	liquid	s.m.	starting material
concd.	concentrated	Me	methyl		
d.	density	min.	minutes	sym	symmetrical
dil.	dilute	m.p.	melting point	tert	tertiary
Et	ethyl			Y	yield

Symbols

Addition	⇓	Elimination	⇑	Rearrangement	↻
Electrolysis	⤸	Exchange	⇅	Ring opening	C
				Ring closure	O

Systematic Survey

Reaction symbol	No.	Reaction symbol	No.	Reaction symbol	No.
HO ⇓ HC		OC ↷ NC	154	HalC ⇅ Hal	450–452
HO ⇓ OC		OC ⇅ H	155–173	HalC ⇅ C	453–454
HO ↷		OC ⇅ O	174–184	SS ⇑ H	455
HO ⇅ C	1–14	OC ⇅ N	185–200	SR ⇅ O	456
HO ⇑ O	15–16	OC ⇅ Hal	201–227	SC ⇓ CC	457–459
HN ⇓ NN	17–19	OC ⇅ S	228–233	SC ⇅ H	460–465
HN ⇓ NC		OC ⇅ C	234–244	SC ⇅ O	466–469
HN ↷		OC ⇑ H	245	SC ⇅ N	470
HN ⇅ O	20–30	OC ⇑ O	246	SC ⇅ Hal	471–496
HN ⇅ N		OC ⇑ N	247	OL ⇑ Hal	497
HN ⇅ C	31–37	OC ⇑ Hal	248	RC ⇓ CC	498–500
HS ⇅ C	38	OC ⇑ C	249–250	RC ⇅ N	501
HC ⇓ OC	39–50	NN ⇅ O	251–265	RC ⇅ Hal	502–507
HC ⇓ NC	51–54	NN ⇅ N	266	CC ⇓ OC	508–521
HC ⇓ CC	55–62	NHal ⇅ H	267	CC ⇓ NC	522–525
HC ↷		NS ⇅ O	268	CC ⇓ CC	526–536
HC ⇅ O	63–82	NS ⇅ Hal	269–276	CC ↷ OC	537–538
HC ⇅ N	83–92	NC ⇓ NN		CC ↷ CC	539–541
HC ⇅ Hal	93–102	NC ⇓ OC	277–279	CC ⇅ H	
HC ⇅ S	103	NC ⇓ NC	280–288	CC ⇅ O	542–603
HC ⇅ C	104	NC ⇓ CC	289–292	CC ⇅ N	604–622
HC ⇑ O	105–110	NC ↷	293	CC ⇅ Hal	623–712
HC ⇑ C	111–113	NC ⇅ H	294–295	CC ⇅ S	713–714
ON ⇅ H	114	NC ⇅ O	296–356	CC ⇅ C	715–718
OS ⇓ S	115–120	NC ⇅ N	357–363	CC ⇑ H	719–732
OS ⇅ Hal	121–125	NC ⇅ Hal	364–385	CC ⇑ O	733–764
OR ⇓ OC	126	NC ⇅ C	386–390	CC ⇑ N	765–767
OR ⇅ Hal	127	NC ⇑ H	391	CC ⇑ Hal	768–781
OC ⇓ HC	128–131	NC ⇑ O	392–397	CC ⇑ S	
OC ⇓ OO	132	NC ⇑ S	398–401	CC ⇑ C	782–785
OC ⇓ OC	133–134	HalS ⇅ O	402	Het ⇓ N	786–789
OC ⇓ NC	135	HalC ⇓ CC	403–407	Het ⇓ S	790
OC ⇓ CC	136–149	HalC ⇅ H	408–419	Het ⇅	791–792
OC ↷ HC	150–152	HalC ⇅ O	420–437		
OC ↷ ON	153	HalC ⇅ N	438–449		

Formation of H—O Bond by:

Addition

Addition to Hydrogen and Carbon   **HO ⇓ HC**
See OC ⇓ HC

Addition to Oxygen and Carbon   **HO ⇓ OC**
See HC ⇓ OC, CC ⇓ OC

β-Hydroxyl Alkyl Amines
See 277.

Rearrangement   **HO ↷**

Hydroxynaphthoquinones
See 581.

Exchange

Carbon ⬆   **HO ⥮ C**

Sodium hydroxide   *NaOH*

Opening of the Coumarin Ring
See 104.

Sodium alcoholate   *NaOR*

Deacetylation of Glycosides   OAc → OH

1. Tetraacetylprotocatechualdehyde-4-β-D-glucoside is dissolved in abs. MeOH. 1 mole Na is added; after its complete reaction a soln. of citric acid in abs. MeOH is added → protocatechualdehyde-4-β-D-glucoside (s.m. 551). Y = 66.8%. L. Reichel and J. Marchand, *Ber. 76*, 1132 (1943); *C.A. 1944*, 4944. Methods, see L. Reichel, *Ann. 553*, 88 (1942); *C.A. 1943*, 5062.

Alkali in pyridine

Ether Cleavage   ROR → ROH

2. Cleavage of phenolic ethers can be accomplished by boiling with an alkali metal in dry pyridine. Ex: BzPh ether with Na in C_5H_5N → phenol; Y = 90%. Also: anisole → phenol; Y = 94%. Phenetole → phenol; Y = 95%. F.e.s. V. Prey, *Ber. 76*, 156 (1943); *C.A. 1943*, 5380.

Potassium bicarbonate $KHCO_3$

Partial Saponification   OAc → OH

3. 1.4 g. 3-β-acetoxy-D-homo-17-androstanone is heated for 3 hrs. with MeOH–$KHCO_3$ on the water bath → 1.05 g. 3-β-hydroxy-D-homo-17-androstanone. M. W. Goldberg and E. Wydler, *Helv. Chim. Acta 26*, 1142 (1943); *C.A. 1944*, 367.

Deacetylation of Glycosides
  See 220.

Barium hydroxide $Ba(OH)_2$
  See 217.

Barium methylate $Ba(OR)_2$

4. Pentaacetyl-β-methyl-D-manno-D-galaheptoside (prepn., see 218) is treated with $(MeO)_2Ba$ → β-methyl-D-manno-D-galaheptoside. Y = 91%. E. M. Montgomery and C. S. Hudson, *J. Am. Chem. Soc. 64*, 247 (1942); *C.A. 1942*, 1906.

5. Maltose octaacetate is shaken with $(MeO)_2Ba$ (prepn., see original) at room temp. → maltose monohydrate. W. A. Mitchell, *J. Am. Chem. Soc. 63*, 3534 (1941); *C.A. 1942*, 1019. Methods, see Weltzien and Singer, *Ann. 443*, 104 (1925).

Aluminum chloride $AlCl_3$

Ether Cleavage   ROR → ROH

6.

2,2'-Dimethoxybenzil is heated for 7 hrs. at 55° with pulverized $AlCl_3$ in $PhNO_2$ → 2,2'-dihydroxybenzil. Y = 50–66%. F.e.s. R. Kuhn, L. Birkofer and E. F. Möller, *Ber. 76*, 900 (1943); *C.A. 1944*, 2950.

7. 2,2'-Dimethoxy diphenyl sulfone is boiled with $AlCl_3$ in xylene → 2,2'-dihydroxy diphenyl sulfone. Y = 60–70%. F.e.s. G. Machek and H. Haas, *J. prakt. Chem. 160*, 41 (1942); *C.A. 1943*, 5040.

Formic acid-acetyl chloride $HCOOH-CH_3COCl$

Degradation of Methylated Polysaccharides   ROR → ROH

8. Methylated polysaccharides can be decomposed at room temp. into simple methylated sugars by HCO_2H and AcCl as a catalyst. After removal of the formic acid, if necessary after previous glucosidation [see K. Freudenberg and W. Jacob, *Ber. 74*, 162 (1941)], the sugars can be distilled *in vacuo*. The procedure is not suitable for free and acetylated polysaccharides, methylated wood, and proteins. K. Freudenberg, T. Ploetz and W. Jacob, *Ber. 75*, 1694 (1942); *C.A. 1944*, 1213.

Pyridinium hydrochloride

Ether Cleavage   ROR → ROH

9. The following compounds can be cleaved with pyridinium hydrochloride and dry HCl at 200–10°: anisol, nerolin, veratrol, guaiacol. V. Prey, *Ber. 75*, 350 (1942); *C.A. 1943*, 3072.

   See also 610.

Hydrochloric acid HCl

Cleavage of Trityl Ethers   ROR → ROH
   See 216.

Glycoside Cleavage

10. g-Strophanthin (rhamnose glycoside of g-strophanthidin) is allowed to stand for a few days with HCl in Me_2CO → g-strophanthidin. Y = 80%. C. Mannich and G. Siewert, *Ber. 75B*, 737 (1942); *C.A. 1943*, 3441.

Hydrobromic acid HBr

Ether Cleavage   ROR → ROH

11. 8-Methoxyquinoline is refluxed in HBr (d. 1.5) for 3–4 hrs. → 8-hydroxyquinoline. Y = 90%. F. E. King and J. A. Sherred, *J. Chem. Soc. 1942*, 415; *C.A. 1942*, 5821.

12. 6-Methoxy-1-naphthoic acid (prepn., see 189) is refluxed with 48% HBr in glacial AcOH → 6-hydroxy-1-naphthoic acid. Y = 90%. L. Long, Jr., and A. Burger, *J. Org. Chem. 6*, 852 (1941); *C.A. 1942*, 763.

Palladium black Pd

Cleavage of Benzyl Ethers   ROR → ROH

13.

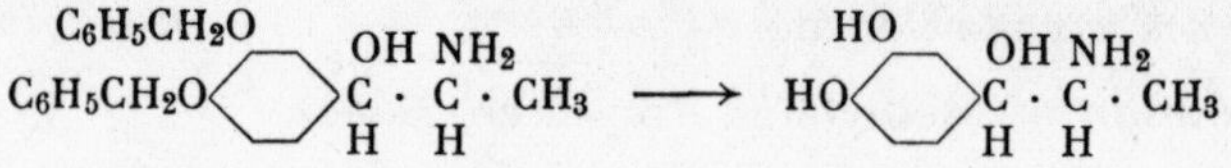

$$C_6H_5CH_2O \diagdown \diagup OH NH_2$$
$$C_6H_5CH_2O\diagup \diagdown C \cdot C \cdot CH_3 \longrightarrow HO\diagdown \diagup OH NH_2$$
$$H H HO\diagup \diagdown C \cdot C \cdot CH_3$$
$$H H$$

1-(3,4-Dibenzylhydroxyphenyl)-2-aminopropanol (prepn., see 292) is dissolved in MeOH and 3N HCl and reduced with a prehydrogenated suspension of 22% Pd–C at room temp. and atm. pressure → 1-(3,4-dihydroxyphenyl)-2-aminopropanol. Y = quant. V. Bruckner and G. v. Fodor, *Ber. 76,* 466 (1943); *C.A. 1943,* 6656.

14. 5-Benzyloxy-2-indolecarboxylic acid (prepn., see 562) is reduced with Pd–C in MeOH → Me 5-hydroxy-2-indolecarboxylate. Y = 70%. F. Bergel and A. L. Morrison, *J. Chem. Soc. 1943,* 49; *C.A. 1943,* 3429.

Cleavage of Trityl Ethers
  See 216.

Elimination

Oxygen ⚹   **HO ⇑ O**

Sodium sulfite Na_2SO_3

Alcohols from Peroxides   · OOH → OH

15.

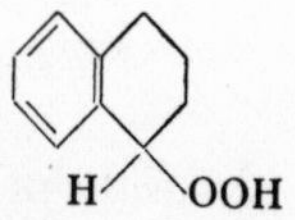

The corresponding alc. is obtained in a smooth reaction by the reduction of the peroxides with Na_2SO_3. Ex: Tetralin peroxide with Na_2SO_3 in H_2O → α-tetralol. Y = 90%. F.e.s. H. Hock and Shon Lang, *Ber. 75,* 313 (1942); *C.A. 1943,* 3749.

16.

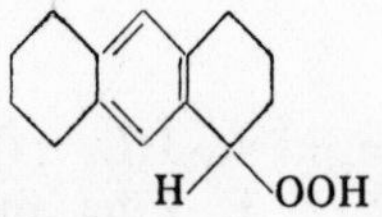

Octahydroanthracene peroxide (prepn., see 132) is stirred with H_2O–Na_2SO_3 in MeOH for 1 hr. at room temp. and for 2 hrs. at 75° → octahydroanthrol. Y = 85%. H. Hock and Shon Lang, *Ber. 76,* 1130 (1943); also, *Ber. 77,* 257 (1944); *C.A. 1944,* 4935.

Formation of H—N Bond by:

Addition

Addition to Nitrogen   HN ⇓ NN

Zinc dust   **Zn**

Hydrazo Compounds from Azo Compounds   N : N → NH · NH

17. **Total Reduction of Disazo Compounds.** 4,4'-Bis(benzeneazo)biphenyl, $C_{24}H_{18}N_4$, is stirred in pyridine with Zn dust and glacial AcOH is added during which the reaction mixture heats up to 28° → 4,4'-bis(benzenehydrazo)biphenyl. Y = almost quant.

    Partial Reduction of Disazo Compounds. 4,4'-Bis(benzeneazo)biphenyl is treated with Zn dust in pyridine with gradual addn. of a little glacial AcOH → 4-benzenehydrazo-4'-benzeneazobiphenyl. Y = 90%. P. Ruggli and K. Hölzle, *Helv. Chim. Acta 26*, 814 (1943); *C.A. 1944*, 2640.

18. **Mild Reduction to Sensitive Hydrazo Compounds.** 2-Aminoazobenzene (0.5 g.) is reduced with Zn and NH_3 at 50–5° in alc. under N_2 → 0.35 g. 2-aminohydrazobenzene. F.e.s. P. Ruggli and K. Hölzle, *Helv. Chim. Acta 26*, 1190 (1943); *C.A. 1944*, 547.

Hydrogen sulfide   **H_2S**

Partial Reduction of Nitrazo Compounds   N : N → NH · NH

19. 4-Aminobiphenyl-4'-azobenzene in NH_3–alc. suspension is treated with H_2S → 0.95 g. 4-nitrobiphenyl-4'-hydrazobenzene. P. Ruggli and K. Hölzle, *Helv. Chim. Acta 26*, 814 (1943); *C.A. 1944*, 2640; also, *Helv. Chim. Acta 26*, 1190 (1943); *C.A. 1944*, 547.

Sulfur dioxide   **SO_2**

Hydrazinocarboxylic Acids   · $NHNH_2$
    See 261.

Addition to Nitrogen and Carbon   HN ⇓ NC
    See HC ⇓ NC

Without additional reagents
See NC ⇓ NC, 490.

Lithium   *Li*

Closure of the Triazine Ring   O
See 285.

Sodium alcoholate   *NaOR*
See NC ⇓ NC NaOR

Rearrangement   HN ↷

O-Acyl from N-Acyl Derivatives   N · Ac → O · Ac
See 154.

Exchange

Oxygen ⋏   HN ⇅ O

Electrolytic   ⚡
See 292.

Sodium amalgam   *Na,Hg*

Amines from Oximes   CHNOH → CH₂NH₂

20. 16 g. $Me_2NCH_2CH_2C(: NOH)Me$ is reduced with 6% Na–Hg in 10%
AcOH → 15 g. 2-amino-4-dimethylaminobutane. E. Ghigi, *Ann. Chim.
applicata* 32, 3 (1942); *C.A. 1943*, 1385.

Amines from Nitro Compounds
See 28.

Zinc   *Zn*

Alkylamino Compounds from Nitro Compounds NO_2 → NHR

21. $C_6H_5NHCOC_6H_4NO_2 + CH_3CHO + 8 H \rightarrow C_6H_5NHCOC_6H_4NHCH_2CH_3$

1 g. *p*-nitrobenzanilide is treated with Zn and H_2SO_4 in alc., while
$AcHNH_3$ is added dropwise → 0.65 g. 4-ethylaminobenzanilide.
G. Lockemann, T. Lobenstein and W. Neumann, *Ber.* 75B, 1911
(1943); *C.A. 1944*, 1216.

N-Amino from *N*-Nitroso Compounds $N \cdot NO \rightarrow N \cdot NH_2$
See 255.

Aluminum   *Al*

Amines from Nitro Compounds $NO_2 \rightarrow NH_2$

22. Et 5-nitro-2-thiophenecarboxylate is treated with activated Al scale in
moist ether while CO_2 is passed through the reaction mixture → Et 5-
amino-2-thiophenecarboxylate. Y = 78%. O. Dann, *Ber. 76*, 419 (1943);
C.A. 1943, 6260.

Aluminum amalgam   *Al,Hg*

Aminoacridines from Nitroacridones

23.

Nitroacridone is reduced to the corresponding aminoacridane with
Na amalgam in CO_2 atm., or with Al amalgam without use of CO_2.
Then $FeCl_3$ oxidizes it to aminoacridone. Ex: 1-Aminoacridine; Y =
70%. 2-Aminoacridine; Y = 70%. 3-Aminoacridine; Y = 75%. A. Albert
and B. Ritchie, *J. Indian Chem. Soc. 60*, 120 (1941); *C.A. 1942*, 5823.

Stannous chloride   *SnCl₂*

Partial Reduction of Dinitro Compounds $NO_2 \rightarrow NH_2$

24. 2,4-Dinitrodimethylaniline (prepn., see 330) in warm EtOH is reduced
with $SnCl_2$ in alc. HCl → 2-amino-4-nitrodimethylaniline. Y = 72%.
E. E. Ayling, J. H. Gorving and L. E. Hinkel, *J. Chem. Soc. 1942*, 755;
C.A. 1943, 1398.

25. The 1-nitro group of 1,2-dinitronaphthalenes can be reduced advan-
tageously with $SnCl_2$ dissolved in glacial $AcOH \cdot HCl$. The 1,5- and
1,8-dinitronaphthalenes, however, are reduced to the corresponding
diamines. 1,5-Dinitronaphthalene is reduced to 5-nitro-1-naphthyla-
mine and 1,6-dinitronaphthalene to 5-nitro-2-naphthylamine with an aq.
Na_2S soln. Ex: 1,6-Dinitronaphthalene is dissolved in hot glacial AcOH
and treated with $SnCl_2$ in glacial $AcOH \cdot HCl$ for 45 min. under 30° →
6-nitro-1-naphthylamine. Y = 60%. $1,5\text{-}C_{10}H_6(NO_2)_2$ (pulverized)
wetted with EtOH, is treated with an aq. soln. of crystalline Na_2S for
15 min. at 95° (improved method by Hodgson and Walter, *J. Chem.
Soc. 1933*, 1346) → $1,5\text{-}C_{10}H_6(NH_2)NO_2$. Y = 60.5%. H. H. Hodgson
and H. S. Turner, *J. Chem. Soc. 1943*, 318; *C.A. 1943*, 6258.

Sulfur   S

Amino Aldehydes from Nitro Hydrocarbons
See 162.

Sodium sulfide $Na_2S(SnCl_2)$
See 25.

Sodium hyposulfite $Na_2S_2O_4$

Amines from Nitroso Compounds $NO \rightarrow NH_2$
See 360.

Amines from Nitro Compounds $NO_2 \rightarrow NH_2$

26. 1-Methyl-9-nitrophenanthrene is treated with $Na_2S_2O_4$ in H_2O–MeOH
     $\rightarrow$ 1-methyl-9-aminophenanthrene. Y $=$ nearly quant. T. Hasselstrom,
     J. Am. Chem. Soc. 63, 2527 (1941); *C.A. 1941*, 739.

Iron   *Fe*

27. *m*-Bromonitrobenzene is treated with iron powder and HCl gas in alc.
     $\rightarrow$ *m*-bromoaniline. Y $=$ 86%. B. W. Speekmann and J. P. Wibaut, *Rec.
     trav. chim. 61*, 383 (1942); *C.A. 1944*, 2327.
     See also 30.

Nickel   *Ni(Cu)*

28. Reductions with HCOOH and Cu or Ni. The decomposition of
     HCOOH into H_2 and CO_2 in the presence of Cu or Ni is used for
     reductions under pressure. This method is particularly suitable for
     the reduction of small amounts of material. When Cu is used as the
     catalyst only the side chain of aromatic compounds is reduced, whereas
     Ni also reduces the nucleus. Catalysts: 1. Cu: Kieselguhr which has
     been cleaned with boiling HNO_3 is wetted with an aq. 10% $Cu(NO_3)_2$
     soln., made yellow (alkaline) with $2N$ soda soln. and dried and
     reduced after an H_2O washing. 2. Ni: Similarly shaken with an aq.
     10% $NiSO_4$ soln. Ex: With Cu: 0.01 mole benzaldehyde $\rightarrow$ 1.92 g. mixt.
     of 56% $PhCH_2OH$ and 18% PhMe $\rightarrow$ $PhNO_2$ $\rightarrow$ $PhNH_2$. Y $=$ 100%.
     With Ni: 0.01 mole $PhNO_2$ $\rightarrow$ 1.64 g. cyclohexylamine. R. R. Davies
     and H. H. Hodgson, *J. Chem. Soc. London 1943*, 281; *C.A. 1943*, 5370.

29. Benzoyl-*o*-nitroaniline is reduced with Raney Ni in alc. $\rightarrow$ benzoyl-
     o-phenylenediamine. Y $=$ 96%. P. Ruggli and J. Rohner, *Helv. Chim.
     Acta 25*, 1533 (1942); *C.A. 1943*, 5947.

Palladium   *Pd*

$$\underset{\underset{NH_2}{|}}{\bigcirc} \overset{COCH_2CHCOOH}{\underset{NH_2}{|}}$$

30. *o*-Nitrophenacylaminoacetic acid · HCl is reduced with Pd black in H_2O and treated with H_2SO_4 → *d,l*-kynurenine sulfate. Y = 87%. The reduction with Fe yields only 75%. A. Butenandt, W. Weidel, R. Weichert and W. v. Derjugin, Z. *physiol. Chem. 279,* 27 (1943); *C.A. 1944,* 2044.

Nitrogen ⅄   HN ⅄ N

Sodium hyposulfite $Na_2S_2O_4$

Reductive Cleavage of Azo Compounds $N{=}N$ → NH_2
   See 173.

Nickel   *Ni*
   See 398.

Carbon ⅄   HN ⅄ C

Sodium hydroxide   *NaOH*

Hydrolysis of Acylated Amines   NHAc → NH_2

31. Acetylsulfanilyl derivs. are hydrolyzed by boiling for 1–1.5 hrs. with 10% NaOH. Ex: Acetylsulfanilyl-2-aminopyridine-5-sulfonic acid (prepn., see 274) → sulfanilyl-2-aminopyridine-5-sulfonic acid. Y = 81%. Acetylsulfanilyl-2-aminopyridinesulfonic acid → sulfanilyl-2-aminopyridinesulfonic acid. Y = 96%. C. Naegeli, W. Kündig and E. Suter, *Helv. Chim. Acta 25,* 1485 (1942); *C.A. 1943,* 5949.
   See also 35.

Potassium hydroxide   *KOH*

Opening of the Hydantoin Ring   C
   See 568.

Alkali alcoholate

Hydrolysis of Acylated Amines   NHAc → NH_2

32. Acetylamino compounds which contain a nitro group in the *o*- or *p*-position are easily hydrolyzed by boiling with alc. and the corresponding Na alcoholate. The acetyl group is thereby split off as the ester.

The method is also suitable for the separation of isomers. Ex: 2,3-Dinitro-4-ethoxyacetanilide is boiled with NaOEt in EtOH → 2,3-dinitro-4-ethoxyaniline. Y = 96%. 4-Nitro-1-acetnaphthalide is boiled for 3 hrs. with NaOMe in MeOH → 4-nitro-1-naphthylamine. Y = 98%. F.e.s. P. E. Verkade and P. H. Witjens, *Rec. trav. chim. 62*, 201 (1943); *C.A. 1944*, 2323.

Calcium hydroxide $Ca(OH)_2$

Hydrolysis of Urea Derivatives to Amines

$$O = C \overset{\displaystyle \diagup NHR}{\diagdown NHR} \longrightarrow 2\ RNH_2$$

$$[C_6H_5CH_2C(CH_3)_2NH]CO \rightarrow 2\ C_6H_5CH_2C(CH_3)_2NH_2$$

33. *sym*-Di-(β-phenyl-α,α'-dimethylethyl) urea is heated with $Ca(OH)_2$ at 230° → α-benzylisopropylamine. Y = 80%. C. Menzter, *Compt. rend. 213*, 581 (1941); *C.A. 1943*, 4061.

Sulfuric acid H_2SO_4

Hydrolysis of Acylated Amines   NHAc → NH₂

34. 2,4-Dinitro-*p*-toluenesulfono-1-naphthalide is treated for 45 min. with H_2SO_4 (d. 1.84) under 20° → 2,4-dinitro-1-naphthylamine [2,4-$(O_2N)_2C_{10}H_5NH_2$]. Y = quant. H. H. Hodgson and S. Birtwell, *J. Chem. Soc. (London) 1943*, 433; *C.A. 1944*, 350.

Bromine Br_2

Replacement of Loosely Bound Methyl Groups by Hydrogen in Methylated Anilines $N(CH_3)_2 \rightarrow NH(CH_3)$

35. 2-Chloro-6-nitro-4-acetamidodimethylaniline is treated with Br_2 in $CHCl_3$ → 2-chloro-6-nitro-4-acetamidomethylaniline. Y = 94%. F.e.s. E. E. Ayling, J. H. Corvin and L. E. Hinkel, *J. Chem. Soc. London 1942*, 755; *C.A. 1943*, 1398 (*C.A. 1942*, 419).

Hydrochloric acid HCl

Hydrolysis of Acylated Amines $NH(COR) \rightarrow NH_2$

36. 1-(N^4-acetylsulfanilamido)-isoquinoline (prepn., see 275) is refluxed with 10% NaOH → 1-sulfanilamidoisoquinoline, $C_{15}H_{13}O_2N_3S$. Y = 80–90%. 4-(N^4-acetylsulfanilamido)-isoquinoline is refluxed with 12% HCl → 4-sulfanilamidoquinoline. Y = 60–80%. J. J. Craig and W. E. Cass, *J. Am. Chem. Soc. 64*, 783 (1942); *C.A. 1942*, 3175.

See also 276, 292.

Palladium   **Pd**

Primary from Secondary Amines   NHR → NH₂
  See 75.

Cleavage of Carbobenzoxyamino Compounds
  See 353.

Palladium oxide   *PdO*

**Hydrogenative Cleavage of Tertiary
to Primary and Secondary Amines**

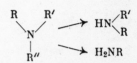

37. Cyclic secondary amines whose H-atom has been replaced by a Bz
    group, undergo cleavage by reduction with PdO and H₂, yielding the
    original secondary amine and toluene. Aromatic rings can be converted
    into hydrogenated rings at the same time. Ex: Tribenzylamine →
    dibenzylamine. Y (of the chlorohydrate) = 97%. Aromatic rings, car-
    boxyl and cyano groups have an activating influence, so that the Bz
    group attached to a secondary N-atom can also be made to undergo
    cleavage. Ex: *N*-benzylaniline → aniline; Y (as chlorohydrate) =
    97.5%. *N,N*-dibenzyl-2-aminonaphthaline → 2-naphthylamine; Y = 88%.
    N,N-dibenzylglycocoll → glycocoll; Y = 95%. Acid amides in which
    one or two amide hydrogen atoms have been replaced by Bz are not
    reduced catalytically under these conditions. F.e.s. L. Birkofer, *Ber.* 75,
    429 (1942); *C.A. 1943*, 3067.

Formation of H—S Bond by:

Exchange

Carbon ⬆   **HS** ⥮ **C**

Sodium–liq. ammonia   *Na,NH₃*

Mercaptans from Thio Ethers   RSR → RSH

38. γ-Benzylthio-α,β-dimethyl-*n*-butyric acid is treated with Na in liq.
NH₃ → γ-mercapto-α,β-dimethylbutyric acid (s.m. 120). Y = 94%.
F. Kögl, J. H. Verbeek, H. Erxleben and W. A. J. Borg, Z. *physiol.*
Chem. 279, 121 (1943); *C.A. 1944*, 3978. Methods, see V. du Vigneaud,
J. Biol. Chem. 111, 393 (1935); *112*, 149 (1935); *130*, 110 (1939).

Sodium hydroxide   *NaOH*

Mercaptans from Ethylene Derivatives
    See 457.

Sodium sulfite   *Na₂SO₃*

Mercaptans from Isothiourea Compounds $\cdot SC\begin{smallmatrix}\diagup NH\\ \diagdown NH_2\end{smallmatrix}$ → SH
    See 493/4.

Formation of H—C Bond by:

Addition

Addition to Oxygen and Carbon   HC ⇓ OC

Sodium amalgam   *Na,Hg*

Secondary Alcohols from Ketones   CO → CHOH

39. 4-Dimethylamino-2-butanone is treated with Na–Hg in 10% AcOH →
4-dimethylamino-2-butanol. Y = 85%. E. Ghigi, *Ann. Chim. applicata*
32, 3 (1942); *C.A. 1943*, 1385.

Magnesium–magnesium iodide   *Mg–MgI$_2$*

Bimolecular Reduction of Aldehydes to Glycols
See 689.

Zinc   *Zn*

Secondary Alcohols from Ketones   CO → CHOH

40.

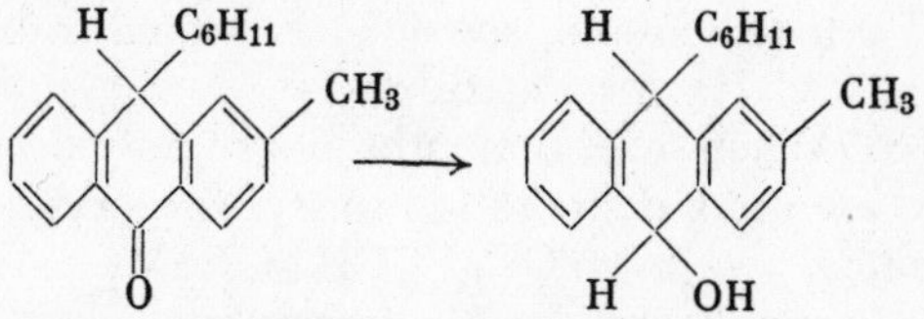

2-Methyl-10-cyclohexyl-9-anthrone (prepn., see 743) is reduced with
Zn dust and aq. NH$_3$ in toluene and ammoniacal CuCO$_3$ soln. by
refluxing for 6 hrs. → 2-methyl-10-cyclohexyl-9-10-dihydro-9-anthranol.
Y = 65%. A. T. Marchevskii and M. T. Ushakov, *J. Gen. Chem. U.S.S.R.*
10, (72) 1369 (1940); *C.A. 1941*, 3626.

Copper–aluminum catalyst   *Cu,Al*

41. Alkyl phenyl ketones can be reduced with a Cu–Al catalyst (prepn.,
see original) at 115° to the corresponding carbinols, and at higher
temps. (150–180°) to the hydrocarbons, with no effect on the C$_6$H$_6$
ring. H$_2$–initial pressure: 100 atm. Y = 95–98%. Ex: Acetophenone →
methylphenylcarbinol → ethylbenzene. V. N. Ipatieff and V. Haensel,
J. Am. Chem. Soc. 64, 520 (1942); *C.A. 1942*, 2534.

Aluminum amalgam   Al,Hg

42.

16 g. Et(diethylaminomethyl)-cyclohexanone carboxylate is reduced
with Al–Hg in ether → 12 g. Et(diethylaminomethyl)-cyclohexanol
carboxylate. C. Mannich and E. Strauss, *Arch. Pharm. 280,* 361 (1942);
C.A. 1944, 1484.

Aluminum alcoholate   Al(OR)₃

Al *tert*-Butoxide for the Meerwein-Ponndorf Reduction

43. Al shavings are dissolved in boiling *tert*-BuOH already containing some
Al *tert*-butoxide; a little HgCl₂ and some C₆H₆ are added → Al *tert*-
butoxide. Y = 80–5%. W. Wayne and H. Adkins, *Organic Syntheses 21,*
8 (1941); *C.A. 1941,* 6235.

Secondary Alcohols from Ketones   CO → CHOH
See 157.

44.

Sulfide Alcohols from Alkyl Phenacyl Sulfides
Me phenacyl sulfide (prepn., see 482) is heated to boiling with (iso-
PrO)₃Al in abs. C₆H₆ for 12–16 hrs. → Me 2-hydroxy-2-phenylethyl
sulfide. Y = 88%. When several months' old slightly decompd. prepns. of
(iso-PrO)₃Al are used, dehydration to styrenes occurs: Me *p*-methoxy-
phenacyl sulfide → *p*-MeOC₆H₄CH : CHSCH₃. F.e.s. V. Prelog,
V. Hahn, H. Brauchli and H. C. Beyermann, *Helv. Chim. Acta 27,*
1209 (1944); *C.A. 1946,* 848.

45. 4-Me-5-acetylthiazole is treated with Al isopropylate and isopropanol
→ 4-Me-5-(α-hydroxyethyl) thiazole, C₆H₉ONS. Y = 71%. P. Baumgarten, A. Dornow, K. Gutschmidt and H. Krehl, *Ber. 75,* 442 (1942);
C.A. 1943, 3091.

See 74.

Cobalt catalyst   Co

46. A mixture of dodecanes (prepn., see 193) is reduced at 190° and 200
atm. with a Co catalyst [compare R. H. Picard and J. Kenyon, *J. Chem.*

Soc. 99, 57 (1911); P. Ceuterick, *Bull. Soc. chim. Belg. 45*, 545 (1936)]
→ a mixture of dodecanols (s.m. 734). Y = 92.5%.

47. 2-Hexadecanone is reduced with a Co catalyst (Fr. Pat. 843,305) in cyclohexane at 200° and 200 atm. → 2-hexadecanol. Y = 95%. F.e.s. F. Asinger and H. Eckold, *Ber. 76*, 579 (1943); *C.A. 1944*, 57.

Nickel (improved method for the prepn. of the catalyst)   *Ni*

48. Fenchone is reduced with Raney Ni (for which an improved method of prepn. is described) at 110° and 120 atm. for 2 hrs. → fenchol. Y = 84%. No hydrogenation could be obtained with Mohr's Pt, PtO$_2$ (according to Adams) and colloidal Pt (according to Skita). W. Hückel, H. Kindler and H. Wolowski, *Ber. 77*, 220 (1944); *C.A. 1945*, 3273.

Hydrogenation of Sugars
Preparation of an Activated Raney Ni Catalyst

49. The catalyst (prepd., as usual, by the fusion of Al and Ni and subsequent boiling with NaOH) is shaken with a solution of PtCl$_4$, 2 HCl + 6 H$_2$O. This catalyst was used with good results in the reduction of sugars. To hasten the absorption of H$_2$ during the hydrogenation small quantities of NaOH were added. G. Jayme and M. Sätre, *Ber. 77*, 248 (1944); *C.A. 1945*, 3522; see also R. Schröter, *Angew. Chem. 54*, 229, 252 (1941); *C.A. 1941*, 6241; M. Delépine and H. Horeau, *Bull. soc. chim. Mém.[s] 4*, 31 (1937); E. Lieber and G. B. L. Smith, *J. Am. Chem. Soc. 58*, 1417 (1936).

Palladium (Mohr)   *Pd*

Hydrogenation of Esters of Arylglyoxylic Acids
   See 712.

Palladium oxide   *PdO*

Secondary Alcohols from Ketones   CO → CHOH

50.

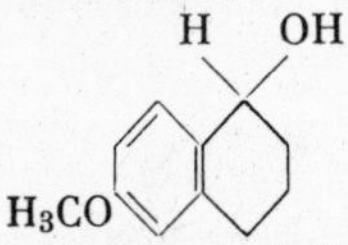

1-Keto-6-methoxy-1,2,3,4-tetrahydronaphthalene is hydrogenated in the presence of PtO → 1-hydroxy-6-methoxy-1,2,3,4-tetrahydronaphthalene. Y = 97%. L. Long, Jr. and A. Burger, *J. Org. Chem. 6*, 852 (1941); *C.A. 1942*, 763.

Addition to Nitrogen and Carbon   HC ⇓ NC

Sodium   *Na*

Amines from Nitriles   CN → CH₂NH₂

51. Tridecanonitrile is reduced in abs. BuOH with Na → tridecylamine
    HCl (s.m. 447). Y = 90–3%. H. Suida and F. Drahowzal, *Ber.* 75, 991
    (1942); *C.A. 1943*, 4683.

    Reduction of Schiff Bases   C: NR → CHNHR
    See 355.

Nickel   *Ni*

Amines from Nitriles   CN → CH₂NH₂

52. The K salt of cyanoacetic acid is reduced with Raney Ni in a satd.
    NH₃–MeOH soln. at 80° and 100 atm. in a shaking autoclave →
    β-alanine. Y = 75%. P. Ruggli and A. Businger, *Helv. Chim. Acta 25*,
    35 (1942); *C.A. 1942*, 4481.

    Hydrogenation of Schiff Bases   C: NR → CHNHR
    See 354.

Platinum oxide   *PtO₂*

Amines from Nitriles   CN → CH₂NH₂

53.

Cinchoninonitrile is reduced with PtO₂ in MeOH · HCl → lepidy-
lamine. Y = 100%. Also: quininonitrile → 6-methoxylepidylamine.
Y = 100%. T. S. Work, *J. Chem. Soc. (London) 1942*, 426; *C.A. 1942*,
6540.

Catalytic Hydrogenation of Cyanohydrins

54.

The cyanohydrin is reduced with PtO₂ in glacial AcOH at room temp.,
sometimes with the addition of concd. HCl to prevent the formation
of sec. amines. Ex: 1. Without concd. HCl: cholestanonecyanohydrin
(1 g.) → 950 mg. crude 3-hydroxy-3-aminomethylcholestane. 2. With

concd. HCl: cyclohexanonecyanohydrin (3 g.) → about 1.7 g. 1-(aminomethyl)-cyclohexanol. K. W. Goldberg and H. Kirchensteiner, *Helv. Chim. Acta 26*, 288 (1943); *C.A. 1944,* 111. See also L. Ruzicka, P. A. Plattner and H. Wild, *Helv. Chim. Acta 26,* 1631 (1943); *C.A. 1944,* 2935.

Platinum–barium sulfate　　　　　　　　　　　　Pt–$BaSO_4$

Reduction of Schiff Bases　　　　　　C:NR → $CHNHR$
　　See 356.

Addition to Carbon　　　　　　　　　　$HC \Downarrow CC$

Electrolytic　　　　　　　　　　　　　　　　　ḷ

Dihydroacridines from Acridines

55.　9-(*o*-Iodophenyl)-acridine → 9-(*o*-iodophenyl)-dihydroacridine. For a description of the electrolysis apparatus, see J. J. Lingane, *Chem. Age 49*, 611 (1943).

Sodium　　　　　　　.　　　　　　　　　　　　Na

Amines
　　See 291.

Partial Reduction of the Triple Bond　　· $C \equiv C$ · → · $CH = CH$ ·
　　See 59.

Mercury　　　　　　　　　　　　　　　　　　Hg

Addition of Water and Alcohols to the Triple Bond
　　See OC $\Downarrow$ CC. Hg.

Nickel　　　　　　　　　　　　　　　　　　　Ni

Preparation of a Raney Ni Catalyst

56.　An excellent Raney Ni catalyst is obtained by the solution of 50% Ni–Al alloy in 20% NaOH. The catalyst, after thorough washing by decantation with H_2O, is very pyrophoric and must be stored under abs. EtOH, methylcyclohexane, or dioxane, in which prepns. it is used. Dioxane may react almost explosively with H and Ni above 210°. R. Mozingo, *Organic Syntheses 21*, 15 (1941); *C.A. 1941,* 6235.

Hydrogenation of the Double Bond　　· CH : CH · → · CH_2 · CH_2 ·
　　See 669.

Hydrogenation of Furyl Compounds

57. Furan is hydrogenated with Raney Ni at 2–4 atm. → tetrahydrofuran. Y = 93%. D. S. Tarbell and C. Weaver, *J. Am. Chem. Soc. 63*, 2939 (1941); *C.A.* 1942, 470.

58. Furyl polyenes, ketones, and esters are reduced to the corresponding tetrahydrofuryl compounds with Raney Ni in alc. at 170–250 atm. The reduction of the side chains starts nearly always at room temp., while that of the furan nucleus commences at 160°. Ex: Et 2-(α-furyl)-acrylate → Et tetrahydro-2-(α-furyl)-propionate. Y = 92%. Furyl acetate → tetrahydrofuryl acetate. Y = 99%. Furfurylidene acetone → 2-hydroxyl-4-(α-tetrahydrofuryl)butane. Y = 76.6%. F.e.s. A. Hinz, G. Meyer and G. Schücking, *Ber. 76*, 676 (1943); *C.A.* 1944, 2334.

Partial Hydrogenation of the Triple Bond $\cdot C \equiv C \cdot \rightarrow \cdot CH : CH \cdot$

59. *cis-trans* **Isomeric Ethylene Derivatives from Acetylene Derivatives.** Catalytic hydrogenation of dialkylacetylenes with Raney Ni yields the *cis* isomers; reduction with Na in liq. NH_3, the *trans* isomers. Prepn: 1. With Ni: The dialkylacetylenes are shaken with Raney Ni under an initial pressure of 60 lbs./sq. in. until the proper amount of H_2 has been taken up [see Covert-Adkins, *J. Am. Chem. Soc.* 54, 4116 (1932)] Y = 75–90%. 2. With Na: The dialkylacetylenes are added dropwise underneath the surface of a soln. of Na in liq. NH_3 over a period of about 40 min. with constant stirring; after another 1–2 hrs. of agitation, they are made to undergo further reaction. F.e.s. K. N. Campbell and L. T. Eby, *J. Am. Chem. Soc. 63*, 216 (1941); *C.A.* 1941, 1377.

60.   NC⟨ ⟩C ≡ C⟨ ⟩CN ⟶ NC⟨ ⟩CH : CH⟨ ⟩CN

p-p'-Dicyanotolan is reduced in dioxane with Raney Ni at 60° → *cis*-4,4'-dicyanostilbene. Y = 87.5%. The *trans* compound is obtained from the *cis* by short boiling in nitrobenzene containing a trace of iodine. S. Bance, H. J. Barber and A. M. Woolmann, *J. Chem. Soc. (London) 1943*, 1; *C.A.* 1943, 2002.

Nickel–formic acid   *Ni–HCOOH*

Hydrogenation of the Nucleus
   See 28.

Palladium–strontium carbonate   *Pd–SrCO₃*

Hydrogenation of the Double Bond $\cdot CH : CH \cdot \rightarrow \cdot CH_2CH_2 \cdot$
   See 606.

Platinum oxide PtO_2

31. Cyclohexane from Cyclohexene Derivatives. 2-(1-Naphthoyl)-4-cyclohexene-1-carboxylic acid, $C_{18}H_{16}O_3$ (prepn., see 697), is reduced with Adams catalyst (PtO_2) in alc. → 2-(1-naphthoyl)-cyclohexane-carboxylic acid. Y = 89%. F.e.s. L. F. Fieser and F. C. Novello, *J. Am. Chem. Soc. 64*, 802 (1942); *C. A. 1942*, 3171.

32. Selective Hydrogenation of the Double Bond. The hydrogenation of the double bond can be controlled by catalytic reduction with PtO_2 and $FeCl_3$ in boiling glacial AcOH or in cold C_6H_6 or toluene. Ex: *trans*-1,2-dibenzoylethylene → dibenzoylethane. Y=85%. Benzalaceto-phenone → benzylacetophenone. C. Weygand and W. Meusel, *Ber. 76*, 498 (1943); *C.A. 1943*, 6661.

Reduction of Lactams   See 79.

Rearrangement   HC ⋔

Silver oxide Ag_2O

Syntheses with Diazomethane
   See OC ⋔ N Ag_2O, CC ⋔ Hal without addnl. reagents

Lead tetraacetate $Pb(CH_3COO)_4$

Ketones from Ethylene Derivatives   · CH = CH · → · CH_2 · CO ·
   See 139.

Ammonium polysulfide $(NH_4)_2S_x$

Amides and Carboxylic Acids   · CH_2COOH
from Methyl Ketones   · $COCH_3$ ⟨
   See OC ⋔ HC · $(NH_4)_2S_x$ · CH_2CONH_2

Exchange

Oxygen ⋏   HC ⋔ O

Electrolytic   ⇶

Alcohols from Carboxylic Acids   COOH → CH_2OH

33. o-$H_2NC_6H_4CO_2H$ is electrolytically reduced in 15% H_2SO_4 at a Pb cathode → o-aminobenzyl alcohol. Y = 69–78%. G. H. Coleman and H. L. Johnson, *Organic Syntheses 21*, 10 (1941); *C.A. 1941*, 6249; see also B. Beilinson and F. M. Hamer, *J. Chem. Soc. (London) 1942*, 98; *C.A. 1942*, 3442.

Hydrocarbons from Ketones $\cdot CO \cdot \rightarrow \cdot CH_2 \cdot$
See 77.

Sodium and alcohol   *NaOR*

Bouveault-Blanc Reduction of Esters to Alcohols $COOR \rightarrow CH_2OH$

64.

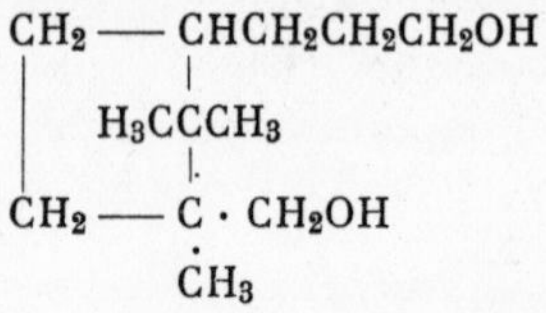

$$CH_2 \!\!-\!\! CHCH_2CH_2CH_2OH$$
$$H_3CCCH_3$$
$$CH_2 \!\!-\!\! C \cdot CH_2OH$$
$$CH_3$$

Dimethylhydrocamphoryl acetate is refluxed with Na in BuOH →
1,2,2-trimethyl-1-(hydroxymethyl)-3-(hydroxypropyl)cyclopentane.
Y = 60%. K. Buser and H. Rupe, *Helv. Chim. Acta 26*, 857 (1943); *C.A. 1944*, 1486.
See also 75.

Sodium amalgam   *Na,Hg*

Acridines from Acridones

65.

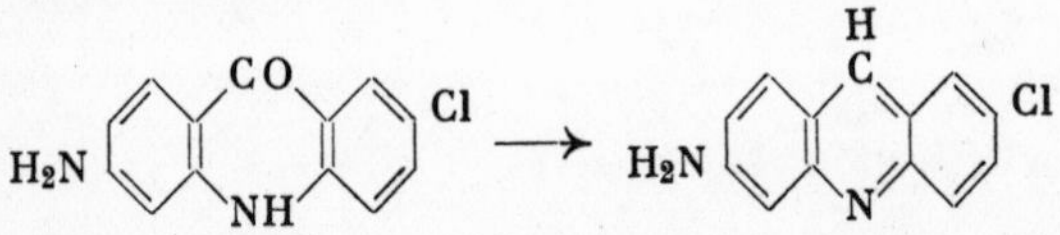

7-Chloro-2-aminoacridone is reduced with Na amalgam in 0.5 N NaOH
→ 7-chloro-2-aminoacridine. Y = 80%. F.e.s. F. R. Bradbury and W. H.
Linnell, *Quart. J. Pharm. Pharmacol. 15*, 31 (1942); *C.A. 1942*, 5822.

Aminoacridines from Nitroacridones
See 23.

Copper catalyst   *Cu*

Hydrocarbons from Aldehydes $\cdot CHO \rightarrow \cdot CH_3$
See 28.

Zinc dust   *Zn*

Hydrocarbons from Ketones $CO \rightarrow CH_2$
See 576.

66. **Hydrocarbons from Quinones.** The *p*-toluidine salt of 1,2,5,6-dibenz-
anthraquinone-4',8'-disulfonic acid is reduced with Zn dust in conc.

NH_3 for 48 hrs. → Zn salt of 1,2,5,6-dibenzanthracene-4′,8′-disulfonic acid. Y = 90–5%. J. Cason and L. F. Fieser, *J. Am. Chem. Soc.* 62, 2681 (1941); *C.A. 1941*, 4376.

Zinc dust, coppered   *Zn,Cu*

Hydrocarbons from Aldehydes $CHO → CH_3$

67. 2-Hydroxy-1-naphthaldehyde is reduced in an acetic acid soln. with coppered Zn dust → 1-methyl-2-naphthol. Y = excellent. R. Robinson and F. Weygand, *J. Chem. Soc. (London) 1941*, 386; *C.A. 1941*, 6965.

Zinc amalgam (Clemmensen reduction)   *Zn,Hg*

68. $4,2,6\text{-}HO(MeO)_2C_6H_2CHO$ is refluxed with amalgamated Zn dust in alc.–AcOH · HCl → $4,3,5\text{-}Me(MeO)_2C_6H_2OH$. Y = 92%. W. Gruber, *Ber. 76*, 135 (1943); *C.A. 1943*, 5047.

     See also 617.

Alkyl Phenols from Phenol Ketones $CO → CH_2$

69. *o*-Heptanoylphenol is boiled with amalgamated Zn and strong HCl for several hrs. with addn. of alc. → *o*-(*n*-heptyl)-phenol. Y = 81–86%. F.e.s. R. R. Read and J. Wood, Jr., *Organic Syntheses 20*, 57 (1940); *C.A. 1940*, 5065.

Hydrocarbons from Ketones

70.

4-Methyl-9-phenalanone is reduced with Zn amalgam and HCl in benzene–MeOH → 4-methylphenalane. Y = 75%. Buu-Hoi and P. Cagniant, *Rev. Scient. 79*, 644 (1941); *C.A. 1944*, 3642.

Hydrocarbons from Quinones

71. Acenaphthenequinone is reduced to acenaphthene according to the modified Clemmensen reduction as proposed by Fieser and Novello (*C. 1941*, I, 1286). Y = up to 90%. Ex: 3-Methylacenaphthenequinone is treated with Zn–Hg in C_6H_6, MeOH and HCl → 3-methylacenaphthene. F.e.s. Buu-Hoi and P. Cagniant, *Compt. rend. 214*, 315–17 (1942); *Rev. Scient. 80*, 176 (1942); *C.A. 1943*, 5717.

Aluminum–copper catalyst   *Al, Cu*

Hydrocarbons from Ketones $· CO → · CH_2$
     See 41.

Aluminum amalgam   *Al,Hg*

Acridines from Acridones
  See 756.

Aminoacridines from Nitroacridones
  See 23.

Stannous chloride   *SnCl₂*

Amines and Aldehydes from Acid Amides

$$C \underset{NH_2}{\overset{O}{<}} \qquad \underset{CH_2NH_2}{\overset{CHO}{<}}$$

72.

$$\underset{N}{CONHCH_3} \longrightarrow \underset{N}{CH_2NHCH_3}$$

By reacting carboxylic acid amides with PCl_5 and consequently
reducing them with $SnCl_2$ and HCl, aldehydes or amines can be
formed. In general, Bz derivatives lead to aldehydes, quinoline
derivatives to amines, and pyridine derivatives to both aldehydes and
amines. Ex: *N*-methylcinchoninamide (1.5 g.) is treated with PCl_5 in
$CHCl_3$ and then with $SnCl_2$ in ether · HCl → *N*-methyllepidylamine
(1.51 g. di-HCl salt). T. S. Work, *J. Chem. Soc. (London) 1942*, 429;
C.A. 1942, 6541. Methods, see Sonn and Müller, *Ber. 52*, 1927 (1919);
C.A. 1920, 1985.

Phosphorus   *P*

Hydrocarbons from Ketones via Alcohols $CO \rightarrow CH_2$

73. 4-Fluorenonecarboxylic acid is refluxed with Zn dust in NaOH in the
     presence of 1 ml. toluene (to prevent foaming) for 2 hrs. → 4-fluorenol-
     carboxylic acid (Y = 85%) which is refluxed for 1 hr. with I and red
     P in AcOH → 4-fluorenecarboxylic acid. Y = 92%. W. E. Bachmann
     and J. C. Sheehan, *J. Am. Chem. Soc. 62*, 2687 (1940); *C.A. 1940*, 7897.

Carboxylic Acids from Keto Acids via Lactones

74. $C_6H_5COCH_2CHCOOR \longrightarrow \overset{\overset{\displaystyle O}{\overline{\qquad\qquad}}}{C_6H_5CH \cdot CH_2 \cdot CH \cdot CO} \longrightarrow C_6H_5CH_2CH_2CHCOOH$

     $\qquad\;\; \overset{\cdot}{C_6H_5} \qquad\qquad\qquad\quad \overset{\cdot}{C_6H_5} \qquad\qquad\qquad\quad \overset{\cdot}{C_6H_5}$

Et α-phenyl-β-benzoylpropionate is reduced with Al iso-PrOH in boiling iso-PrOH → α,γ-diphenyl-γ-butyrolactone. Y = 95%. This is heated
with HI and red P → α,γ-diphenylbutyric acid. Y = 95%. F. Bergmann,
H. E. Eschinazi and D. Schapiro, *J. Am. Chem. Soc. 64*, 557 (1942);
C.A. 1942, 2547.

Copper–chromium oxide catalyst Cu, Cr_2O_3

Optically Active α-Amino Alcohols from
Racemic α-Bromo Fatty Acids $CHBrCOOH \rightarrow CHNH_2CH_2OH$

75.

$$
\begin{array}{llll}
COOC_2H_5 & COOC_2H_5 & CH_2OH & CH_2OH \\
\dot{C}HBr \longrightarrow & \dot{C}HNHCH_2C_6H_5 \longrightarrow & \dot{C}HNHCH_2C_6H_5 \longrightarrow & \dot{C}HNH_2 \\
\dot{C}H_3 & \dot{C}H_3 & \dot{C}H_3 & \dot{C}H_3
\end{array}
$$

Racemic α-bromo fatty acid esters are transformed into the rac. α-benzylamino fatty acid esters with benzylamine. These are then reduced to the corresponding α-benzylamino alcohols (which crystallize well) by the method of Bouveault-Blanc with Cu–Cr₂O₃ catalyst. They can then be separated into the optically active antipodes, which, without racemization, are easily reduced to the corresponding α-amino alcohols with Pd. Ex: Et *dl*-α-bromopropionate → Et *dl*-α-benzylamino-propionate → *dl*-α-N-benzylalaninol → *l*-N-benzylalanilol and *d*-N-deriv. which are reduced with Mohr's Pd in the presence of oxalic acid → *l*-alaninol, *d*-alaninol, respectively (last step, Y = 95%). F.e.s. A. Stoll, J. Peyer and A. Hofmann, *Helv. Chim. Acta 26*, 929 (1943); *C.A. 1944*, 1500.

Palladium   *Pd*

Reduction of Arylglyoxylic Acid Esters $CO \rightarrow CH_2$
   See 712.

β-Arylalkylamines

76. 1. For the prepn. of β-arylalkanolamines by the reduction of isonitroso-alkyl aryl ketones, aryl aminoalkyl ketones, and other N-containing compounds, see 2. Y = 50–80%.

$$
\begin{array}{ll}
C_6H_5COC:NOH \longrightarrow & C_6H_5COCHNH_2 \\
\quad\dot{C}_2H_5 & \quad\dot{C}_2H_5
\end{array}
$$

Ex: 1-Isonitrosopropyl phenyl ketone → 1-phenyl-2-aminobutane. 1-Isonitrosohydrindone → 2-aminohydrindene. 1-Isonitrosomethyl naphthyl ketone → 2-(1-naphthyl)-ethylamine. Phenyl 1-methylamino-butyl ketone → 1-phenyl-2-methylaminopentane.
2. From 1-aryl-1-alkanol-2-amines.

$$C_6H_5CH(OH)CH(CH_3)NH_2 \longrightarrow C_6H_5CH_2CH(CH_3)NH_2$$

The esters of hydroxyl compounds which have been arylated in the 1-position can readily be reduced to hydroxyl-free compounds. They are reduced under esterification conditions with Pd–BaSO₄ in glacial AcOH, while some HClO₄ is added at 80–90°. Ex: Ephedrine chloro-hydrate → (+)-2-phenyl-N-methylisopropylamine chlorohydrate.

Also: 1-(4-methoxyphenyl)-2-aminobutanol → 1-(4-methoxyphenyl)-2-aminobutane. F.e.s. K. W. Rosenmund, E. Karg and F. K. Marcus, *Ber. 75*, 1850 (1942); *C.A. 1944*, 1219.

Platinum   *Pt*

Hydrocarbons from Ketones $CO \rightarrow CH_2$

77.

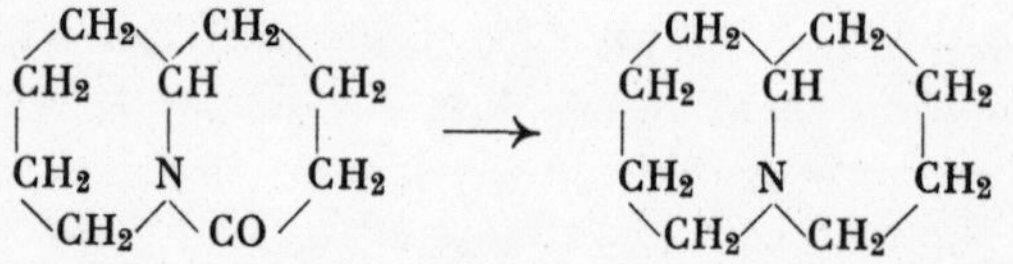

α-Norlupinone is reduced electrolytically for 6 hrs. in 50% H_2SO_4 (8 amp., 0.16 amp./cm.^{2}) → norlupinane. Y = 70%. α-Norlupinone is reduced catalytically in dil. HCl with Pt (from PtO_2) by warming at 25° for 16 hrs. → norlupinane. Y = quant. F. Galinovsky and E. Stern, *Ber. 76*, 1034 (1943); *C.A. 1944*, 3653.

δ-Hydroxyaldehydes from δ-Lactones

78. 4-Methyl-δ-mannonolactone is hydrogenated with Pt (from PtO_2) at room temp. and ordinary pressure → 4-methyl-α-D-mannose. Y, as benzylphenylhydrazone, = 70%. O. T. Schmidt and H. Müller, *Ber. 76B*, 344 (1943); *C.A. 1943*, 5946.

Reduction of Lactams

79.

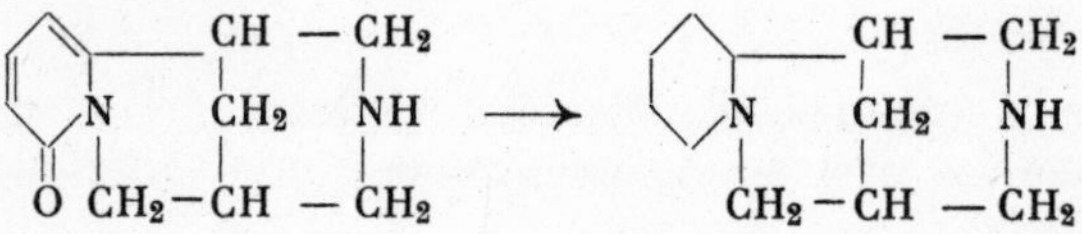

The catalytic reduction of lactams is not suitable in general, but with compounds of high molecular weight such as alkaloids containing a lactam ring, it gives excellent yields. Ex: *N*-methyl-2-pyridone is reduced with Pt (from PtO_2) in dil. HCl at 17° for 42 hrs. → *N*-methylpiperidine. Y = quant. Similarly: cytisine → tetrahydrodesoxycytisine. Addition of H, 157 cc. (155 cc. theor.). F.e.s. F. Galinovsky and E. Stern, *Ber. 77*, 132 (1944); *C.A. 1945*, 938.

Via intermediates

Hydrocarbons from Oxo Compounds via Hydrazones by the Wolff-Kishner Method $CO \rightarrow CH_2$

80. Catalytic Decomposition of Hydrazones. Aromatic aldehyde hydrazones. The behavior of hydrazones of aromatic aldehydes on warming with powdered KOH has been studied. The hydrazones are prepared

from the aldehydes, respectively, azines with $N_2H_4 \cdot H_2O$ in the presence of alc. when necessary ($Y = 70$–91%); the azines with $N_2H_4 \cdot$ salts in dil. alc. ($Y = 81$–97%). The hydrazones are decomposed with KOH at 80–$150°$. The evolution of nitrogen is so vigorous at times that only periodic heating in a horizontally sealed tube leads to a regular conversion. Ex: BzH → toluene; $Y = 79\%$. 2-Chlorobenzaldehyde → 2-chlorotoluene; $Y = 82\%$. 2-Aminobenzaldehyde → 2-toluidine; $Y = 66\%$. 3-Pyrenealdehyde → 3-methylpyrene; $Y = 84\%$. F.e.s. G. Lock and K. Stach, *Ber. 76,* 1252 (1943); *C.A. 1945,* 1395.

81. 3,17-Androstanedione disemicarbazone is heated with Na and $H_2NNH_2 \cdot H_2O$ in alc. for 8 hrs. → androstane. $Y = 80\%$. A. Wettstein, H. Fritzsche, F. Hunziker and K. Miescher, *Helv. Chim. Acta 24E,* 332 (1941); *C.A. 1942,* 5183. Methods, see H. Wieland and W. Kapitel, *Z. physiol. Chem. 212,* 269 (1932); *C.A. 1933,* 511. J. D. Dutcher and O. Wintersteiner, *J. Am. Chem. Soc. 61,* 1992 (1939); *C.A. 1939,* 7813.

82. 10 g. β-(5-methyl-2-furyl)butyraldehyde is refluxed for 5 hrs. with KOH and hydrazine hydrate in some methanol → 6.5 g. 5-methyl-2-*sec*-butylfuran. K. Alder and C. H. Schmidt, *Ber. 76,* 183 (1943); *C.A. 1943,* 4702.

Hydrocarbons from Oxo Compounds via the Aniles
    See 91.

Nitrogen ⚹   HC ⚹ N

Zinc dust   *Zn*

83. **Phenols from Quinones.** 7 g. trimethyl-*p*-benzoquinone is warmed on a water bath with $NH_2OH \cdot HCl$ in dil. HCl → 6.5 g. of the monooxime deriv., 10 g. of which is reduced with $Na_2S_2O_4$ in alc.–H_2O → 7 g. crude 2,3,6-trimethyl-4-aminophenol; this is diazotized with $AmNO_2$ in alc.–concd. HCl and subsequently reduced with Zn dust → 2,3,6-trimethylphenol. $Y =$ up to 50%. P. Karrer and P. Leiser, *Helv. Chim. Acta 27,* 678 (1944); *C.A. 1945,* 519.

Stannous chloride $SnCl_2$

Amines and Aldehydes from Acid Amides
    See 72.

Hypophosphorous acid H_3PO_2

Replacement of Amino Groups by Hydrogen $\cdot NH_2 \rightarrow \cdot H$

84. **General Method.** Bi-*o*-anisidine is diazotized with $NaNO_2$ and the diazonium salt soln. decomposed with ice cold aq. 30% H_3PO_2 → 3,3′-dimethoxybiphenyl. Y = 66–78%. Also: *o*-toluidine → $(3\text{-MeC}_6H_4)_2$. Y = 76–82%. N. Kornblum, *Organic Syntheses 21*, 30 (1941); *C.A. 1941*, 6252.

85. 2,4-Diethyl-6-bromoaniline is diazotized with $NaNO_2$ and HCl in AcOH soln. and treated with H_3PO_2 → 3,5-diethylbromobenzene. Y = 70%. H. R. Snyder, R. R. Adams and A. V. McIntosh, Jr., *J. Am. Chem. Soc. 63*, 3280 (1941); *C.A. 1942*, 1025.

Cuprous oxide Cu_2O

86. **The Effect of Cu_2O on Diazotized Amines in Acid EtOH Solution.** Diazotized amines can be deaminated in acid soln. by the reducing effect of Cu_2O. The method seems to be of general use, because particularly those molecules with prominent cation substituents (nitramines or aminoanthraquinones) give excellent yields. Method: The amine is dissolved in glacial AcOH, diazotized with $NaNO_2$ in H_2SO_4, and added, with stirring, to a suspension of Cu_2O in alc. The deaminized product appears at once without significant side reactions. Cu_2O dissolves almost completely as Cu_2SO_4 and by its oxidation of the alc. to the aldehyde, the "nascent" Cu substantially facilitates the decomposition of the diazonium group. This method is especially suitable for small amounts of amine. Ex: *o*-Nitroaniline → nitrobenzene. Y = 89%. 2-Nitro-1-naphthylamine → β-nitronaphthalene. Y = 79%. 1-Aminoanthraquinone → anthraquinone. Y = 75%. F.e.s. H. H. Hodgson and H. S. Turner, *J. Chem. Soc. (London) 1942*, 748; *C.A. 1943*, 1421. See also H. H. Hodgson, E. Leigh and G. Turner, *J. Chem. Soc. (London) 1942*, 744; *C.A. 1943*, 1422.

87. 1,6-Dinitro-2-naphthylamine is diazotized and the diazonium salt soln. is treated with Cu_2O in an organic solvent (see below) → 1,6-dinitronaphthalene.

Solvent	Yield, %
$HOCH_2CH_2Cl$	69.5
EtOH	57.6; 65.5
MeOH	60.2

For yields with other solvents, see H. H. Hodgson and H. S. Turner, *J. Chem. Soc. (London) 1943*, 86; *C.A. 1943*, 4385.

88. The removal of N_2 from diazonaphthols under reducing conditions proceeds faster and with higher yields if freshly prepared Cu or a

Cu-Al mixt. is used instead of Al. Instead of refluxing in an alc. soln., the AcOH–H_2SO_4 soln. of the diazo compound is added dropwise to the alc. suspension of freshly precipitated Cu_2O. Ex: 6-Nitro-2-diazo-1-naphthol → 6-nitro-1-naphthol. Y = 60–70%. F.e.s. H. H. Hodgson and H. S. Turner, *J. Chem. Soc. (London) 1944*, 8; *C.A. 1944*, 2031.

89. 3-Nitro-1-naphthylamine, dissolved in AcOH, is stirred into a soln. of $NaNO_2$ in H_2SO_4 (d. 1.84) below 20° and the diazonium salt soln. is treated with a suspension of Cu_2O in alc. → 2-nitronaphthalene. Y = nearly quant. H. H. Hodgson and D. E. Hathway, *J. Chem. Soc. (London) 1944*, 21; *C.A. 1944*, 2030.

90. Deamination with Cu_2O in H_2SO_4–AcOH (as free of H_2O as possible) gives yields of about 70% with the naphthalene series and < 40% with the benzene series. Ex: 2,4-Dinitro-1-naphthylamine → 1,3-dinitro-naphthalene. Y = 82%. 2-Nitroaniline → nitrobenzene. Y = 28%. (Prepn., by three different methods, see refs. that follow.) F.e.s. H. H. Hodgson, S. Birtwell and E. Marsden, *J. Chem. Soc. (London) 1944*, 112; *C.A. 1944*, 3640. Compare with: *J. Chem. Soc. (London) 1943*, 433; *C.A. 1943*, 4385.

Palladium   Pd

Hydrocarbons from Aldehydes via Anils   · CHO → · CH₃

91. The aldehyde anil is reduced with Pd prepd. on Norite in a Ni autoclave at 20 atm. Ex: Orcylaldehyde anil → 4,5-dimethylresorcinol. Y = 61.7%. Veratraldehyde anil → homoveratrole. Y = 72%. P. Karrer and E. Schick, *Helv. Chim. Acta 26*, 800 (1943); *C.A. 1944*, 1503.

Via intermediate products

Replacement of Amino Groups by Hydrogen via Chloro Compounds   · NH₂ → · Cl → · H

92. 2-Aminothiazole put through the Sandmeyer reaction → 2-chlorothiazole which is reduced with Zn dust in glacial AcOH → thiazole. Y = 60%. F.e.s. J. McLean and G. D. Muir, *J. Chem. Soc. 1942*, 383; *C.A. 1942*, 5815.

Halogen ⚹   HC ⚹ Hal

Magnesium   Mg

Methylation   See 596.

Nickel *Ni*

Replacement of Chlorine by Hydrogen $\cdot Cl \rightarrow \cdot H$

93. 1,3-Dimethylbicyclo-[3.3.1]-5-chlorononane (1 g.) is reduced with Ni (catalyst according to W. Beckmann, *Thesis,* Hamburg, 1925) in H_2O–alc. in the presence of some KOH at 70–80° → 0.7 g. 1,3-dimethylbicyclo-[3.3.1]-nonane. P. Rabe and K. Appuhn, *Ber. 76,* 982 (1943); *C.A. 1944,* 3259.

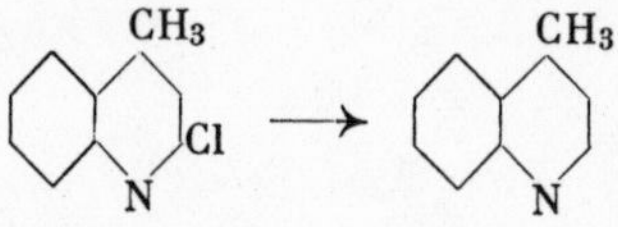

94. 2-Chlorolepidine is reduced with Raney Ni in the presence of KOH in EtOH for 16 hrs. → lepidine. Y = 94%. S. E. Krahler and A. Burger, *J. Am. Chem. Soc. 63,* 2367 (1941); *C.A. 1941,* 7406.

95. 2,6-Dichloropyridine-4-carboxylic acid is reduced with Ni in dil. NaOH at 50° and 4 atm. → pyridine-4-carboxylic acid. Y = 78%. Similarly: 2,6-dibromopyridine-4-carboxylic acid → pyridine-4-carboxylic acid. When the reduction is carried out with Pt in glacial AcOH, piperidine-4-carboxylic acid is obtained, which also is produced from pyridine-4-carboxylic acid under the same conditions. J. P. Wibaut, *Rec. trav. chim. 63,* 141 (1943); *C.A. 1945,* 2073. Methods, see Keller, *Ber. 50,* 305 (1917).

96. 6-Chloro-2,3,4-trimethylpyridine (5.15 g.) is treated with Raney Ni in the presence of MeONa in MeOH → 3.31 g. 2,3,4-trimethylpyridine. V. Prelog, A. Komzak and E. Moor, *Helv. Chim. Acta 25,* 1654 (1942); *C.A. 1943,* 5971.

Palladium *Pd*

97.

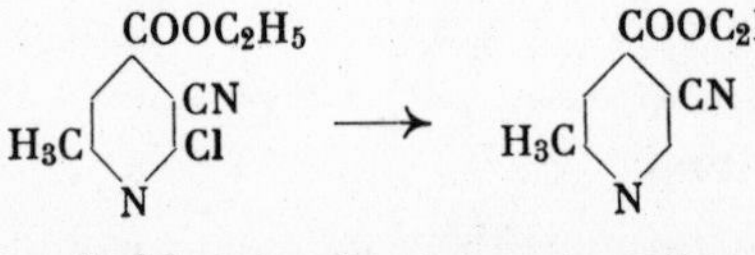

Et 2-methyl-5-cyano-6-chloroisonicotinate is reduced with Pd (5% Pd on $BaCO_3$) in abs. EtOH → Et 2-methyl-5-cyanoisonicotinate. Y = 95%. M. J. Reider and R. C. Elderfield, *J. Org. Chem. 7,* 286 (1942); *C.A. 1942,* 5173.

98. 2-Amino-4-hexyl-6-chloropyrimidine hydrogenated with Pd on charcoal → 2-amino-4-hexylpyrimidine. Y = 87%. F.e.s. J. M. Sprague, L. W.

Kissinger and R. M. Lincoln, *J. Am. Chem. Soc. 63*, 3028 (1941); *C.A. 1942*, 426.

See also 108.

Palladium–barium sulfate   Pd–BaSO₄

Aldehydes from Acid Chlorides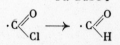

99. Mesitoyl chloride is reduced with Pd–BaSO₄ in boiling xylene → 2,4,6-Me₃C₆H₂CHO. Y = 70–80%. R. P. Barnes, *Organic Syntheses 21*, 110 (1941); *C.A. 1941*, 6249.

00. **Aldehydes from Acid Chlorides with the "Catalyst Poison" of Rosenmund and Zetzsche.** β-Naphthoic acid reduced with PCl₅ → β-naphthoyl chloride (Y = 90–95%) with Pd–BaSO₄ in the presence of a poisoned catalyst prepared from quinoline and S in xylene at 140–150° → β-naphthaldehyde (Y = 74–81%). F.e.s. E. B. Hershberg and J. Cason, *Organic Syntheses 21*, 84 (1941); *C.A. 1941*, 6253. Methods, see Rosenmund and Zetzsche, *Ber. 54*, 436 (1921); *C.A. 1921*, 2435.

01. Similarly: 3 g. elemenoyl chloride, C₃₀H₄₉OCl is reduced in abs. toluene → 2.16 g. elemenal. F.e.s. L. Ruzicka, E. Rey, M. Spillmann and H. Baumgartner, *Helv. Chim. Acta 26*, 1659 (1943); *C.A. 1944*, 2946.

Platinum oxide   PtO₂

02. Thiourea is used instead of quinoline-S for addn. to the PtO₂ catalyst in the Rosenmund and Zetsche method. [*Ber. 51*, 594 (1918); *C.A. 20*, 1936.] Ex: Benzoyl chloride → benzaldehyde; Y = nearly quant. C. Weygand and W. Meusel, *Ber. 76*, 503 (1943); *C.A. 1943*, 666.

Sulfur ⚡   HC ⚡ S

Hydrogen peroxide or nitric acid   H₂O₂ or HNO₃

Replacement of the Mercapto Group by Hydrogen   · SH → ·H

03. 2-Mercapto-4,5-dimethylthiazole is treated with H₂O₂ in a strong HCl soln. or with dil. HNO₃ → 4,5-dimethylthiazole. Y = 60–65%. E. R. Buchman, A. O. Reims and H. Sargent, *J. Org. Chem. 6*, 764 (1941); *C.A. 1942*, 1606.

Carbon ↟   HC ⥮ C

Sodium hydroxide   NaOH

Hydrolytic Opening of the Coumarin Ring   C

104.

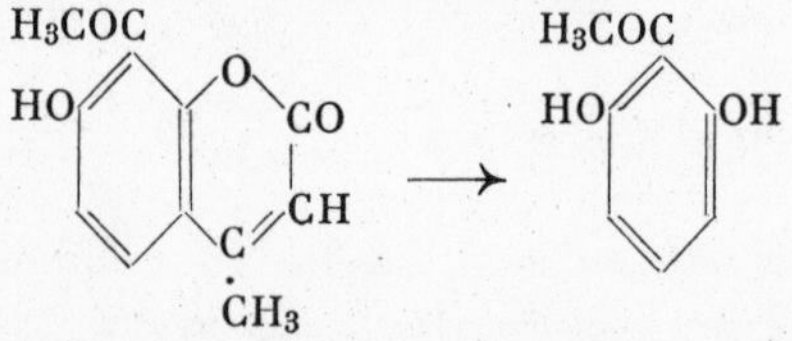

4-Methyl-7-hydroxy-8-acetylcoumarin (prepn., see 538) is heated with 10% aq. NaOH while N_2 is passed through for several hrs. → 2,6-$(HO)_2C_6H_3Ac$. Crude Y = 87–92%. A. Russell and J. R. Frye, *Organic Syntheses 21*, 22 (1941); *C.A. 1941*, 6249.

Cupric salt–Zn Cu^{++}–Zn

Reductive Cleavage   See 547.

Lead dioxide–potassium hydroxide PbO_2–KOH
   See 534.

Elimination

Oxygen ↟   HC ⇑ O

Copper (see copper–chromium oxide catalyst)   *Cu*

Titanium dioxide–formic acid TiO_2–HCOOH

Aldehydes from Carboxylic Acids   · COOH → · CHO

105.   This method can be used only for aliphatic carboxylic acids containing more than 7 C-atoms. The apparatus consists of two soft steel tubes which fit into each other; the play between the tubes is taken up by a low-melting fusible alloy. Method: a sealed glass tube containing the starting product is placed into the inner tube and heated from the outside at practically a horizontal position. Ex: Lauric acid with HCOOH in the presence of TiO_2 is heated for 3 hrs. at 260° and allowed to stand for 2 hrs. → lauraldehyde. Conversion = 31%. Yield is 90% when the acid which has not been converted is taken into consideration.

Acid → aldehyde	Conversion, %	Y, %
Nonoic acid → nonaldehyde	22	78
Salicylic acid → aldehyde	92	92
p-Chlorobenzoic acid → aldehyde	41	89

Butyric, heptoic, and phenylacetic acids do not react, while p-nitrobenzoic acid yields mostly nitrobenzene. F.e.s. R. R. Davies and H. H. Hodgson, *J. Chem. Soc. (London) 1943*, 84; *C.A. 1943*, 4360.

Phosphorus   **P**

Hydrocarbons from Alcohols $\cdot OH \rightarrow \cdot H$
See 73.

Copper–chromium oxide catalyst Cu–Cr_2O_3

06. 2,3-$Me_2C_6H_3CH_2OH$ with Cu-Cr-Ba oxide catalyst under pressure → 1,2,3-$C_6H_3Me_3$. Y = 92%. For further details, see L. I. Smith and L. J. Spillane, *J. Am. Chem. Soc. 62*, 2639 (1940); *C.A. 1940*, 7892.

Iodine   **I**
See 73.

Palladium   **Pd**

7. Mandelic acid is hydrogenated with Mohr Pd at room temp. in the presence of some H_2SO_4 or $HClO_4$ in glacial AcOH → $PhCH_2CO_2H$. Y = 90%. The formation of the mol. compds. of the acid by the addn. of H_2SO_4 or $HClO_4$ speeds up the hydrogenation and enables it to go in a different direction. F.e.s. K. Kindler and Dschi-yin-Kwok, *Ann. 554*, 9 (1943); *C.A. 1943*, 5383.
   See also 76.

Via halogen compounds

Hydrocarbons from Hydroxy Compounds $\cdot OH \rightarrow \cdot H$
8. 2-Methyl-4-amino-6-hydroxypyrimidine (14.5 g.) is refluxed for 3 hrs. with $POCl_3$ → 12.3 g. 2-methyl-4-amino-6-chloropyrimidine; 0.5 g. of this is reduced in aq. HCl with 0.1 g. Pd–C (20% Pd chloride) → 2-methyl-4-aminopyrimidine $\cdot$ HCl (0.5 g.). Zoltan Földi and co-workers, *Ber. 75B*, 755 (1942); *C.A. 1943*, 3434.

Aldehydes from Carboxylic Acids
via Acid Chlorides $\cdot COOH \rightarrow \cdot CHO$
See 100.

Via nitrogen compounds

Aldehydes from Carboxylic Acids
via Acid Hydrazides $\cdot CONHNH_2 \rightarrow \cdot CHO$

9.

Nicotinic acid hydrazide in pyridine is treated with $PhSO_2Cl$ → *sym*-

nicotinyl-(phenylsulfonyl)hydrazine $(Y = 88\%)$. This is treated with Na_2CO_3 in $HOCH_2CH_2OH$ at $160°$ → 3-pyridinecarboxyaldehyde $(Y = 36\%)$.

The following methods for preparing aldehydes from carboxylic acids failed: (1) Reduction of the nicotinic acid imidochloride with $SnCl_2$. (2) Acid saponification of the addn. product of nicotinic acid chloride (respectively, cyanide) to quinoline. (3) Reduction of the nicotinic acid chloride with palladized charcoal.

L. Panizzon, *Helv. Chim. Acta 24E*, 24 (1941); *C.A. 1942*, 5175. Compare Buchman and Richardson, *J. Am. Chem. Soc. 61*, 891 (1939); *C.A. 1939*, 4242. Methods, see J. S. McFadyen and T. S. Stevens, *J. Chem. Soc. 1936*, 584; *C.A. 1936*, 5196.

110. Et 6-quinolinecarboxylate (40 g.) is heated for 2 hrs. at $110°$ with 50% hydrazine hydrate → 35 g. 6-quinolinecarboxylic acid hydrazide which is treated with *p*-toluene-SO_2Cl → *p*-toluenesulfonyl-6-quinolinecarboxylic acid hydrazide. This is heated with glycol and NaOH at $150°$ → 6-quinolinecarboxaldehyde $(Y = 45\%)$. F.e.s. A. H. Cook, I. M. Heilbron and L. Steger, *J. Chem. Soc. 1943*, 413; *C.A. 1944*, 104.

Carbon ⋏   HC ⇑ C

Without additional reagents

Decarboxylation   RCOOH → RH

111.

Flavazolecarboxylic acid (10 g.) is heated in a current of CO_2 → 4.3 g. flavazole. H. Ohle and A. Iltgen, *Ber. 76*, 1 (1943); *C.A. 1943*, 5066.

Copper compounds
    See 610.

112. 2,7-Dimethylpyrido-[2,3-g]quinoline-3,8-dicarboxylic acid (prepn., see 400) is heated at $215°$ with Cu powder and $CuCrO_2$ in quinoline $(Y = 30\%)$; or (with smaller yields) with Cu powder and BaO in a vacuum sublimation app. at $240–50°$ and 11 mm. pressure → 2,7-dimethylpyrido-[2,3-g]quinoline. P. Ruggli and F. Brandt, *Helv. Chim. Acta 27*, 274 (1944); *C.A. 1944*, 6288.

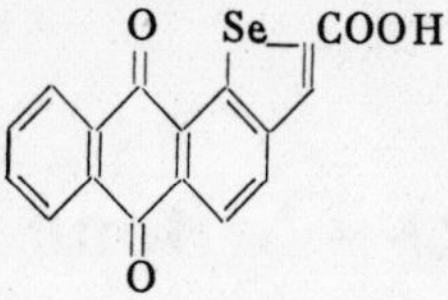

13. 1,2-(Selenopheno-2,'3')-anthraquinone-5'-carboxylic acid (prepn., see 507) is heated at 230–240° with basic $CuCo_3$ in quinoline → 1,2-(selenopheno-2',3')-anthraquinone. Y = 94%. F.e.s. E. B. Hershberg and L. F. Fieser, *J. Am. Chem. Soc. 63*, 2561 (1941); *C.A. 1942*, 458.

Acetic acid–sulfuric acid $CH_3COOH–H_2SO_4$
    See 558, 559.

Hydrochloric acid   *HCl*

α-**Hydroxypyrroles from 5-Bromopyrrole-2-carboxylic Acids**
    See 227.

Formation of O—N Bond by:

Exchange

Hydrogen ⬆   **ON ⇅ H**

Sodium nitrite   *NaNO₂*

Nitro Compounds from Amines   · NH₂ → · NO₂

114. Diazonium cobaltinitrites, $(R \cdot N_2)_3 Co(NO_2)_6$ (prepn., see 259) are decompd. in the cold by aq. $NaNO_2$ in the presence of CuO and $CuSO_4$ (some decompose without $CuSO_4$). Nitroaryl compounds are obtained in excellent yields. Ex: Without $CuSO_4$: o-Nitroaniline → o-dinitrobenzene; Y = 67.4%. p-Chloroaniline → p-chloronitrobenzene; Y = 82.5%. α-Naphthylamine → α-nitronaphthaline; Y = 20%. With $CuSO_4$: α-naphthylamine → α-nitronaphthalene; Y = 68%. F.e.s. H. H. Hodgson and E. Marsden, *J. Chem. Soc. 1944*, 22; *C.A. 1944*, 2021.

Formation of O—S Bond by:

Addition

Addition to Sulfur   OS ⇓ S

Nitric acid   *HNO₃*

Sulfonic Acids from Disulfides   R · S · S · R → 2 RSO₃H
   See 485.

Ozone   *O₃*

Sulfones from Sulfides   R₂S → R₂SO₂

15. Small amts. of sulfones can be prepd. in quant. yields by the action of
O₃ on thio ethers. Ex: Me₂S → Me₂SO₂ (dimethyl sulfone). F.e.s.
H. Böhme and H. Fischer, *Ber. 75*, 1310 (1942); *C.A. 1943, 4686*.

Hydrogen peroxide   *H₂O₂*

Sulfoxides   R₂S → R₂SO

16. (CH₂)₄S (prepn., see 484) is treated with H₂O₂ in Me₂CO (Y =
88%), or without solvent (Y = 90%) → tetramethylene sulfoxide (s.m.
268). F.e.s. D. S. Tarbell and C. Weaver, *J. Am. Chem. Soc. 63*, 2939;
C.A. 1942, 470.

Sulfones ·   R₂ → R₂SO₂

17. (CH₂)₄S (prepn., see 484) with the theoretical amt. of 30% H₂O₂ →
tetramethylene sulfone. Y = 97%. D. S. Tarbell and C. Weaver, *J. Am.
Chem. Soc. 63*, 2939 (1941); *C.A. 1942, 470*.

Potassium permanganate   *KMnO₄*

Sulfones from Sulfides   R₂S → R₂SO₂
   See 492.

Sulfonamides and Sulfinamides   · SONH₂ → · SO₂NH₂
   See 269.

Halogen   *Hal.*

Sulfonyl Chlorides from Thiocyanates $\cdot$ SCN $\rightarrow$ $\cdot$ SO$_2$Cl

118. Primary-isobutyl thiocyanate is treated with Cl in an aq. suspension at 5° → prim.-isobutanesulfonyl chloride. Y = 91%. F. Asinger and F. Ebeneder, *Ber.* 75, 344 (1942); *C.A. 1943,* 3048.

Sulfonic Acids from Disulfides   R $\cdot$ S $\cdot$ S $\cdot$ R $\rightarrow$ 2 RSO$_3$H

119. Addn. of Br to cystine in HCl soln. → cysteic acid. Y = 81–90%. H. T. Clarke, *Organic Syntheses* 20, 23 (1940); *C.A. 1940,* 5052.

Sulfonic Acids from Mercaptans $\cdot$ SH $\rightarrow$ $\cdot$ SO$_3$H

120. γ-Mercapto-α,β-dimethylbutyric acid (prepn., see 38) is neutralized with Ba(OH)$_2$ $\cdot$ 8 H$_2$O and, after addn. of BaCO$_3$, oxidized with Br$_2$ in the cold → Ba γ-sulfo-α,β-dimethylbutyrate. Y = 83%. F. Kögl, J. H. Verbeek, H. Erxleben and W. A. J. Borg, *Z. physiol. Chem.* 279, 121 (1943); *C.A. 1944,* 3978. Methods, see P. A. Levene, *J. Biol. Chem.* 75, 344 (1927).

Exchange

Halogen ⬆   **OS** ⥮ **Hal**

Alkali hydroxide

    See 123.

Organic bases

Sulfuric Acid Esters from Phenols $\cdot$ OH $\rightarrow$ $\cdot$ OSO$_3$H

121. Sulfuric acid esters can be prepared very readily by adding ClSO$_3$H to PhOH in PhNMe$_2$ or C$_5$H$_5$N and after making the soln. alkaline with strong aq. KOH, the K-salt of phenol sulfate is extracted with hot 95% EtOH. The yields are excellent. Ex: 1- and 2-C$_{10}$H$_7$OH in PhNMe$_2$ → 1- and 2-naphtholsulfonic acid. PhOH in C$_5$H$_5$N → phenolsulfonic acid. J. Feigenbaum and C. A. Neuberg, *J. Am. Chem. Soc.* 63, 3529 (1941); *C.A. 1942,* 1022.

Sulfuric Acid Esters of Sterols

122.

$$ROH \xrightarrow{\quad C_6H_5N \cdot SO_3 \quad} ROSO_3H \cdot NC_5H_5$$

H$_2$O, H$^+$ ↖   ↙ KCl

ROSO$_3$K

Sterols may be isolated and separated as steryl sulfates because of their ease of formation in quantitative yields and their insolubility in lipide solvents in contrast to the digitonides. Preparation: The sterols are heated with $C_5H_5NSO_3$ at 50–60°. The pyridinium sulfate which precipitates is decomposed into the K salt of the steryl sulfate with 10% KCl. The sterol is regenerated by heating the steryl sulfate with H_2O and some H_2SO_4. A. E. Sobel and P. E. Spoerri, *J. Am. Chem. Soc. 64*, 361 (1942); *C.A. 1942*, 1942.

Esters of Methanesulfonic Acid   · OH → · OSO₂CH₃

23. **Masking of Phenolic Hydroxy Groups through Esterification with Methanesulfonic Acid.** The methane sulfonates of phenols, C_6H_5-OSO_2CH_3, are only slightly affected by acid but are hydrolyzed by alkali. They can usually be prepared in good yields, either by mixing the phenol with a slight excess of $MeSO_2Cl$ in C_5H_5N or by treating the alkaline solution of the phenol with an excess of $MeSO_2Cl$ (or its solution in a suitable solvent like C_6H_6). These Ph methyl sulfonates are easily crystallized. They can be prepared from simple or higher phenols. Partial masking is also possible. The resistance against acid hydrolysis is great; prolonged boiling with concentrated HCl has no effect. Hydrolysis takes place at room temperature upon extended storage, however, in an aq. *N*-alkaline, aq. Me_2CO solution. Hydrolysis proceeds even more readily under the same conditions with the methane sulfonate of a higher phenol homologue, which has been fully masked; further hydrolysis can be accomplished only by refluxing. Ex: PhOH in aq. KOH (cooled) is stirred vigorously with $MeSO_2Cl$ in C_6H_6 → Ph methane sulfonate; Y = 90%. Resorcinol → bis(methane sulfonate) resorcinol; Y = 95%. F.e.s. B. Helferich and P. Papalambrou, *Ann. 551*, 235 (1942); *C.A. 1943*, 5040.

24. Tetraacetylglycol-*β*-D-glucoside (1 g.) is treated with $MeSO_2Cl$ in abs. C_5H_5N in the cold → 1 g. tetraacetylmethane sulfonic glycol-*β*-D-glucoside. B. Helferich and J. Werner, *Ber. 75*, 1446 (1942); *C.A. 1944*, 1213.

p-Toluene Sulfonate   · OH → · OSO₂C₇H₇

25. p-$MeC_6H_4SO_2Cl$ added to 1-dodecanol in C_6H_5N at 20° → dodecyl-*p*-toluene sulfate. Y = 88–90%. F.e.s. C. S. Marvel and V. C. Sekera, *Organic Syntheses 20*, 50 (1940); *C.A. 1940*, 5048.

See also 233.

Formation of Bond between Oxygen and Remaining Elements by:

Addition

Addition to Oxygen and Carbon   OR ⇓ OC

Without additional reagents

**Phosphoric Acid Esters
and Alkylene Oxides**

$$R \cdot CH \overset{\displaystyle\diagdown}{\underset{CH_2}{\cdot}} O \longrightarrow \overset{\displaystyle RCHOH}{\underset{CH_2OPO_3^{--}}{\cdot}}$$

126. 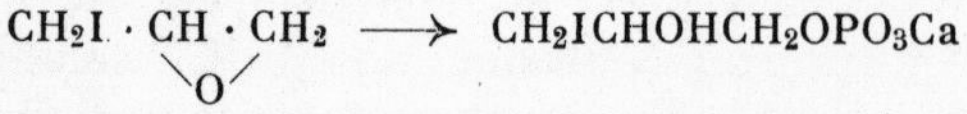 $CH_2I \cdot CH \cdot CH_2 \longrightarrow CH_2ICHOHCH_2OPO_3Ca$
                        $\diagdown O \diagup$

1 Mole epiiodohydrin is acted upon by 2 moles 89% H_3PO_4 and the reaction product is neutralized with $CaCO_3$ and $Ca(OH)_2 \rightarrow$ Ca iodopropanediol phosphate. Y = 71%. E. Eidenbenz and M. Depner, *Arch. Pharm. 280*, 227 (1942); *C.A. 1943*, 4077.

Exchange

Halogen ⋏   OR ⋔ Hal

Phosphorus oxychloride   POCl₃

Phosphoric Acid Esters

127. *m*-Cresol (54 g.) is refluxed for 8 hrs. with POCl₃ under anhyd. conditions → 40 g. tri-*m*-cresol phosphate. F.e.s. F. L. Breusch and H. Keskin, *Rev. faculté sci. univ. Istanbul 7A*, 182 (1942) (in German); *C.A. 1944*, 1483.

Formation of O—C Bond by:

Addition

Addition to Hydrogen and Carbon   OC ⇓ HC

Silver oxide   Ag$_2$O

Carboxylic Acids from Aldehydes   CHO → COOH

128. Aldehydes of high mol. wt. can be oxidized quantitatively to the corresponding acids with Ag$_2$O. Ex: Enanthal is stirred into a suspension of Ag$_2$O in 10% NaOH over a period of 1 hr. at 95°; after 6 hrs. HNO$_3$ (d. 1.40) is slowly added at 70° → enanthic acid. Y = 97.5%. F.e.s. F. Asinger, *Ber. 75*, 656 (1942); *C.A. 1942*, 6135.

129. Δ^3-Tetrahydrobenzaldehyde is treated with Ag$_2$O in alc. KOH → Δ^3-tetrahydrobenzoic acid. Y = 62.5%. H. Fiesselmann, *Ber. 75*, 881 (1942); *C.A. 1943*, 3417. Methods, see Deléphine, *Bull. soc. chim. Mém.* (4) 5, 879 (1909).

Lead compounds

Secondary Alcohols from Hydrocarbons   CH$_2$ → CHOH

130.

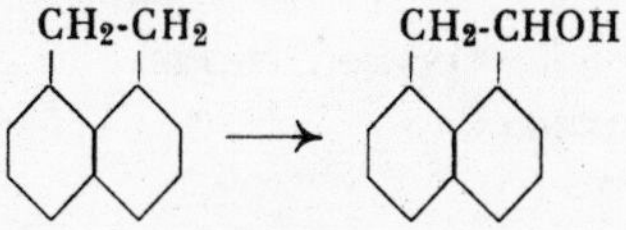

CH$_2$-CH$_2$ → CH$_2$-CHOH

Acenaphthene in glacial AcOH is treated with Pb$_3$O$_4$ at 60–70° → acenaphthenyl acetate (Y = 80–82%). This is refluxed with aqueous MeOH and NaOH → 1-acenaphthanol (Y = 70–74%). J. Cason, *Organic Syntheses 21*, 1 (1941); *C.A. 1941*, 6254.

2-Hydromethylpyrroles from
2-Hydroxymethylpyrroles   · CH$_3$ → · CH$_2$OH
See 159.

Persulfate   S$_2$O$_8$$^{--}$

Replacement of Hydrogen by Hydroxyl   · H → · OH

131.

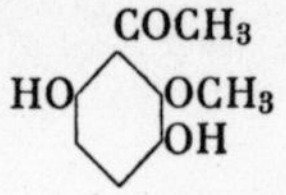

$$COCH_3$$

2,6-HO(MeO)C$_6$H$_3$Ac (16 g.) in 10% NaOH is treated with K$_2$S$_2$O$_8$ → 5 g. 6,2,5-MeO(HO)$_2$C$_6$H$_2$Ac. K. Wallenfels, *Ber.* 75, 785 (1942); *C.A. 1943*, 3425.

Addition to Oxygen   OC ⇓ OO

Without additional reagents

Peroxides   ·H → ·OOH

132.

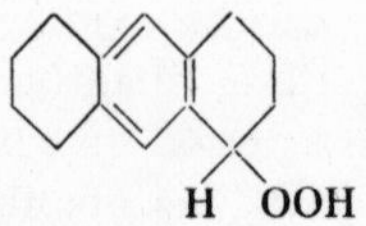

H   OOH

Octahydroanthracene is shaken with dry oxygen for 12 hrs. at 75° and isolated via the Na salt → octahydroanthracene peroxide (s.m. 16, 246). Y = 15%. H. Hock and Shon Lang, *Ber.* 76, 1130 (1943); *C.A. 1944*, 4935. See also *Ber.* 77, 257 (1944); *C.A. 1945*, 3526.

Addition to Oxygen and Carbon   OC ⇓ OC

Sulfuric acid   H$_2$SO$_4$

Opening of Heterocyclic Oxygen Rings.
γ-Diketones from Furans   C

133. 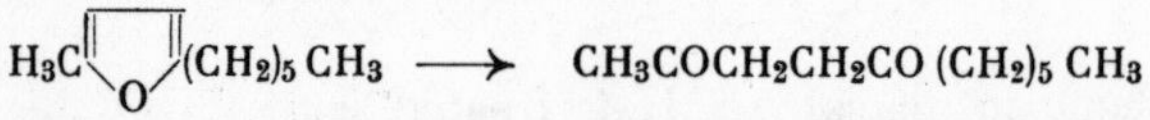   H$_3$C⎯⎯(CH$_2$)$_5$ CH$_3$ ⟶ CH$_3$COCH$_2$CH$_2$CO (CH$_2$)$_5$ CH$_3$

5-Methyl-2-hexylfuran is heated with a little H$_2$SO$_4$ in AcOH for 1.5 hrs. at 120° → 2,5-hendecanedione. Y = 86%. [For further syntheses of γ-diketones see H. Hunsdiecker, *Ber.* 75, 477 (1942); *C.A. 1943*, 3403.]

134. Pentaacetyl-β-methyl-D-manno-D-galaheptofuranoside is treated with 4% H$_2$SO$_4$ in 70 : 30 Ac$_2$O–AcOH → aldehydo-D-manno-D-galaheptose hexaacetate. Y = 94%. E. M. Montgomery and C. S. Hudson, *J. Am. Chem. Soc.* 64, 247 (1942); *C.A. 1942*, 1906.

Addition to Nitrogen and Carbon   OC ⇓ NC

Hydrogen peroxide H_2O_2

Acid Amides from Nitriles $\cdot C \equiv N \longrightarrow \cdot C \diagdown^{O}_{NH_2}$

35. 3-Cyanopyridine is hydrolyzed with a 6% H_2O_2 soln. in the presence of NaOH → nicotinamide. Y = up to 20%. Nicotinamide was obtained only in traces by partial hydrolysis with 90% H_2SO_4. A. Georg and P. Bachmann, *Helv. Chim. Acta 26*, 358 (1943); *C.A. 1944*, 100.

Quinazoline Ring from Isatin Ring   See 293.

Addition to Carbon   OC ⇓ CC

Without additional reagents

Organomercury Compounds   See RC ⇓ CC

Silver benzoate–iodine $C_6H_5COOAg–I$

**Glycols from Ethylene
Derivatives** $\cdot CH : CH \cdot \rightarrow \cdot CH(OH) \cdot CH(OH) \cdot$
See 146.

Mercury Hg

**Addition of Water to Triple Bond Ketones
from Acetylene Derivatives** $\cdot C \equiv CH \rightarrow \cdot COCH_3$

136.

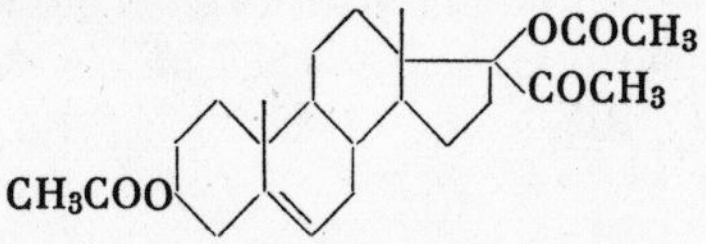

Δ^5-17-Ethynylandrostene-3(β),17(α)-diol diacetate (1 g.) is refluxed for 72 hours with (p-MeC$_6$H$_4$SO$_2$NH)$_2$Hg in 96% alcohol and the Hg precipitated with H_2S → Δ^5-3(β),17(α)-diacetoxypregnen-20-one (1.05 g.). M. W. Goldberg, R. Aeschbacher and E. Hardegger, *Helv. Chim. Acta 26*, 680 (1943); *C.A. 1944*, 1514. Compare E. Hardegger and C. Scholz, *Helv. Chim. Acta 28*, 1355 (1945); *C.A. 1946*, 1895.

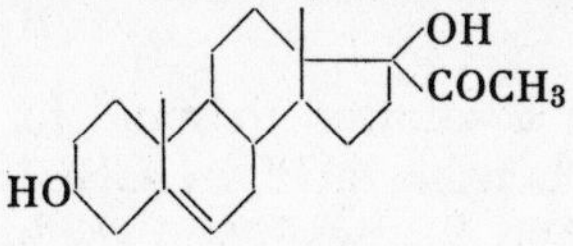

137. Δ^5-17-Ethynylandrostene-3,17-diol (4 g.), HgCl$_2$, PhNH$_2$, C$_6$H$_6$, and
      H$_2$O are heated at 60° for 20 hrs. → 3.8 g. Δ^5-pregnene-3,17-diol-20-
      one. H. E. Stavely, *J. Am. Chem. Soc. 63*, 3127 (1941); *C.A. 1942*, 486.

Addition of Alcohols to the Triple Bond   · C ≡ C · →· CH = C(OR) ·

138. Methyl butyl propiolate is treated with abs. MeOH and a catalyst
      (prepd. from red HgO, ether–BF$_3$, abs. MeOH, and trichloracetic
      acid) at 50° → Me *n*-butyl-β-methoxyacrylate. Y = 52%. F.e.s. A. O.
      Zoss and G. F. Hennion, *J. Am. Chem. Soc. 63*, 1151 (1941); *C.A. 1941*,
      3601.

Zinc chloride   ZnCl$_2$

Coumaran and Chromane Derivatives from Dihydric Phenols
      See 698.

Lead tetraacetate   Pb(CH$_3$COO)$_4$

Ketones from Ethylene Derivatives   · CH = CH · → · CH$_2$ · CO ·

139.

Isoeugenol Me ether is converted to the acylated glycol with
Pb(OAc)$_4$ in glacial AcOH, according to Criegee [*Ann. 481*, 302
(1930)]; this is treated with 20% H$_2$SO$_4$ without isolation. The saponification of the acetyl group converts it to the ketone → veratrylacetone
(3,4-dimethoxyphenylacetone). Y = 37%. F.e.s. A. V. Wacek, *Ber. 77*,
85 (1944); *C.A. 1945*, 917.

Perbenzoic acid

Ring Opening. Lactones from Ketones   C

140.

3-Cholestanone (1 g.) is allowed to stand for 16 hrs. in the dark at
room temp. with perbenzoic acid in CHCl$_3$ → 610 mg. lactone.
F.e.s. V. Burckhardt and T. Reichstein, *Helv. Chim. Acta 25*, 1434
(1942); *C.A. 1943*, 5980. See also U. Prelog, L. Ruzicka, P. Meister
and P. Wieland, *Helv. Chim. Acta 28*, 618 (1945); *C.A. 1946*, 891.

Bromoacetamide

α-Hydroxy Halogen Compounds
from Ethylene Derivatives   · CH = CH · → · CH(Br) · CH(OH) ·
See 405.

Ozone   *O₃*

Aldehydes and Ketones   · CH = CH · → · CO

41.

(3-(β)-Acetoxy-11 (α)-hydroxyetiocholanyl) methyldiphenylethylene
is treated with O₂ + 4% O₃ at the rate of 100 cc./min. (in acetate) for
2.5 min. at −80°. Dry air is blown through at −80°; the ozonide
is carefully cleaved with Zn dust and glacial AcOH and the reaction
mixture is heated to room temp. with constant shaking until the spot
test with KI paper is negative. The separation is completed with
Girard Reagent T [A. Girard and G. Sandulesco, *Helv. Chim. Acta 19,*
1095 (1936); *Organic Syntheses 18*, 10 (1938)] and the product
acetylated with Ac₂O–pyridine → 3 (β),11 (α)-pregnanediol-20-one
3-acetate. Y = 63%. F.e.s. J. v. Euw, A. Lardon and T. Reichstein,
Helv. Chim. Acta 27, 821 (1944); *C.A. 1945*, 938.

42. Ozonides react with Raney Ni to give aldehydes or ketones and NiO.
The yields of aldehydes and ketones are comparable to those obtained
by Fischer by a less convenient method, and are at least twice those
obtained by earlier methods. N. C. Cook and F. C. Whitmore, *J. Am.
Chem. Soc. 63*, 3540 (1941); *C.A. 1942*, 1010.

Carboxylic Acids   · CH = CH · → · COOH

43. Ozonides of olefins of high mol. wt. can be cleaved by adding a hot
alkaline suspension of Ag₂O dropwise at 90–95°, and stirring for several hrs. Olefins mixed with satd. hydrocarbons can also be cleaved in
this manner. Isomerization does not seem to occur. Ex: 1-Tridecylene
is ozonized at −5° in CHCl₃ → 1-tridecylene ozonide. Y = 99%. This
is added dropwise to a suspension of Ag₂O in 10% NaOH over a period
of 40 minutes at 90° → lauric acid. Crude Y = 94%. F.e.s. F. Asinger,
Ber. 75, 656 (1942); *C.A. 1942*, 6135.

Hydrogen peroxide H_2O_2

Flavones   O
  See 245.

Opening of the Isatin Ring   C
  See 281.

Glycols from Ethylene Derivatives $\cdot C = C \cdot \rightarrow \cdot C(OH) \cdot C(OH) \cdot$
  See 145.

Thionyl chloride $SOCl_2$

Ketones from Ethylene Derivatives $\cdot C = C \cdot \rightarrow \cdot CO$

144.

Ethylene compounds can be cleaved to two keto groups by successive treatment with $SOCl_2$ and H_2O. Ex: Bixanthylene is refluxed for 1 hr. with $SOCl_2$ and the reaction product is shaken with H_2O at 30° → xanthone. Y = quantitative. F.e.s. A. Schönberg and W. Asker, *J. Chem. Soc. 1942*, 725; *C.A. 1943*, 884.

Potassium permanganate $KMnO_4$

Glycols from Ethylene Derivatives $\cdot C = C \cdot \rightarrow \cdot C(OH) \cdot C(OH) \cdot$

145. **Stereoisomers.** Alk. $KMnO_4$ oxidation causes *cis* addition, while H_2O_2-AcOH oxidation probably causes *trans* addition. α-(*trans?*)-9-octadenedioic acid is heated with H_2O_2 in glacial AcOH at 70–80°. The partly esterified crude products are saponified by heating with 20% KOH → meso(?)-9,10-dihydroxyoctadecanedioic acid, m.p. 158.5–159.5°.

α-(*trans?*)-9-octadenedioic acid is oxidized in the cold with 1% $KMnO_4$ in dil. NaOH → racem(?)-9,10-dihydroxyoctadecanedioic acid, m.p. 122.5–123.5°. H. Hunsdiecker, *Ber. 77*, 185 (1944); *C.A. 1945*, 2975.

Iodine–silver benzoate $I-AgOOCC_6H_5$

146. 1-Octadecene is treated with BzOAg and I → 1,2-octadecanediol. Y = 73%. F.e.s. C. Niemann and C. D. Wagner, *J. Org. Chem. 7*, 227 (1942); *C.A. 1942*, 5136. (Methods, see Prévost, *C.A. 27*, 3195).

Osmium tetraoxide OsO_4

HO H HO H

47.

The addition of OsO_4 to the double bond is accelerated appreciably in the presence of tertiary bases. The pyridine addition products of the monoesters are obtained in quant. yields; these are easily purified by recrystallization. By this new method, osmium compounds of olefins can be prepared which do not react without the use of pyridine. The hydrolytic cleavage of the pyridine compound with cold diluted aq. KOH in the presence of mannitol lends itself particularly well to the prepn. of the diols from the monoesters. The K osmiate formed is thus bound as the water-soluble diester (or its K salt). The high solubility of the mannitol diesters and their salts in water, and their corresponding insolubility in organic solvents, makes the isolation of pure glycols easier. Ex: Phenanthrene, OsO_4, and C_5H_5N are allowed to stand for 7 days in thiophene-free $C_6H_6 \rightarrow$ 9,10-dihydrophenanthrene-9,10-diol osmiate ($+ 2 C_5H_5N$), (Y = 95%), which is shaken in methylene chloride with aq. KOH and mannitol for about 1 hr. → dihydrophenanthrene-9,10-diol (Y = 64%). F.e.s. R. Criegee, B. Marchand and H. Wannowins, *Ann.* 550, 99 (1942); *C.A. 1943*, 2720.

48. α-Bufotalin is treated with OsO_4 in abs. ether → α-bufotalene glycol. Y = almost quant. H. Wieland and H. Behringer, Hesse and K. Gäbelein, *Ann.* 549, 209 (1941); *C.A. 1943*, 1438.

CH₃
ĊH (CH₂)₂ CH : C (CH₃)₂

→

CH₃
ĊH (CH₂)₂CH : C (CH₃)₂

49. Cryptosterol is allowed to stand at room temp. with OsO_4 in ether for 2 days; the precipitate, brown OsO_4 ester is decomposed with Na_2SO_3; the reaction product is saponified with MeOH–KOH → cryptostene-triol. Y = 60%. H. Wieland and W. Benend, *Ber.* 75, 1708 (1942); *C.A. 1943*, 5978.

Rearrangement

Hydrogen–Carbon Type   OC ↷ HC

Sodium hydroxide   *NaOH*

Flavanones from Chalcones

150. 2′,4,5-Trihydroxychalcone 4-β-D-glucoside (for prepn., see 551) is allowed to stand for 6 days at room temp. with NaOH → 3′,4′-dihydroxyflavanone 4′-β-D-glucoside, $C_{21}H_{22}O_9$. Y = 83.6%. L. Reichel and J. Marchand, *Ber. 76*, 1132 (1943); *C.A. 1944*, 4944.

Silver oxide Ag_2O

Syntheses with Diazomethane
See CC ⑂ Hal. without additional reagents.

Ammonium polysulfide $(NH_4)_2S_x$

151. **Amides and Carboxylic Acids**
     from Methyl Ketones
$$\cdot COCH_3 \begin{cases} \cdot CH_2COOH \\ \cdot CH_2CONH_2 \end{cases}$$

3-Pyridyl Me ketone in aq. $(NH_4)_2S$ is heated for 6 hrs. at 160–170° → mixt. of 3-pyridineacetamide and the acid. Y = up to 70%. M. Hartmann and W. Bosshard, *Helv. Chim. Acta 24*, 28E (1941); *C.A. 1942*, 5175. Methods, see Willgerodt, Houben-Weyl, Vol. III, 867.

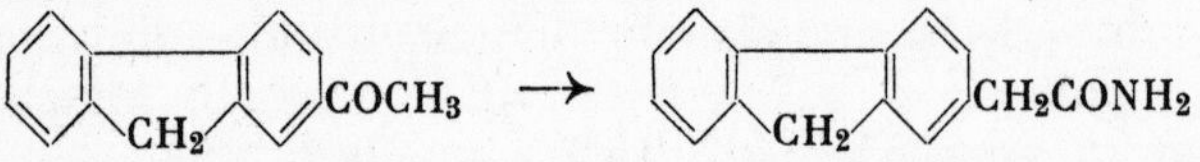

152. 8-Acetylfluorene is heated at 160° in dioxane for 10 hrs. with $(NH_4)_2S_x$ in a sealed tube → 2-fluoreneacetamide. Y = 70%. W. E. Bachmann and J. C. Sheehan, *J. Am. Chem. Soc. 62*, 2687 (1940); *C.A. 1940*, 7897.

Hydrochloric acid HCl

Flavanones
See 552, 553.

Oxygen–Nitrogen Type   OC ↷ ON

Without additional reagents

**Substituted Aspartic Acids from Aromatic
Oximes and Maleic Anhydride**

153.

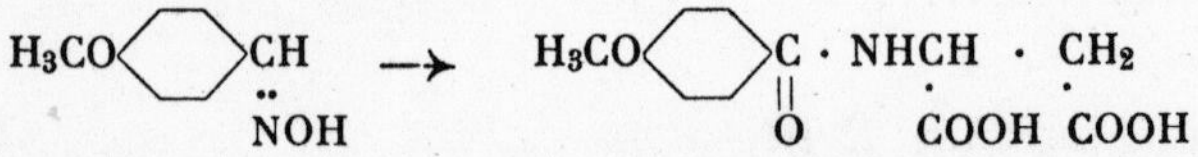

α-Anisaldoxime is heated with maleic anhydride in C_6H_6 → p-methoxybenzoylaspartic acid (Y = 70%). This is not a general reaction: the position and nature of the substituents have a profound influence on the course of the reaction. F.e.s. G. La Parola, *Gazz. chim. Ital. 73*, 94 (1943); *C.A. 1944*, 5211.

Nitrogen–Carbon Type

Hydrochloric acid

O-Acyl from N-Acyl Derivatives

OC ↻ NC

HCl

NAc → OAc

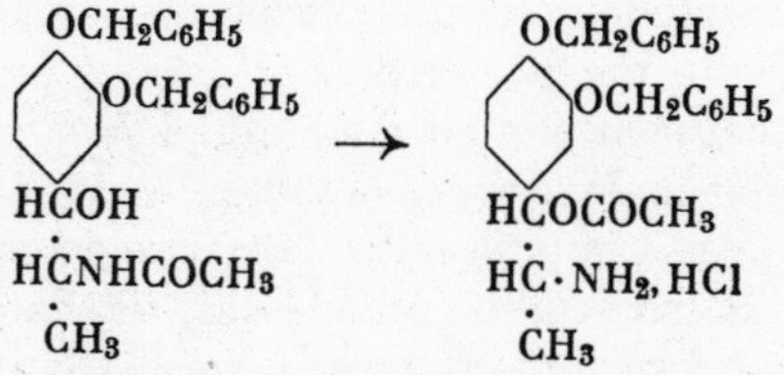

1-(3,4-Dibenzyloxyphenyl)-2-acetamido-1-propanol is dissolved in an equimol. amt. of 4% MeOH–HCl and the soln. allowed to stand in an evacuated desiccator → 1-(3,4-dibenzyloxyphenyl)-2-aminopropyl acetate–HCl. Y = nearly quant. V. Bruckner and G. v. Fodor, *Ber. 76*, 466 (1943); *C.A. 1943*, 6656. See also G. v. Fodor, *Ber. 76*, 1216 (1943); *C.A. 1945*, 286.

Exchange

Hydrogen ⋏

Silver–copper catalyst

Aldehydes from Alcohols

OC ⥮ H

Ag–Cu

CH_2OH → CHO

Cu–Ag–pumice gives the best yields among four catalysts for the catalytic oxidn. of alcs. with air at 300–350°. These four are: (*1*) Cu-kieselguhr; (*2*) Cu–Ag–kieselguhr; (*3*) Cu–Ag–pumice; and (*4*) Ag on Cu gauze. For apparatus and method see original. Ex: Butyl alcohol → butaldehyde. Y = 96%. Dodecyl alcohol → dodecaldehyde. Y = 88%. $PhCH_2OH$ → benzaldehyde. Y = 76.5%. R. R. Davies and H. H. Hodgson, *J. Chem. Soc. 1943*, 282; *C.A. 1943*, 5370.

Fehling solution

Benzil Compounds from Benzoins

$CH(OH) \cdot CO$ → $CO \cdot CO$

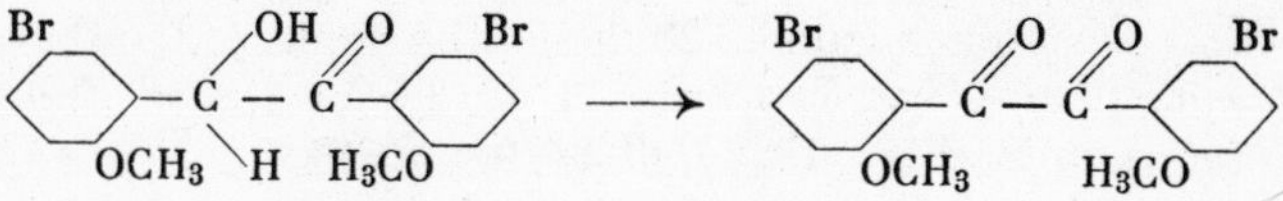

5,5'-Dibromo-2,2'-dimethoxybenzoin (5 g.) (for prepn., see 513) is refluxed with just the required amt. of Fehling soln. in 70% alc. → 4.5 g. 5,5'-dibromo-2,2'-dimethoxybenzil. R. Kuhn, L. Birkofer and E. F. Möller, Ber. 76, 900 (1943); C.A. 1944, 2950.

Aluminum alcoholate   *Al(OR)₃*

Aldehydes from Alcohols   CH₂OH → CHO

157. The conversion of an alcohol into the corresponding aldehyde by a less volatile aldehyde (with the Al alkoxide as catalyst) and the influence of an ethylene linkage in the reactant aldehyde were investigated. The reaction involved in Meerwein's method (*C.A. 19*, 3250; *31*, 656) is reversible, but if a less volatile aldehyde is selected as the reactant, the more volatile aldehyde can be removed by distillation, and equilibrium prevented. The function of the Al alkoxide is to activate one of the alc. H atoms for the purpose of hydrogen bonding. This view is supported by the fact that cinnamaldehyde (whose double bond is in the side chain favors formation of the H bond) gives better yields than benzaldehyde. Ex: Al powder is washed with C_6H_6, hot 5% NaOH, H_2O, and alc. Then it is treated for 30 minutes with a 0.5% alc. soln. of $HgCl_2$ and rinsed with alc. The powder is then added (with cooling) to clean (washed with dil. NaOH, dil. $NaHSO_3$, and H_2O, and dried with Na_2SO_4) Bz alcohol and treated with cinnamaldehyde. The mixture is refluxed in a 10-plate Raschig column (reflux ratio 1:10) → benzaldehyde. Y = 94.5%, on the basis of cinnamaldehyde used. Yield of cinnamic alcohol = 88.6%.

n-Butanol → n-butaldehyde. Yield on basis of aldehyde used: 47.8% with BzH, and 72% with cinnamaldehyde. R. R. Davies and H. H. Hodgson, *J. Indian Chem. Soc. 62*, 109 (1943); *C.A. 1943*, 6254.

Aluminum phenolate   *Al(OC₆H₅)₃*

Ketones from Secondary Alcohols   · CH(OH) · → · CO ·

158.

3(α),12(β)-21-pregnanetriol-20-one 21-acetate (2.45 g.) is refluxed with Al(OPh)₃ (prepn., see original) in abs. C_6H_6 and anhyd. Me_2CO → 1 g. 12(β)-21-pregnanediol-3,20-dione 21-acetate. Al(OPh)₃ gives better results than Al isopropylate. H. G. Fuchs and T. Reichstein, *Helv. Chim. Acta 26*, 511 (1943); *C.A. 1944*, 1516.

Lead tetraacetate $Pb(CH_3COO)_4$

2-Hydroxymethyl- and 2-Formylpyrroles
from 2-Methylpyrroles

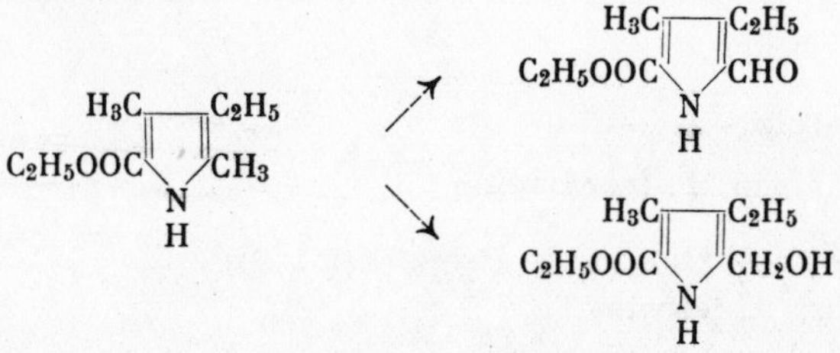

1. 2,4-Dimethyl-3-ethyl-5-carbethoxypyrrole is treated with 1 mole of $Pb(OAc)_4$ at 20–25° → 4-methyl-2-hydroxymethyl-3-ethyl-5-car-bethoxypyrrole. Y = nearly quant.

2. 2,4-Dimethyl-3-ethyl-5-carbethoxypyrrole is treated with one mole of $Pb(OAc)_4$ at room temp., and with a second mole of $Pb(OAc)_4$ on a boiling water bath → 4-methyl-3-ethyl-2-formyl-5-carbethoxypyrrole. Crude Y = 80%. F.e.s. W. Siedel and F. Winkler, *Ann. 554*, 162 (1943); *C.A. 1943*, 5399.

Nitrogen oxides

Aldehydes from Alcohols $CH_2OH \rightarrow CHO$

60. 4-Cyanobenzyl alc. (10 g.) and N_2O_4 in $CHCl_3$ → 8–9 g. 4-NCC_6-H_4CHO. J. N. Ashley, H. J. Barber, A. J. Ewins, G. Newbery and A. D. H. Self, *J. Chem. Soc. 1942*, 103; *C.A. 1942*, 3496.

Quinones from Hydroquinones

61. Dibenzoylhydroquinone in C_6H_6 is treated with N oxides → dibenzoylquinone. Y = 74%. R. Pummerer, E. Buchta, E. Deimler and E. Singer, *Ber. 75*, 1976 (1943); *C.A. 1944*, 1214.

Sulfur   S

Amino Aldehydes from Nitro Hydrocarbons

62. Boiling *p*-nitrotoluene is treated dropwise for one hour with a boiling soln. of S in 17% aq. NaOH and heated for an addl. 2 hrs. → *p*-aminobenzaldehyde (Y = 52%). Also: *o*-chloro-*p*-nitrotoluene → *o*-chloro-*p*-aminobenzaldehyde (Y = 46%). The loosely bound S of the polysulfides plays an important role in the oxidation of the Me to the CHO group. EtOH proves to be the best solvent, while free alkali must be present. H. G. Beard, H. H. Hodgson and R. R. Davies, *J. Chem. Soc. 1944*, 4; *C.A. 1944*, 2024.

Ammonium polysulfide $(NH_4)_2S_x$

Amides and Carboxylic Acids
from Methyl Ketones

$\cdot COCH_3 \begin{cases} CH_2COOH \\ CH_2CONH_2 \end{cases}$

See 151.

Selenium dioxide SeO_2

Aldehydes from Hydrocarbons

$CH_3 \rightarrow CHO$

Use of Selenium Dioxide in Preparation of Quinoline Aldehydes

163. In the prepn. of quinoline aldehydes from the corresponding homologues the SeO_2 used should be freshly prepared; SeO_2 which is sublimed immediately after prepn. can also be used. Old SeO_2 gave only traces of aldehydes with quinaldine and lepidine, but excellent yields (80%) of benzoin-type compounds, *e.g.*, 1,2-di-4-quinolylethylenes.

Quinaldine is oxidized with freshly prepared SeO_2 in dioxane at 45° → quinoline-2-aldehyde (Y = 50%). Also: lepidine → quinoline-4-aldehyde (Y = 58%). H. Kaplan, *J. Am. Chem. Soc. 63*, 2654 (1941); *C.A. 1942*, 478.

Ketones from Hydrocarbons

$CH_2 \rightarrow CO$

164.

Fluorene (2 g.) is heated with SeO_2 and H_2O at 230–240° in a closed tube → 1.5 g. fluorenone. F.e.s. G. M. Badger, *J. Chem. Soc. 1941*, 535; *C.A. 1942*, 457. R. M. Martin, *J. Chem. Soc. 1941*, 679; *C.A. 1942*, 446.

Chromite catalyst

Carbonyl from Hydroxy Compounds

$CH(OH) \rightarrow CO$

165. Primary and secondary alcohols with 4 or more C-atoms can be dehydrogenated catalytically in the liquid phase with good yields, in the presence of ethylene as a hydrogen acceptor. Favorable reaction conditions are: 40 g. alcohol to 0.5–2.5 g. catalyst; pressure of C_2H_4 (at 280°) 70–130 atm.; reaction time 1/2 hr. A mixed Cu–Zn–Ba chromite catalyst proved to be most satisfactory. (For prepn. of catalyst and effect of its constituents on the reaction, see original.) W. Reeve and H. Adkins, *J. Am. Chem. Soc. 62*, 2874 (1940); *C.A. 1940*, 7846.

Chromic acid $CrO_4 --$

Aldehydes from Hydrocarbons

$CH_3 \rightarrow CHO$

66.

3,4-$(NO_2)_2C_6H_3Me$ is oxidized by CrO_3 in concd. H_2SO_4-$Ac_2O \rightarrow$ 3,4-dinitrobenzylidine diacetate (Y = 36%) which is boiled with 12% HCl $\rightarrow$ 3,4-dinitrobenzaldehyde (Y = quant.). Methods: Thiele and Winter, *Ann. 311*, 353 (1900). H. Goldstein and R. Voegeli, *Helv. Chim. Acta 26*, 1125 (1943); *C.A. 1944*, 78.

Ketones from Secondary Alcohols

$CH(OH) \rightarrow CO$

67. 3-Octanol (117 g.) is oxidized with a Beckmann mixture ($K_2Cr_2O_7$, H_2SO_4, H_2O) at 40–60° $\rightarrow$ 102 g. 3-octanone. Y. R. Naves, *Helv. Chim. Acta 26*, 1034 (1943); *C.A. 1943*, 6819.

Quinones from Hydrocarbons—"Film Reactor"

68. 2-Methylnaphthalene is treated with CrO_3 in "film reactor" $\rightarrow$ 2-methyl-1,4-naphthoquinone. Y = 45%. W. J. C. de Kok, J. J. Leendertse and H. I. Waterman, *Chem. Weekblad 37*, 579 (1940); *C.A. 1942*, 4799, 4800. H. Veldstra and P. W. Wiardi, *Rec. trav. chim. 62*, 75 (1943); *C.A. 1944*, 2951.

Carboxylic Acids from Hydrocarbons

$CH_3 \rightarrow COOH$

69. 3,4-Dinitrotoluene is oxidized by CrO_3 in concentrated H_2SO_4 at 45–50° $\rightarrow$ 3,4-dinitrobenzoic acid (s.m. 203). Y = 85–90%. H. Goldstein and R. Voegeli, *Helv. Chim. Acta 26*, 475 (1943); *C.A. 1944*, 78.

Potassium permanganate $KMnO_4$

70. 5-Acetamido-2-bromotoluene is oxidized with $KMnO_4$ and $MgSO_4$ for 6 hrs. $\rightarrow$ 5-acetamido-2-bromobenzoic acid. Y = 75%. H. Goldstein and G. Preitner, *Helv. Chim. Acta 27*, 888 (1944); *C.A. 1945*, 918.

71.

α-Picoline with $KMnO_4$ in dil. aq. solution on the steam bath $\rightarrow$ picolinic acid (hydrochloride). Y = 50–51%. A. W. Singer and S. M. McElvain, *Organic Syntheses 20*, 79 (1940); *C.A. 1940*, 5084.

Chlorine Cl_2

72. 3-Picoline · HCl is dissolved in H_2O and Cl is introduced at 110–115°, in the presence of light $\rightarrow$ nicotinic acid · HCl. After 5 hrs.' chlorina-

tion the conversion is 19.2%. Y = almost quant. F. Stitz, *Oesterr. Chem.-Ztg. 45,* 159 (1942); *C.A. 1944,* 2040.

Ferric sulfate $Fe_2(SO_4)_3$

173. **Quinones from Phenols via Aminophenols.** 2-3-Dimethylphenol is coupled with diazotized sulfanilic acid in an alkaline soln. The azo compound is cleaved by reduction with $Na_2S_2O_4$ and the aminophenol formed is oxidized with $Fe_2(SO_4)_3$ during continuous steam distn. under reduced pressure → o-xyloquinone. Y = 61%. L. I. Smith and F. L. Austin, *J. Am. Chem. Soc. 64,* 528 (1942); *C.A. 1942,* 2533.

Via nitrogen compounds

Kröhnke's Syntheses
   See 197–199.

Phenols from Hydrocarbons via Amines   · H → · OH
   See 192.

Via halogen compounds

**α-Hydroxycarboxylic Acids from Carboxylic Acids
via α-Halogencarboxylic Acids**   · CH_2COOH → $CH(OH)COOH$
   See 451.

**Aldehydes from Hydrocarbons
via Halogen Compounds**   · CH_3 → · CHO
   See 410.

Oxygen ⋏   OC ⥮ O

Without additional reagents

Acetylation   · OH → · OAc

174. 4-Methyl-7-hydroxycoumarin (prepn. see 591) is refluxed with Ac_2O → 4-methyl-7-acetoxycoumarin (s.m. 538). Crude Y = 90–96%. A. Russel and J. R. Frye, *Organic Syntheses 21,* 22 (1941); *C.A. 1941,* 6249.

Sodium   *Na*

Chromone
   See 546.

Copper sulfate $\qquad\qquad$ $CuSO_4$

Isopropylidene Derivatives of Glycols

$$\begin{matrix} COH \\ \cdot \\ COH \end{matrix} \rightarrow \begin{matrix} CO \\ \cdot \\ CO \end{matrix} {>} CR$$

5. 1,2-Hexadecanediol and acetone with anhyd. $CuSO_4 \rightarrow$ isopropylidene-1,2-hexadecanediol. Y = 90%. The glycol can be recovered with very dilute aq. MeOH–HCl. F.e.s. C. Niemann and C. D. Wagner, *J. Org. Chem. 7,* 227 (1942); *C.A. 1942,* 5136.

Pyridine

Acetylation of Carbohydrates

6. 6-Methyl-D-sorbitol is allowed to stand in Ac_2O and C_5H_5N at room temp. for 24 hrs. $\rightarrow$ pentaacetyl-6-methyl-D-sorbitol, $C_{17}H_{26}O_{11}$. Y = 80%. L. Vargha and T. Puskas, *Ber. 76,* 859 (1943); *C.A. 1944,* 2930.

Zinc chloride $\qquad\qquad$ $ZnCl_2$
   See 180.

Boron trifluoride $\qquad\qquad$ BF_3

Acetylation $\qquad\qquad$ $\cdot\,OH \rightarrow OAc$

7.

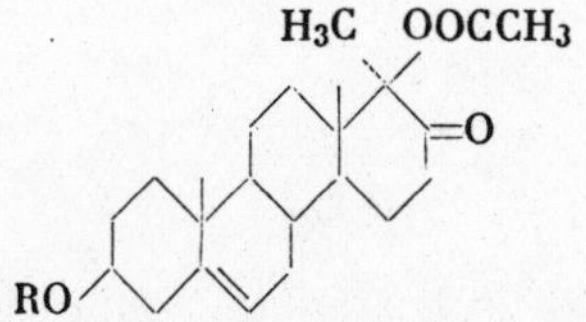

OH groups which do not react during boiling with C_5H_5N–Ac_2O, can be acetylated by employing a mixt. of BF_3–glacial AcOH–Ac_2O. The OH group in the 17a position as in the following compound is an example: $3(\beta)$, 17a (β)-dihydroxy-17a-methyl-*D*-homo-5-androsten-17-one is allowed to stand with Ac_2O and the BF_3–ether complex at room temp. for 16 hrs. $\rightarrow$ $3(\beta)$, 17a (β)-diacetoxy-17a-methyl-*D*-homoandrostan-17-one. Y = 70%. F.e.s. C. W. Shopee and A. Prins, *Helv. Chim. Acta 26,* 201 (1943); *C.A. 1944,* 371.

Ketene $\qquad\qquad$ $CH_2 : C : O$

General Method for Preparation of Acid Anhydrides

$$2\,COOH \rightarrow \begin{matrix} CO \\ CO \end{matrix} {>}O$$

Ketene and $Me(CH_2)_4CO_2H$ are reacted and the product is separated from the acetic acid formed by several hrs. of fractional distn.

→ caproic anhydride. Y = 80–87%. J. W. Williams and J. A. Krynitsky, *Organic Syntheses 21*, 13 (1941); *C.A. 1941*, 6237.

Phosphorus pentoxide P_2O_5

Isopropylidene Derivatives
See 468.

Phosphoric acid H_3PO_4

Acetylation   · OH → · OAc

179. Alcohols, phenols, polyphenols, and amines can be acetylated with Ac_2O in the presence of 7–8% concd. H_3PO_4 as catalyst; the reaction is sometimes quite violent. The following compounds were acetylated: MeOH, glycerine, glucose, phenol, salicylic acid, β-naphthol, quinone, aniline, and triethanolamine. R. Ciusa and G. Sollazo, *Ann. chim. applicata 33*, 72 (1943); *C.A. 1944*, 5794.

Sulfuric acid H_2SO_4

Acylation of Nonreactive Hydroxyl Groups   · OH → · OAc

180.

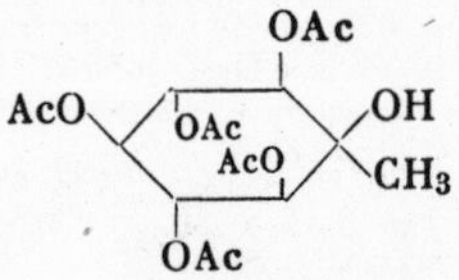

Isomytilitol pentaacetate is heated to boiling with 7–10 parts Ac_2O in the presence of a little concd. H_2SO_4 or anhydr. $ZnCl_2$ for 3 min. → isomytilitol hexaacetate. T. Posternak, *Helv. Chim. Acta 27*, 457 (1944); *C.A. 1944*, 4912.

Acetylation

181. 3,6-Dihydroxy-2,4,5-trimethylbenzyl chloride is treated with Ac_2O and some H_2SO_4 → 3,6-diacetoxy-2,4,5-trimethylbenzyl chloride. Y = almost quant. L. I. Smith and R. B. Carlin, *J. Am. Chem Soc. 64*, 524 (1942); *C.A. 1942*, 2533.

Esterification of Carboxylic Acids   COOH → COOR

182. 2-Thiophenecarboxylic acid is treated with abs. EtOH and concd. H_2SO_4 → Et 2-thiophenecarboxylate. [Y = 93%. Also: Pyromucic acid → pyromucic acid Et ester.] Y = 96%. O. Dann, *Ber. 76*, 419 (1943); *C.A. 1943*, 6260. Methods: B. B. Corson, E. Adams and R. W. Scott, *Organic Syntheses 10*, 48 (1930); *C.A. 1930*, 1844.

Perchloric acid   HClO₄

Differential Acetylation of Hydroxyl
Groups in Hydroxyamino Acids   · OH → · OAc

3. In acetylation with Ac₂O in glacial AcOH, the acetylation of α-amino groups is increasingly suppressed, while that of the OH group is catalytically promoted with increasing concentration of HClO₄. It was known that in benzene compounds an acid reaction favored acetylation of the OH group, while an alkaline reaction favored that of the N group. Method: The soln. of the hydroxyamino acid in AcOH is allowed to react with an excess of Ac₂O in the presence of an excess of HClO₄. Ex: *O*-acetyl-*l*-hydroxyproline, *O*-acetyl-*l*-tyrosine. F.e.s. W. Sakami and G. Toennies, *J. Biol. Chem.* **144**, 203 (1942); *C.A. 1942*, 5842.

Hydrochloric acid   HCl

Acetals   · CHO → · CH(OCH₃)₂

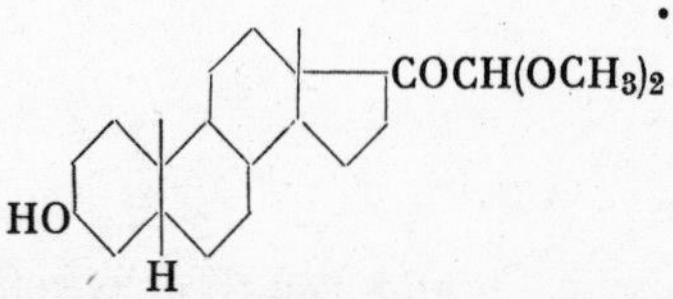

3(β)-pregnanol-20-one-21-al (110 mg.) is refluxed with 1% MeOH · HCl for 1 hr. → 70 mg. dimethylacetyl derivative. L. Ruzicka, V. Prelog and P. Wieland, *Helv. Chim. Acta* **26**, 2050 (1943); *C.A. 1944*, 4610.

Chromone
   See 546.

Benzylpyrylium Salts
   See 603.

Nitrogen   OC ↑↓ N

Without additional reagents

Alkylation with Diazo Paraffins
Ethers   ROH → ROR

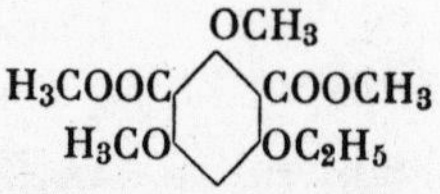

1,3-Di Me-4-hydroxy-2,6-dimethoxybenzene dicarboxylate is treated with diazoethane (from nitrosoethylurethan) in ether → 1,3-di Me-2,6-dimethoxy-4-ethoxybenzene dicarboxylate. Y = 87%. W. Gruber, *Ber.* **76**, 135 (1943); *C.A. 1943*, 5047.

Esters   COOH → COOR

186. Dry, pulverized 1,2-MeOC$_{10}$H$_6$CO$_2$H (25 g.) is slowly introduced into a soln. of 13 g. diazomethane in ether → 2-methoxy-l-naphthoic acid Me ester. Y = 85%. F. L. Warren, M. Gindy and F. G. Baddar, *J. Chem. Soc. 1941*, 687; *C.A. 1942*, 454.

187. 5-Nitro-2-thiophenecarboxylic acid is allowed to stand overnight with MeCHN$_2$ in ether → Et 5-nitro-2-thiophenecarboxylate. O. Dann, *Ber. 76*, 419 (1943); *C.A. 1943*, 6260.

Aqueous and alcoholic alkalis

Carboxylic Acids from Nitriles   CN → COOH

188. 3,5-Diethylbenzonitrile (prepn. see 665) is boiled with NaOH, (CH$_2$OH)$_2$, and 20% H$_2$O → 3,5-Et$_2$C$_6$H$_3$CO$_2$H. Y = 85%. H. R. Snyder, R. R. Adams and A. V. McIntosh, Jr., *J. Am. Chem. Soc. 63*, 3280, 1941; *C.A. 1942*, 1025.

189.

COOH

CH$_3$O

6-Methoxy-l-naphthonitrile (prepn. see 664) is refluxed with KOH in PrOH → 6-methoxy-l-naphthoic acid (s.m. 12). Y = 93%. L. Long, Jr., and A. Burger, *J. Org. Chem 6*, 852 (1941); *C.A. 1942*, 763.

Opening of the Hydantoin Ring   C
   See 568.

Oxazolidinedione   O
   See 316.

Silver oxide   Ag$_2$O

**Carboxylic Acid Esters
from Diazoacetyl Compounds**   COCHN$_2$ → CH$_2$COOR

190.   COCHN$_2$ CH$_2$COOCH$_3$
                COOCH$_3$ →   COOCH$_3$
              N   N

2-Carbomethoxy-3-diazoacetylpyridine is dissolved in MeOH and shaken with Ag$_2$O → β-homoquinolinic acid di-Me ester (Y = 50–70%). 2-Amino-3-diazoacetylpyridine cannot be converted to 2-amino-pyridine-3-acetic acid. K. Miescher and H. Kägi, *Helv. Chim. Acta*, 24, 1471 (1941); *C.A. 1942*, 4820.

Sodium nitrite   *NaNO₂*

Phenols and Phenolic Esters

· NH₂ ⟨ · OOR / · OH

1. Arylazo-2-naphthylamines are decomposed with the calcd. amt. of
Na–NaNO₂ in glacial Ac₂O at 70°. The acetate formed is practically
completely hydrolyzed by the H₂O produced during the reaction. Ex:
p-Nitrophenylazo-2-naphthylamine → acetate deriv. (Y = 61%).
o-Nitrophenylazo-2-naphthylamine → naphthol deriv. (Y = 100%).
o-Carboxyphenylazo-2-naphthylamine → naphthol deriv. (Y = 100%).
F.e.s. H. H. Hodgson and C. K. Foster, *J. Chem. Soc. 1942*, 30; *C.A.
1942*, 3501.

Introduction of Hydroxyl Group into Aromatic Nucleus · H → · OH

2.

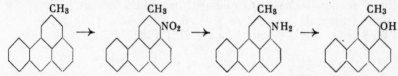

2-Methyl-meso-benzanthrone (5 g.) (prepn., see 589) is heated with
88% HNO₃ in PhNO₂ at 40–50° → 3.6 g. 3-nitro deriv., 3 g. of which is
reduced with Na₂S → 2.2 g. 3-NH₂ deriv.; 1 g. of this is diazotized in
50% H₂SO₄, and heated on the water bath until N₂ evolution ceases →
1 g. 3-hydroxy-2-methyl-meso-benzanthrone. D. H. Hey, R. J. Nicholls
and C. W. Pritchett, *J. Chem. Soc. 1944*, 97; *C.A. 1944*, 3644.

Ring Expansion
   See 539–541.

Stannous chloride   *SnCl₂*
   See 193.

Ozone, hydrogen peroxide   *O₃,H₂O₂*

Dodecanone Mixture (prepn. see 46)
and Mononitrododecane Mixture (prepn. see 302)

)3. 1. By treating with O₃ in a mixture of 15% KOH and MeOH at
−3 to −5°. Y = 97.7%.
   2. By oxidation with alkaline H₂O₂ soln. Y = 56%.
   3. By reduction with SnCl₂ in concd. HCl [method by Konovalow,
J. Russ. Phys. Chem. Soc. 30, 960 (1898); *C.A. 1899, I*, 597] and cleavage of the oxime. Y = 81%.
   4. By conversion to the pseudonitrole (Y = 98%) with NaNO₂ in a
mixture of 25% KOH–MeOH and its cleavage by concd. H₂SO₄
(Y = 45%). F. Asinger, *Ber. 77*, 73 (1944); *C.A. 1945*, 906.

Carboxylic acids $R \cdot COOH$

Phenols from Diazonium Sulfates

194. 4-Nitrophenylazo-2-naphthalenediazonium sulfate (prepn. see 256) is treated with glacial AcOH and H_2O → 4-nitrophenylazo-2-naphthol. Y = quant. F.e.s. H. H. Hodgson and C. K. Foster, *J. Chem. Soc. 1942*, 435; *C.A. 1942*, 6524.

Cleavage of Semicarbazones $\cdot C = N \cdot NHCONH_2 \rightarrow C = O$

195. 3-Octanone semicarbazone is steam distd. in the presence of oxalic acid → 3-octanone. Y = 96.5%. Y. R. Naves, *Helv. Chim. Acta 26*, 1034 (1943); *C.A. 1943*, 6819.

196. β-Ionol semicarbazone is treated with aq. phthalic acid while steam is passed through the soln. → β-ionol. Y = 94%. Y. R. Naves and P. Bachmann, *Helv. Chim. Acta 26*, 2151 (1943); *C.A. 1944*, 4260.

Dilute mineral acids

α,β-Unsaturated Aldehydes $\cdot CH = CHCH_2Br \rightarrow \cdot CH = CH \cdot CHO$

$$RCH:CHCH_2OH \longrightarrow RCH:CHCH_2OSO_2C_6H_4CH_3 \longrightarrow RCH:CHCH_2 \cdot NC_5H_5$$

197.

$$\swarrow \quad OSO_2C_6H_4CH_3$$

$$RCH:CHCHO \longleftarrow \quad RCH:CHCH:NC_6H_4N(CH_3)_2$$
$$\overset{\|}{O}$$

The transformation of halogen compds., $R \cdot CO \cdot CH_2X$ and $R \cdot CH : CHCH_2X$, to the corresponding aldehydes, $R \cdot CO \cdot CHO$ and $R \cdot CH : CH \cdot CHO$, according to Kröhnke [*C.A. 30*, 6714] was used in the prepn. of unsatd. aliphatic aldehydes. The difficulty of preparing the requisite halides from the corresponding alc. in pure form led to a modification of Kröhnke's process in which the alc. was converted to the toluenesulfonic ester, which was then transformed to the pyridinium salt. The yields of farnesal, for instance, were much higher by this method than from farnesyl bromide. Ex: Farnesol (6 g.) in absolute phosgene-free $CHCl_3$ was mixed with anhyd. pyridine and freshly purified p-MeC$_6$H$_4$SO$_2$Cl and, after 70 hrs., was warmed at 50° for 3 hrs. The oily residue after evapn. of the $CHCl_3$ and pyridine was extracted with ether and petroleum ether, and the purified residue was taken up in $CHCl_3$, and was washed with H_2O to remove pyridinium chloride → 8 g. farnesylpyridiniumtoluene sulfonate, which was converted to the nitrone with p-nitrosodimethylaniline in the presence of NaOH in EtOH; this is taken up in petroleum ether and decomposed with 2 N HCl → 2 g. farnesal. P. Karrer and A. Epprecht, *Helv. Chim. Acta* 24, 1039 (1941); *C.A. 1942*, 2524.

α-Keto Aldehydes from α-Halogen Ketones   COCH₂Hal → COCHO

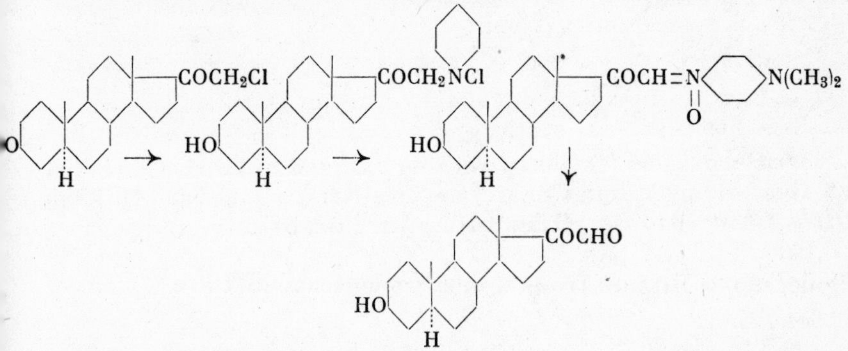

98. 21-Chloroallo-3(β)-pregnanol-20-one (1.0 g.) is warmed for 0.5 hr. at 100–110° with dry pyridine → 1.19 g. pyridinium chloride deriv., 863 mg. of which is converted to the nitrone with p-ONC₆H₄NMe₂ in the presence of NaOH in alc. The nitrone is taken up in ether and cleaved by dil. HCl in a separatory funnel → 430 mg. 3(β)-allopregnanol-20-one-21-al. F.e.s. L. Ruzicka, V. Prelog and P. Wieland, *Helv. Chim. Acta* 26, 2050 (1943); *C.A. 1944*, 4610. L. Ruzicka, O. Jeger and J. Norymberski, *Helv. Chim. Acta* 27, 1185 (1944); *C.A. 1945*, 4859. Methods: F. Kröhnke and E. Börner, *Ber.* 69, 2006 (1936); *C.A. 1936*, 6714.

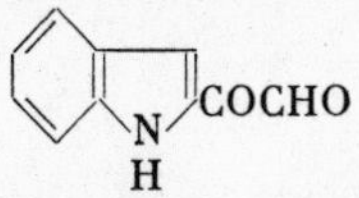

99. Indanylpyridinium bromide (prepn., see 789) and p-Me₂NC₆H₄NO are treated with NaOH in an aq. alc. soln. → (2-indolylcarbonyl)-N-(p-dimethylaminophenyl) nitrone which is converted with dil. H₂SO₄ → indolylglyoxalhydrate. Y = nearly quant. F.e.s. G. Sanna, *Gazz. chim. ital.* 72, 363 (1942); *C.A. 1943*, 6662.

Acetic acid–concentrated sulfuric acid   CH₃COOH–H₂SO₄

Replacement of Nitroso by Acetyl Groups   · NO → · OOC · CH₃
See 292.

Sulfuric acid   H₂SO₄

Ring Opening of o-Nitrophenols
See 622.

Via intermediate products

Ketones from Ketoximes $C = NOH \rightarrow C = O$

200.

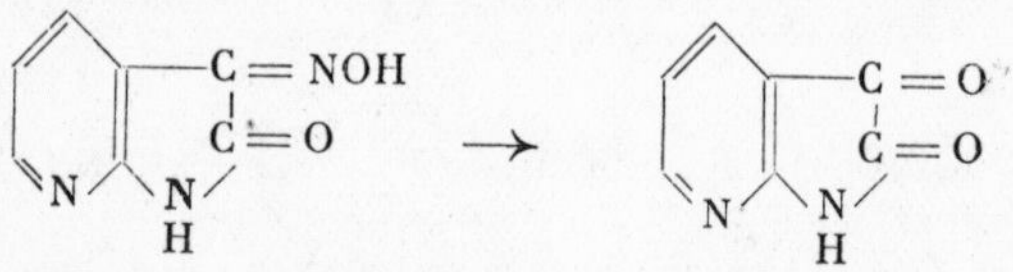

7-Pyrisatin-3-oxime is reduced with Zn dust and oxidized with $FeCl_3$ in HCl → 7-pyrisatin. Crude Y = 73%. Net Y = 40–50%. H. Kägi, *Helv. Chim. Acta 24,* 141E (1941); *C.A. 1942,* 5176.

Dodecanone Mixture from Mononitrododecane Mixture
   See 193.

Halogen ⋏   **OC ⫯ Hal**

Without additional reagents

Ethers $R \cdot O \cdot R$

201. Chloroquinaldines and -lepidines when heated at 180° with excess PhOH give the phenyl ethers in almost quant. yields. Ex: 4-Chloro-quinaldine → 4-phenoxyquinaldine. 2-Chlorolepidine → 2-phenoxy-lepidine. F.e.s. O. G. Backeberg and J. L. C. Marais, *J. Chem. Soc. 1942,* 381; *C.A. 1942,* 5821.

Acetylation $\cdot OH \rightarrow \cdot OAc$

202. $OHCH_2CH_2SO_3Na \rightarrow C_6H_5CH_2COOCH_2CH_2SO_3Na$

Anhyd. Na isethionate (14.6 g.) (prepn. of Ca salt, see 461) is heated with $PhCH_2COCl$ at 130–140° for 4 hrs. → 10 g. Na O-(phenylacetyl) isethionate. F.e.s. A. A. Goldberg, *J. Chem. Soc. 1942,* 716; *C.A. 1943,* 868.

Esters from Carboxylic Acids
via Acid Chlorides $\cdot COOH \rightarrow COCl \rightarrow COOR$

203. 3,4-Dinitrobenzoic acid (prepn., see 169) is refluxed with $SOCl_2$ and consequently distd. → 3,4-dinitrobenzoic acid chloride (Y = 82%) which is added to MeOH → Me 3,4-dinitrobenzoate (Y = 95%). H. Goldstein and R. Voegeli, *Helv. Chim. Acta 26,* 475 (1943); *C.A. 1944,* 78.

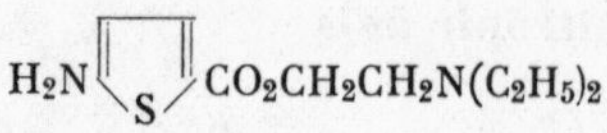

04. 5-Nitrothiophenecarboxylic acid is boiled with 5 times the theoretical amt. of $SOCl_2$ until the soln. clears, and distilled → acid chloride (Y = 93%); this is boiled with $Et_2NCH_2CH_2OH$ in C_6H_6 and treated with soda soln. → 2-(diethylamino)ethyl ester. Y = 81%. F.e.s. O. Dann, *Ber. 76*, 419 (1943); *C.A. 1943*, 6260.

Sodium hydroxide   *NaOH*

Hydroxy- from Chloropyridines   · Cl → · OH

05. 2-Chloropyridine-5-sulfonylaminoacetic acid is boiled with 16% NaOH for 7 hrs. → 2-hydroxypyridine-5-sulfonylaminoacetic acid. Y = 87%. C. Naegeli, W. Kündig and H. Suter, *Helv. Chim. Acta 25*, 148 (1942); *C.A. 1943*, 5949.

Oxazolone Ring   O
    See 313.

Potassium hydroxide   *KOH*

**α-Hydroxycarboxylic Acids
from α-Halogenocarboxylic Acids**   · Hal → · OH
    See 451.

Sodium alcoholate   *NaOR*

Ethers   ROR

06. o-$BrC_6H_4CH_2Br$ is refluxed for 15 minutes with EtONa in abs. EtOH → o-bromobenzyl Et ether. Y = 98%. F. G. Holliman and F. G. Mann, *J. Chem. Soc. 1942*, 737; *C.A. 1943*, 1396.

07. 2-Amino-6-chloro-4-methylpyrimidine is treated with Na in abs. MeOH → 2-amino-6-methoxy-4-methylpyrimidine. Y = 82%. Also: 6-amino-2-methoxy-4-methylpyrimidine. Y = 74%. H. J. Backer and A. B. Grevenstuk, *Rec. trav. chim. 61*, 291 (1942); *C.A. 1944*, 2326.

08. $2,5$-$O_2N(HO)C_6H_3Me$ and $PhCH_2Cl$ are refluxed for 8 hrs. with EtONa in abs. EtOH → 2-nitro-5-benzyloxytoluene, $C_{14}H_{13}O_3N$ (s.m. 562). Y = 95%. F. Bergel and A. L. Morrison, *J. Chem. Soc. 1943*, 49; *C.A. 1943*, 3429.

09. 2-Chloro-4-methyl-8-nitroquinoline is refluxed with NaOH, MnO_2, and Co_2O_3 in MeOH → 2-methoxy-4-methyl-8-nitroquinoline, $C_{11}H_{10}O_3N_2$. Y = 87%. O. H. Johnson and C. S. Hamilton, *J. Am. Chem. Soc. 63*, 2867 (1941); *C.A. 1942*, 477.

Potassium carbonate K_2CO_3

Ethers from Esters

$RCOOR' \rightarrow ROR''$

210.

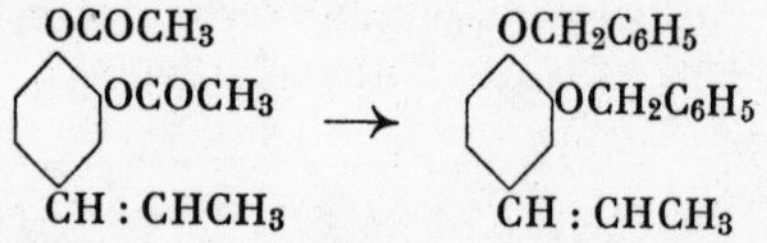

3,4-Diacetoxypropenylbenzene (prepn., see 242) is refluxed on a water bath with $PhCH_2Cl$ and anhyd. K_2CO_3 in abs. MeOH for 8 hrs. in a current of $CO_2 \rightarrow$ 3,4-dibenzyloxy-1-propenylbenzene. Crude Y = 55%. V. Bruckner and G. v. Fodor, *Ber.* 76, 466 (1943); *C.A. 1943,* 6656.

Potassium acetate CH_3COOK

Replacement of Bromo- by Acetoxy Groups

$\cdot Br \rightarrow \cdot OAc$

211. 4-AcO-3-MeOC$_6$H$_3$CHBrAc is warmed with AcOK in EtOH $\rightarrow$ 4-AcO-3-MeOC$_6$H$_3$CH(OAc) Ac. Y = quant. A. v. Wacek, *Ber.* 77, 85 (1944); *C.A. 1945,* 917.

Organic bases

Trityl Ethers

$R \cdot O \cdot R$

212.

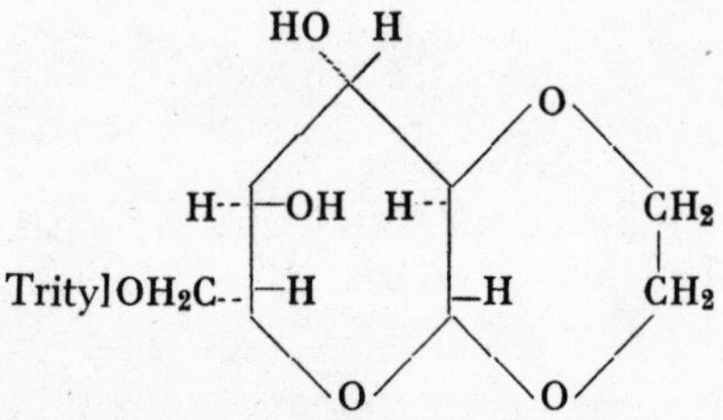

Glycol-β-D-glucoside anhydride (0.5 g.) is heated on a water bath with triphenylchloromethane in abs. pyridine for 3 hrs. $\rightarrow$ 0.5 g. 6-trityl-glycol-β-D-glucoside anhydride. B. Helferich and J. Werner, *Ber.* 75B, 1446 (1943); *C.A. 1944,* 1213.

213. Trityl ethers of glycols which can be used as organic solvents. Preparation: (1) Tritylation of ether alcohols: 0.5 cc. ether alcohol with 0.5 equiv. Ph$_3$CCl and 1 cc. C$_5$H$_5$N are heated in a 15-cc. flask on a water bath.

(2) Ditritylation of glycols: 0.1 cc. ethylene glycol with 2 equivs. Ph$_3$CCl in 1–2 cc. C$_5$H$_5$N are heated for from 15 mins. to 1 hr. on a water bath.

(3) Monotritylation of glycols: 0.25 cc. ethylene glycol is heated for 5 mins. with 0.5 equivs. Ph_3CCl in 1 cc. C_5H_5N on a water bath and the reaction product extd. with 95% EtOH in which the ditrityl ether is insol. Ex: β-Ethoxyethyl(Cellosolve) trityl ether. Y = 80–85%. Ethylene glycol monotrityl ether. Y = 50%. Ethylene glycol ditrityl ether. Y = 60–70%. F.e.s. M. K. Seikel and E. H. Huntress, *J. Am. Chem. Soc. 63,* 593 (1941); *C.A. 1941,* 2111.

Esters   COOR

4. Benzoylation. Toluhydroquinone is treated with benzoyl chloride in C_5H_5N → 2,5-dibenzoyltoluhydroquinone. Y = 82.7%. F.e.s. G. Zemplén, R. Bognár and S. Morvay, *Ber. 76,* 1165 (1943); *C.A. 1945,* 1398.

5. Esters of Fatty Acids. α-Stearoyl-β-palmitoyl glyceride is treated with a $CHCl_3$ soln. of myristoyl chloride in dry quinoline → α-stearoyl-β-palmitoyl-γ-myristoyl glyceride. Y = 88%. P. E. Verkade, *Rec. trav. chim. 62,* 393 (1943); *C.A. 1944,* 3250.

Monoacyl Glycols

6.

CH_2OH		$CH_2OTrityl$		$CH_2OTrityl$		CH_2OH
CH_2OH	→	CH_2OH	→	$CH_2OStearoyl$	→	$CH_2OStearoyl$

Monoacyl glycols are obtained by reductive cleavage of the corresponding acyltrityl glycols in the presence of Pd–C in EtOH. The method is not applicable to those monoacyl glycols which contain a reducible functional group. Ex: $(CH_2OH)_2$ and Ph_3CCl in C_5H_5N → monotrityl glycol (Y = 69%)—with stearoyl chloride in C_5H_5N → stearoyltrityl glycol (Y = 81%). Reduction by passing HCl into the petr. ether soln. (not always applicable) or with a catalyst prepared from $PdCl_2$ in abs. alcohol at 50° for 5 hrs. → monostearoyl glycol. Y = 91% and 94%, respectively. F.e.s. P. E. Verkade, F. D. Tollenaar and T. A. P. Posthumus, *Rec. trav. chim. 61,* 373 (1942); *C.A. 1943,* 5371.

Silver oxide Ag_2O

Glucosides   R·O·R

7.
$$C_6H_{11}O_5 \cdot O \diagup\diagdown \begin{matrix} OCH_3 \\ COCH_3 \end{matrix}$$

Isopeonol (3 g.) and acetobromoglucose are treated with Ag_2O in anhyd. quinoline → 5.8 g. tetraacetylglucoisopeonol, 3 g. of which is shaken with $Ba(OH)_2$ in H_2O for 16 hrs. → 1.1 g. glucoisopeonol. F. Mauthner, *J. prakt. Chem. 161,* 284 (1943); *C.A. 1944,* 5809.

Silver carbonate Ag_2CO_3

Methyl Glucosides

218. α-Acetobromo-D-manno-D-galaheptose $(C_{17}H_{23}O_{11}Br)$ is condensed with MeOH in the presence of Ag_2CO_3 (usual methods of Königs and Knorrl) $\rightarrow$ pentaacetyl-β-methyl-D-manno-D-galaheptoside (s.m. 4). Y = 90%. E. M. Montgomery and C. S. Hudson, *J. Am. Chem. Soc.* 64, 247 (1942); *C.A. 1942*, 1906.

Steroid Glucosides

219. Until now, only small yields of steroid saccharides could be obtained from alcohols and acylhalogenoses. The yields can be improved considerably if part of the H_2O, along with some solvent, is continuously removed by azeotropic distln. Benzene, toluene, and $CHCl_3$ are suitable solvents. Ex: *t*-Androsterone in C_6H_6 is treated with Ag_2CO_3 and the C_6H_6 distd. with the dropwise addn. of acetobromo-D-glucose in C_6H_6 $\rightarrow$ *t*-androsterone-β-D-glucoside tetraacetate (Y = 51.4%) and free glucoside (Y = 34.4%). F.e.s. C. Meystre and K. Miescher, *Helv. Chim. Acta* 27, 231 (1944); *C.A. 1944*, 4612. Also *Helv. Chim. Acta* 27, 1153 (1944).

220. Desoxycorticosterone in abs. benzene is treated with acetobromoglucose in abs. ether and shaken with freshly prepd. Ag_2CO_3 for 24 hrs. at 20°, then filtered over Na_2SO_4 and washed with Me_2CO $\rightarrow$ desoxycorticosterone-tetraacetyl-β-glucoside. (Y = approx. 20%. Use of Ag_2O according to Johnson, *C.Z. 1942*, II, 291, yields only 10–14%.) This product is hydrolyzed with K_2CO_3 in MeOH–H_2O for 14 hrs. at 20° $\rightarrow$ desoxycorticosterone-β-glucoside (Y = almost quant.). K. Miescher, W. H. Fischer and C. Meystre, *Helv. Chim. Acta* 25, 40 (1942); *C.A. 1942*, 4513.

Silver acetate CH_3COOAg

Esters • OAc

221.

10-Bromo-9-anthrone is shaken with AcOAg in glacial AcOH $\rightarrow$ 10-acetoxy-9-anthrone. Y = 83%. F.e.s. L. F. Fieser and H. Heymann, *J. Am. Chem. Soc.* 64, 376 (1942); *C.A. 1942*, 1925.

Magnesium   *Mg*

Acylation of Alcohols

2. Of all the metals which were investigated, Mg. influences the course of the reaction during the acylation of alcohols with acid chlorides most favorably. This is more noticeable during the esterification of secondary and tertiary, than of primary, alcohols. A. Spasov, *Ber. 75*, 780 (1942); *C.A. 1942*, 7010.

3. Reaction of Mg upon a mixture of Me_3COH and $AcCl \rightarrow Me_3COAc$. Y = 45–55%. A. Spasov, *Organic Syntheses 20*, 21 (1940); *C.A. 1940*, 5049.

Acylation of Phenols

4. The HO-acyl derivs. of phenols are prepd. in almost quant. yields in the presence of Mg, without which decidedly lower yields are obtained. This method is especially useful for ether-soluble esters, because the isolation of ether-insoluble esters is made very difficult by the sepn. of the excess Mg. Method: 0.1 Mole phenol is heated for 0.5–1 hr. at 90° with 0.1–0.12 mole acyl chloride and 1.2 g. Mg shavings in 20–25 g. benzene. Ex: Phenyl acetate, Y = 92%; phenyl benzoate, Y = 93%; hydroquinone diacetate, Y = 95%. F.e.s. A. Spasov, *Ber. 75*, 779 (1942); *C.A. 1942*, 7010.

Sulfuric acid H_2SO_4

Ketones from Unsaturated Halogenides

5.
$$CH_3CCl = CHCH_2CH_2COOH \rightarrow CH_3COCH_2CH_2CH_2COOH$$
The (γ-chlorocrotyl) group is converted to a $CH_3COCH_2CH_2$ group upon the addition of H_2SO_4. Ex: 5-Chloro-4-hexene-1-carboxylic acid is melted and added to concd. $H_2SO_4 \rightarrow$ 5-hexanone-1-carboxylic acid. O. Wichterle, *Chem. Listy 37*, 180 (1943); *C.A. 1945*, 1841.

Replacement of Halogens by Oxo Groups $CCl_2 \rightarrow CO$

6. $\alpha,\alpha,\alpha',\alpha'$-2,5-Hexabromo-*p*-xylene (prepn., see 418) is mixed with $H_2SO_4 \cdot H_2O$ and heated at 130–140° and 25 mm. pressure $\rightarrow$ 2,5-dibromoterephthalaldehyde (s.m. 377). Y = 84%. Similarly: 2,5-dichloro deriv. P. Ruggli and F. Brandt, *Helv. Chim. Acta 27*, 274 (1944); *C.A. 1944*, 6288.

See also 410.

Manganese dioxide MnO_2

Ethers   ROR
See 209.

Hydrochloric acid   *HCl*

Hydroxy- and Alkoxypyrroles from Bromopyrrolecarboxylic Acids

227.

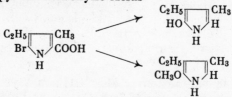

1. 5-Bromo-3-methyl-4-ethyl-2-pyrrolecarboxylic acid (I) is decarboxylated by warming on a water bath with concd. HCl → 2-hydroxy-4-methyl-3-ethylpyrrole. Y = 40%.
2. (I) is decarboxylated with concd. HCl in MeOH → 2-methoxy-4-methyl-3-ethylpyrrole. Y = 60%. F.e.s. W. Siedel, *Ann. 554*, 144 (1943); *C.A. 1943*, 5401.

Cobalt oxide   *Co₂O₃*

Co_2O_3

Ethers   ROR
   See 209.

Via intermediate products   See 197–199.

Sulfur ↟   OC ⫫ S

Alkali hydroxide

Alkylation of Sugars   ROH → ROR
228. Glucose is methylated with Me_2SO_4 and NaOH in the presence of CCl_4 at 50–55°. The α- and β-methyltetramethyl glucosides obtained are saponified with 2 N HCl → tetramethyl-D-glucose. Y = 46–55%. E. S. West and R. F. Holden, *Organic Syntheses 20*, 97 (1940); *C.A. 1940*, 5055.

Alkylation of Phenols
229. 5-Hydroxy-4-nitro-1,3-dimethylbenzene and aqueous NaOH are evaporated to dryness *in vacuo;* the pulverized Na salt is dried by azeotropic distillation with benzene until all water is removed and is boiled for 5.5 hrs. in a benzene solution of dimethyl sulfate. Y = 93.5%. R. Adams and H. W. Stewart, *J. Am. Chem. Soc. 63*, 2859 (1941); *C.A. 1942*, 421.

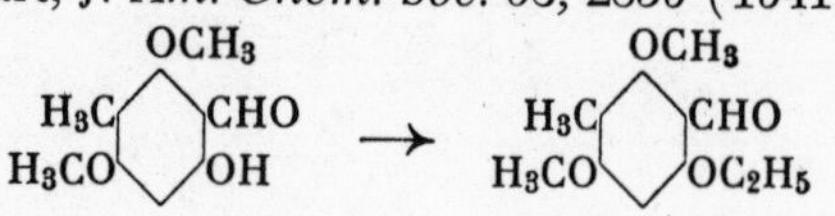

0. 2-Hydroxy-4,6-dimethoxy-5-methylbenzaldehyde is treated with Et_2SO_4 in 10% KOH → 2-ethoxy-4,6-dimethoxy-5-methylbenzaldehyde. Y = 89%. W. Gruber, *Ber. 76*, 135 (1943); *C.A. 1943*, 5047.

1. *o*-Xylohydroquinone is treated with Me_2SO_4 and KOH in boiling MeOH → *o*-xylohydroquinone di-Me ether, $C_{10}H_{14}O_2$. Y = 96%. L. I. Smith and F. L. Austin, *J. Am. Chem. Soc. 64*, 528 (1942); *C.A. 1942*, 2533.

Alkylation of Hydroperoxides   · OOH → · OOR

2.

The methylation of hydroperoxides was accomplished with thymol blue [whose change takes place in the alkaline region (pH 8.0–9.6)] as the indicator. Ex: Tetralin peroxide is dissolved in abs. di-Et ether and anhyd. MeOH and treated with ether. The soln. of Me_2SO_4 and KOH in methanol, maintaining the orange color of the thymol blue at all times → tetrahydronaphthyl Me peroxide. Y = 70%. F.e.s. H. Hock, Shon Lang (and W. Duyfjes), *Ber. 75B*, 300 (1942); *C.A. 1943*, 3748.

Sodium acetate CH_3COONa

Epimerization of Saturated Sterines

3.

3(β)-Hydroxyalloetiocholanic acid Me ester is dissolved in dry pyridine and decomposed with p-$MeC_6H_4SO_2Cl$ at 0°. After 18 hrs. at room temp. the product (tosylate deriv., Y = nearly quant.) is refluxed for 1 hr. with anhyd. NaAc in glacial AcOH → Me 3(α)-acetoxyalloetiocholanate. Y = 50%. F.m.s. P. A. Plattner and A. Fürst, *Helv. Chim. Acta 26*, 2266 (1943); *C.A. 1944*, 3986.

Carbon ⚛   OC ⚛ C

Sodium hydroxide   *NaOH*

Indole- and Pyrrolecarboxylic Acids   · $COCH_2Br$ → · COOH
See 789.

Silver oxide Ag_2O

Carboxylic Acids from Ozonides   · C : C · → · COOH
See 143.

Zinc   **Zn**

Aldehydes and Ketones from Ozonides $\cdot C : C \cdot \rightarrow \cdot CO \cdot$
    See 141.

Aluminum bromide, pyridine $AlBr_3, C_5H_5N$

Acetyl pyridinium chloride

Phosphoric acid HPO_3

Cleavage of Phenol Ethers   ROR $\Big\langle$ ROH
Phenol Esters from Phenol Ethers   ROOR

234. 1. H_3PO_4 proved to be excellent for cleavage. Ex: 1 part guaiacol is heated with 3 parts of 100% H_3PO_4 for 5–6 hrs. at 220° → PhOH. Y = 100%.

2. $AlBr_3$ and its C_5H_5N salts are good for the cleavage of most phenol ethers. Simple diaryl ethers such as diphenyl ether cannot be cleaved with $AlBr_3$ or H_3PO_4.

3. By cleaving the phenol ethers with the C_5H_5N compounds of the acid chlorides the phenol esters can be obtained at once. The latter are particularly useful for the identification of the phenol. V. Prey, *Ber.* 75, 537 (1942); *C.A. 1943*, 3412.

Sulfuric acid H_2SO_4

Coumarin Ring   O
    See 591.

Vanadium pentoxide V_2O_5

Catalytic Vapor-Phase Oxidation of Volatile Organic Compounds

235.

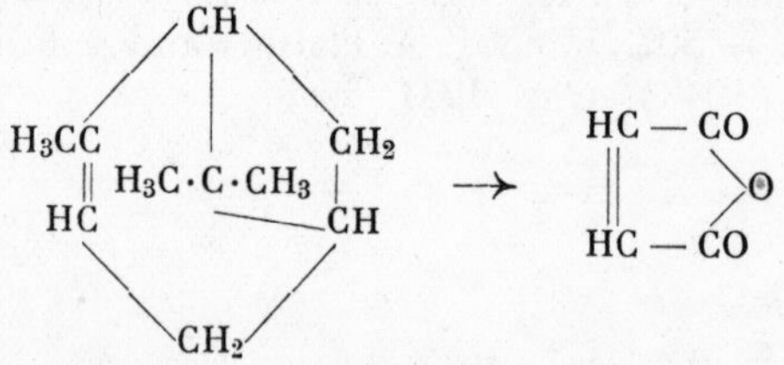

An apparatus is described which permits the study of the catalytic vapor-phase oxidation of volatile organic compounds like terpenes in the laboratory. For the literature and prepn. of the catalyst, see the original. Ex: Pinene vapor is passed over V_2O_5 → maleic anhydride. Y = 29%. C. K. Clark and J. E. Hawkins, *Ind. Eng. Chem.* 33, 1174, 1177 (1941); *C.A. 1941*, 6952.

Chromic acid and permanganate $CrO_4{}^{--}, MnO_4{}^-$

Aldehydes from Ethylene Derivatives

$$\cdot CH:CH\cdot \rightarrow CHO$$

236.

Experiments show that alkaline $KMnO_4$ is more efficient than $K_2Cr_2O_7$ for the oxidation of stilbene derivs. $K_2Cr_2O_7$, however, is more efficient for the oxidn. of unsatd. groups in $R \cdot CH : CH \cdot CH_3$ to $R \cdot CHO$. The results are in accordance with the electronic theories, according to which the stability of the double bond is much greater in stilbene than in isosafrole and isoeugenol. Ex: An aq. soln. of $KMnO_4$ is added over a period of 20 mins. below 10° to an aq. (neutralized with Na_2CO_3) soln. of 4,4′–dichlorostilbene-2,2′–disulfonic acid. The soln. is warmed to 50° to coagulate the MnO_2 and filtered → 4-chlorobenzaldehyde-2-sulfonic acid. Y = 52%. No significant changes in the yield are obtained by changing the amt. of $KMnO_4$ or adding I_2 or V_2O_5 as catalysts. Isosafrole is stirred with H_2SO_4 and H_2O at 30–40° and oxidized with a soln. of $Na_2Cr_2O_7$ → piperonal. Y without dispersion agents = 70%; with sulfanilic acid as dispersion agent = 86.5%; with "Dispersol" = 80%. F.e.s. R. R. Davies and H. H. Hodgson, *J. Chem. Soc. Ind. 62*, 90 (1943); *C.A. 1943*, 5948.

Carboxylic Acids from Ethylene Derivs. $\cdot C:C\cdot \rightarrow \cdot COOH$
See 752.

Sodium hypochlorite   *NaOCl*

Carboxylic Acids from Methyl Ketones $COCH_3 \rightarrow COOH$

237. $CH_2=C(CH_3)COCH_3 \longrightarrow CH_2=C(CH_3)COOH$

Me isopropenyl ketone is added to NaOCl in NaOH → **methacrylic** acid. Y = 41%. T. White, *J. Chem. Soc. 1943*, 238; *C.A. 1943*, **5019**.

238.

Also: 2 g. 5-chloro-6-methoxy-2-acetonaphthone → 1.5 g. 5-chloro-6-methoxy-2-naphthoic acid. R. Robinson and J. Willenz, *J. Chem. Soc. 1941*, 393; *C.A. 1941*, 6966.

Oxidation of Side Chains

239.

γ-Keto-γ-5-hydrindenebutyric acid → 5-hydrindenecarboxylic acid.
Y = good. F. J. McQuillin and R. Robinson, *J. Chem. Soc. 1941*, 586;
C.A. 1942, 490.

Periodic acid HIO_4

240.

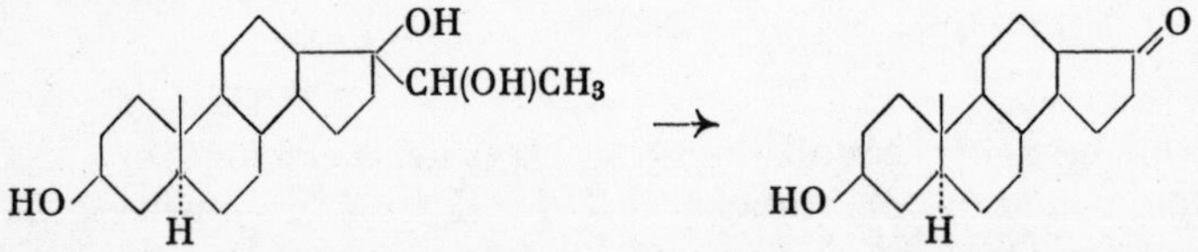

Allopregnane-3,17,20-triol (50 mg.) is treated with HIO_4 in MeOH
for 24 hrs. → 33 mg. isoandrosterone. H. E. Stavely, *J. Am. Chem.
Soc. 63*, 3127 (1941); *C.A. 1942*, 486.

Periodate $IO_4{}^-$

241.

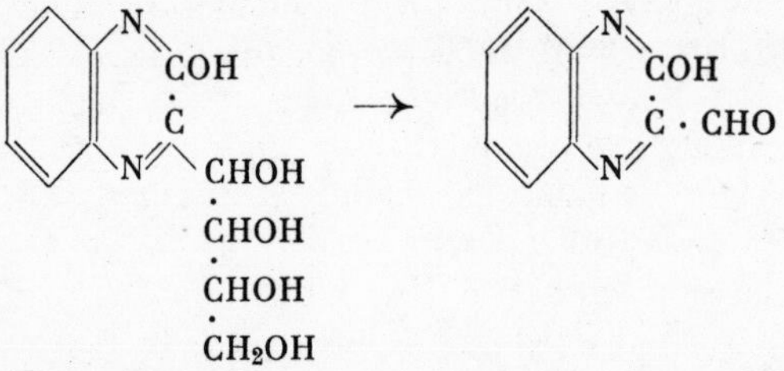

2-Hydroxy-3-(tetrahydroxybutyl)quinoxaline is treated with KIO_4 →
2-hydroxy-3-quinoxaldehyde. Y = 90%. H. Ohle and G. Noetzel, *Ber.
76*, 624 (1943); *C.A. 1944*, 107.

Nickel   *Ni*

Aldehydes and Ketones from Ozonides   ·C : C· → ·CO
     See 142.

Via intermediate products

**Opening of the Ether Linkage. Esters and
Straight Chain Ethers from Cyclic Ethers**

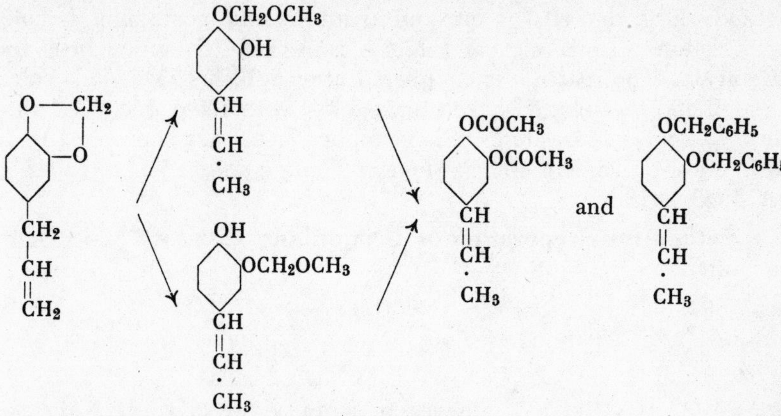

$$OCH_2OCH_3$$
$$OH$$

$$O-CH_2$$
$$-O$$

$$CH$$
$$\parallel$$
$$CH$$
$$\cdot$$
$$CH_3$$

$$CH_2$$
$$CH$$
$$\parallel$$
$$CH_2$$

$$OH$$
$$OCH_2OCH_3$$
$$CH$$
$$\parallel$$
$$CH$$
$$\cdot$$
$$CH_3$$

$$OCOCH_3$$
$$OCOCH_3$$
$$CH$$
$$\parallel$$
$$CH$$
$$CH_3$$

and

$$OCH_2C_6H_5$$
$$OCH_2C_6H_5$$
$$CH$$
$$\parallel$$
$$CH$$
$$\cdot$$
$$CH_3$$

242. Safrole is heated with NaOH in MeOH at 150–60° and 15–18 atm. pressure [Ciamician and Silber, *Ber.* **25**, 1470 (1892)] → mixt. of 2,4- and 2,5-MeCH : $CH(MeOCH_2O)C_6H_3OH$. Y = 65%, on the basis of recovered isosafrole.

(*a*) Heated with Ac_2O for 4 hrs. at 210–20° (Y = 90%) or (*b*) by refluxing for 2 hrs. with Ac_2O and a few drops concd. H_2SO_4 in xylene [K. Ono and M. Imoto, *Bull. Chem. Soc. Japan* **10**, 323 (1935). Y = 80% → 3,4-$(AcO)_2C_6H_3CH$: CH-Me (s.m. 210).

Dissolved in EtOH and boiled in abs. alc. with a few drops of concd. H_2SO_4 after addn. of $PhCH_2Cl$ and anhyd. K_2CO_3 → 3,4-dibenzyloxy-1-propenyl-benzene (Y = 51.5%; s.m. 292).

V. Bruckner and G. v. Fodor, *Ber.* **76**, 466 (1943); *C.A.* **1943**, 6656.

Via Ozonides
See 141–143.

General Method for Preparation of Aromatic Acids by Degradation of Methyl Aryl Ketones   Ar · CO · CH₃ → Ar · COOH

243. Isonitroso derivs. of alkyl aryl ketones decompose on warming or through the action of $SOCl_2$ into HCN and the corresponding aromatic acid. When the OH radical of the isonitroso group is etherized, the esters of these acids are obtained in good yields; such isonitroso compounds undergo decompn. at room temp. according to the following equation:

$$Ar \cdot CO \cdot CH : NOR \longrightarrow Ar \cdot COOR + HCN$$

Method: 30 g. dry HCl is introduced into a soln. containing 1 mole of the ketone in abs. alc., and 120 g. isoAmONO is added little by little at $0°$. The reaction is completed after 8–10 hrs. Dil. soda soln. is added and the soln. is shaken for 4–5 hrs. with 130 g. Me_2SO_4, and finished product is isolated. Ex: Acetophenone $\rightarrow$ Me benzoate (Y = 90%). F.e.s. G. Darzens and C. Mentzer, *Compt. rend. 214*, 113 (1942); *C.A. 1943*, 3418.

New Method for Preparation of 1-Naphthoic Acid $CH_2CN \rightarrow COOH$

244.

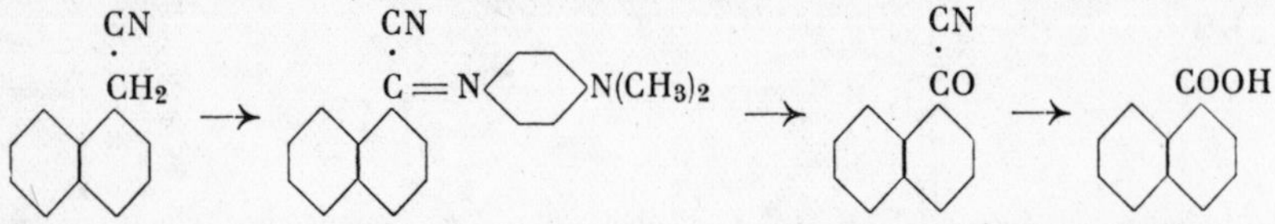

When $1\text{-}C_{10}H_7CH_2CN$ is allowed to stand with $p\text{-}NOC_6H_4NMe_2$ in the presence of a trace of alkali it forms $C_{10}H_7C(CN):NC_6H_4NMe_2$ in excellent yields. This is hydrolyzed rapidly to give $C_{10}H_7COCN$ which on hydrolysis with alkali yields 1-naphthoic acid. By this method 1-naphthoic acid has become readily available, as $1\text{-}C_{10}H_7CH_2CN$ can easily be prepd. from 1-chloromethylnaphthalene. Buu-Hoi and P. Cagniant, *Bull. soc. chim. 9*, 725 (1942); *C.A. 1943*, 5393.

Elimination

Hydrogen ⬆　　　　　　　　　　　　　　　OC ⇑ H
(Oxo- from hydroxy compounds, see OC ⬆ H)

Hydrogen peroxide　　　　　　　　　　　　　　　H_2O_2

Flavones from Chalcones　　　　　　　　　　　　O

245. 2′,4,5-Trihydroxychalcone-4-β-D-glucoside (prepn., see 551) is treated with H_2O_2 and 16% NaOH $\rightarrow$ 3,3′4′-trihydroxyflavone-4′-β-D-glucoside, $C_{21}H_{20}O_{10}$. Y = 94%. L. Reichel and J. Marchand, *Ber. 76*, 1132 (1943); *C.A. 1944*, 4944.

Ferric chloride　　　　　　　　　　　　　　　$FeCl_3$

Synthesis of Tocopherol　　See 678.

Oxygen ⬆　　　　　　　　　　　　　　　　OC ⇑ O

Hydrobromic acid　　　　　　　　　　　　　　　*HBr*

Synthesis of Tocopherol　　See 678.

Ferrous sulfate   *FeSO₄*

Ketones from Peroxides $C\underset{H}{\overset{OOH}{\diagup}}$ → C : O

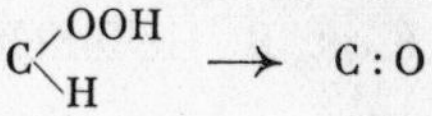

246.

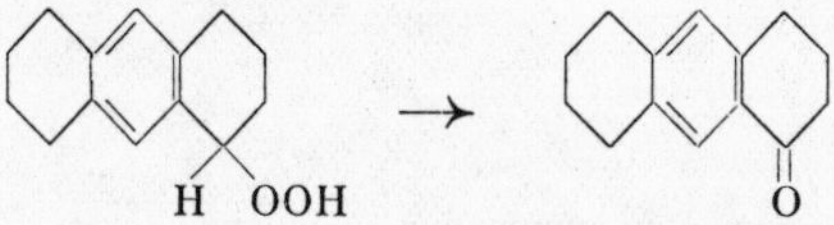

Octahydroanthracene (prepn., see 132) is refluxed on a steam bath with aq. FeSO₄ for 1 hr, → 1-octahydroanthracenone. Y = 64%. H. Hock and S. Lang, *Ber. 76*, 1130 (1943); *C.A. 1944*, 4935.

Nitrogen ⚡   **OC ⇑ N**

Without additional reagents

Dinitrophenylurethan   · OH → · OCONHR

247.

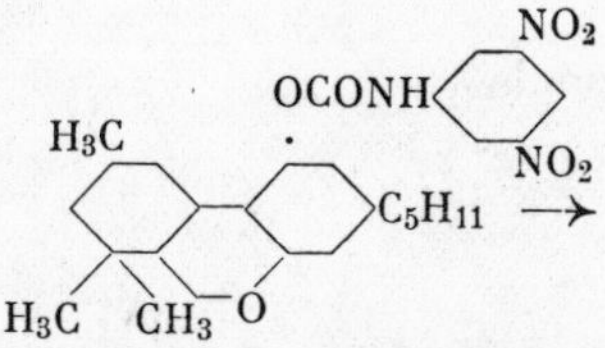

Tetrahydrocannabinol and 3,5-dinitrobenzazide (from 3,5-dinitrobenzoyl chloride and NaN₃) in C₆H₆ are refluxed for 3 hrs. and, after addn. of abs. EtOH, are heated for another hour → tetrahydrocannabinoldinitrophenylurethan. T. H. Bembry and G. Powell, *J. Am. Chem. Soc. 63*, 2766 (1941); *C.A. 1942*, 472.

Halogen ⚡   **OC ⇑ Hal**

Sodium alcoholate   *NaOR*

Cyclic Ethers   O

248.

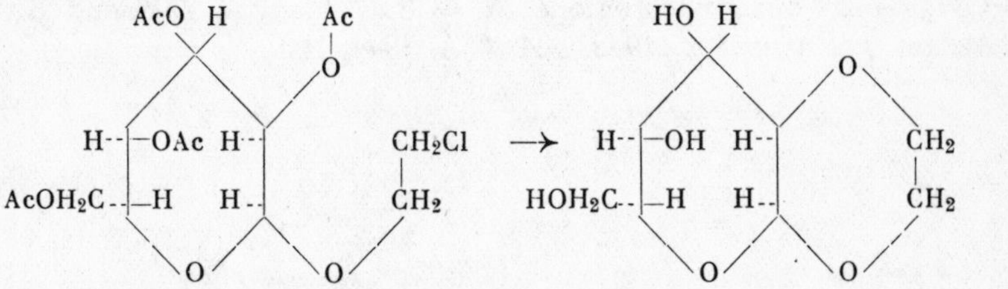

Tetraacetyl-β-D-glucosidoethylenechlorohydrin is boiled for 7.5 hrs.

with NaOH in alc. → glycol-β-D-glucoside anhydride. Y = 90%.
F.e.s. B. Helferich and J. Werner, *Ber. 75*, 1446 (1943); *C.A. 1944*, 1213.

Carbon ⚰   OC ⇑ C

Without additional reagents

Aldehydes from α-Hydroxy Acids   · CH(OH)COOH → · CHO

249. A partial reaction of an improved method of degradation of carboxylic acid according to Blaise and Guerin, *Ber. of Schimmel & Co. 11*, 17 (1929). Pure α-hydroxylauric acid is heated gradually to 190° in an atm. of CO_2, whereby H_2O is split off. Consequent refluxing at 190–200° for 15 min. splits off CO → hendecanal. Y = 96%. R. R. Davies and H. H. Hodgson, *J. Soc. Chem. Ind. 62*, 128 (1943); *C.A. 1943*, 6641.

Sulfuric acid H_2SO_4

Saponification of Acetals   · CH(OR)$_2$ → · CHO
    See 290.

Hydrochloric acid   *HCl*

Saponification of Aldehyde Diacetates   · CH(OOR)$_2$ → CHO
    See 166.

Hydriodic acid   *HI*

3-Alkylchromone   O

250.

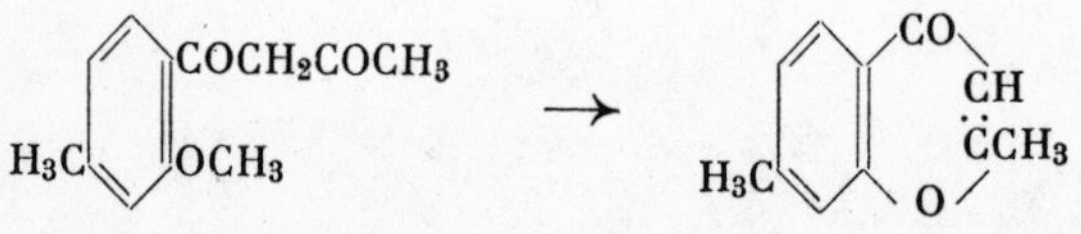

(2-Methoxy-4-methylbenzoyl)acetone is boiled for 3 hrs. with HI (d. 1.96) → 2,7-dimethylchromone. Y = 83%. F.e.s. A. Zaki and R. C. Azzam, *J. Chem. Soc. 1943*, 434; *C.A. 1944*, 100.

Formation of N—N Bond by:

Exchange

Oxygen ↑ NN ⇅ O

Without additional reagents

Nitramines $\cdot NH_2 \rightarrow \cdot NH(NO_2)$

251. $$2\,C_6H_{11}NH_2 + \begin{matrix} COOC_2H_5 \\ | \\ COOC_2H_5 \end{matrix} \longrightarrow \begin{matrix} CONHC_6H_{11} \\ | \\ CONHC_6H_{11} \end{matrix} \longrightarrow \begin{matrix} CON(NO_2)C_6H_{11} \\ | \\ CON(NO_2)C_6H_{11} \end{matrix} \longrightarrow 2\,C_6H_{11}NH(NO_2)$$

2 Moles cyclohexylamine are treated with 1 mole $(CO_2Et)_2$ → *N,N′*-dicyclohexyloxamide (Y = 91%) which is heated on a water bath with anhyd. HNO_3 → *N,N′*-dinitro-*N,N′*-dicyclohexyloxamide (Y = 95%). This is heated at 100° in a sealed tube with a concd. aq. NH_3 soln. → cyclohexylnitramine (Y = 90%). K. A. de Vries, *Rec. trav. chim. 61,* 223 (1942); *C.A. 1944,* 2312. Methods, see Franchimont and Klobbie, *Rec. trav. chim. 8,* 295 (1889).

Electrolytic ↯

Azo Compounds Which Cannot Be Prepared by Usual Methods from *o*- and *p*-Nitrophenol $2\,R—NO_2 \rightarrow RN{=}NR$

252.
2 CH3OCH2O
NO2
CH3OCH2O
N = N
OCH2OCH3

Methylene glycol Me *p*-nitrophenyl ether (prepn., see original) is reduced electrolytically with a Ni cathode (6 amp., 4.8–3.2 v.) and a Pb anode. The anode soln. consists of hot, satd. Cl-free NaOH, while the cathode soln. contains a boiling mixture of the *p*-nitro ether and NaAc as a conducting salt in aq. EtOH → 4,4′-bis-(methoxymethoxy)azobenzene. Y = 69–73%. Also: Methylene glycol Me *o*-nitrophenyl ether → 2,2′-bis-(methoxymethoxy)azobenzene. Y = 40–64%. K. Brand and W. Schreber, *Ber. 75,* 156 (1942); *C.A. 1943,* 3413.

Sodium carbonate *Na_2CO_3*

Triazine ○

See 607.

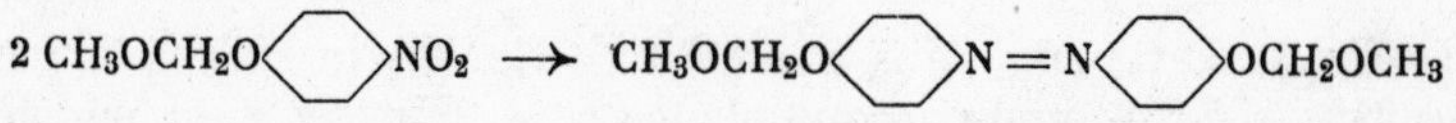

Sodium acetate CH_3COONa

Stabilizing of Diazonium Salts with Piperazine

253.

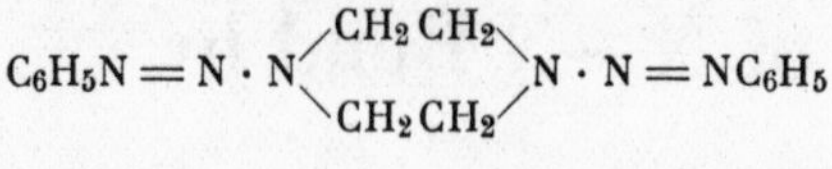

$$C_6H_5N = N \cdot N \underset{CH_2CH_2}{\overset{CH_2CH_2}{\diagup\diagdown}} N \cdot N = NC_6H_5$$

The compound formed from 2 moles diazonium salt and 1 mole piperazine has a high content of stabilized and separable diazonium salt which can be regenerated. Ex: 4-Chloro-*o*-toluidine diazotized as usual and slowly added to a cold aqueous soln. of piperazine and excess aq. NaOAc → *N,N'*-bis-(3-chloro-6-methylphenylazo)piperazine. The piperazine compound can be cleaved again by heating with 80% H_2SO_4 at 45°. P. J. Drumm, W. F. O'Connor and J. Reilly, *Sci. Proc. Roy. Dublin Soc. 22*, 223 (1940); *C.A. 1940*, 4389.

Sodium nitrite $NaNO_2$

N-Nitroso Compounds. Nitrosamines $\cdot NH_2 \to \cdot NH \cdot NO$

254. $1\text{-}C_{10}H_7NHAc$ (18.5 g.) is diazotized with $NaNO_2$ in H_2SO_4 below 20° → 0.7 g. *N*-nitrosoaceto-1-naphthalide. The prepn. of this compound had been tried in vain up till then. H. H. Hodgson and E. Marsden, *J. Chem. Soc. 1943*, 285; *C.A. 1943*, 5391.

See also 346.

N-Aminoquinolines from Quinolines via N-Nitrosoquinolines

255.

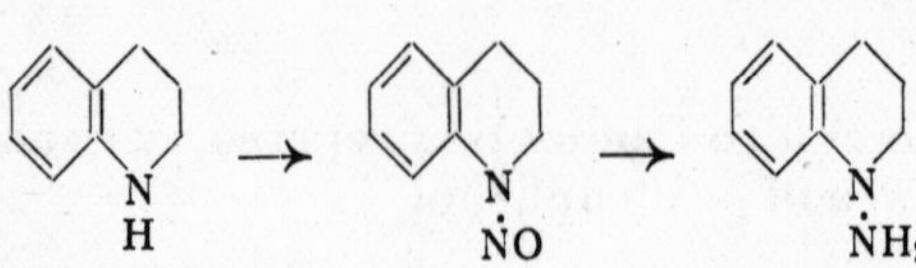

1,2,3,4-Tetrahydroquinoline is treated with $NaNO_2$ in HCl below 10° → 1-nitroso-1,2,3,4-tetrahydroquinoline (Y = 92%), 22 g. of which is dissolved in $AcOH-H_2O-EtOH$ and treated with a suspension of Zn dust in 90% alc. at 60–75° → 1-amino-1,2,3,4-tetrahydroquinoline (11 g., isolated as the sulfate). F. G. Holliman and F. G. Mann, *J. Chem. Soc. 1942*, 737; *C.A. 1943*, 1396.

Diazonium Salts $\cdot NH_2 \to \cdot N \equiv N^+ SO_4H^-$

256.

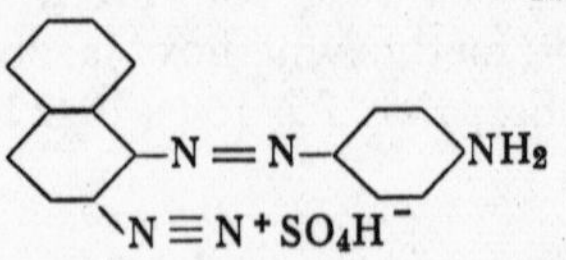

Diazonium salts are formed from a series of arylazo-2-naphthylamines by the following methods:

1. Diazonium chloride: by the addn. of solid $NaNO_2$ to the HCl soln. of the amine in glacial AcOH and subsequent pptn. with EtOH–ether. Y = moderate.

2. Diazonium sulfate: by addn. of nitrosyl sulfuric acid–glacial AcOH soln. of the amine at 18–20°. Although the sulfate is contaminated with inorganic material, the yields are good.

3. Diazonium sulfate: by addn. of glacial AcOH to a paste containing the amine, $NaNO_2$, and H_2SO_4.

Ex: 4-Nitrophenylazo-2-naphthylamine → 4-nitrophenylazo-2-naphthalenediazonium sulfate (s.m. 194). F.e.s. H. H. Hodgson and C. K. Foster, *J. Chem. Soc. 1942*, 435; *C.A. 1942*, 6524.

Improved Method for Preparation of Benzenediazonium Salts
$\cdot NH_2 \rightarrow \cdot N \equiv N^+ Cl^-$

57. $PhNH_2 \cdot HCl$ is diazotized with EtONO in glacial AcOH and anhyd. dioxane (1:1) and the diazonium salt is pptd. in crystaline form by addn. of an excess of dioxane. Y of clean salt = over 95%. W. Smith and C. E. Waring, *J. Am. Chem. Soc. 64*, 169 (1942); *C.A. 1942*, 1914.

Diazonium Borofluorides
$\cdot NH_2 \rightarrow \cdot N \equiv N^+ BF_4^-$

58. Diazonium borofluorides (s.m. 501) from aromatic amines, hydrofluoboric acid, and $NaNO_2$, according to E. B. Starkey, *Organic Syntheses 19*, 40 (1939). Ex: *p*-Phenetidine; Y = 87%. *p*-Aminobenzoic acid; Y = 84%. *o*-Aminobenzoic acid; Y = 46%. F.e.s. A. Wayne Ruddy, E. B. Starky and W. H. Hartung, *J. Am. Chem. Soc. 64*, 828 (1942); *C.A. 1942*, 3160.

Diazonium Cobaltinitrite

59.
$$\left[\langle \bigcirc \rangle N = N \right]_3^{+++} \left[Co(NO_2)_6 \right]^{---}$$

Amines are diazotized in HCl or H_2SO_4 (the vol. of liquid is kept as small as possible). The soln. is neutralized and the filtrate treated with Na cobaltinitrite. Ex: Aniline → benzenediazonium cobaltinitrite; Y = 88%. *o*-Nitraniline → *o*-nitrobenzenediazonium cobaltinitrite (s.m. 114); Y = 99%. F.e.s. H. H. Hodgson and E. Marsden, *J. Chem. Soc. 1944*, 22; *C.A. 1944*, 2021.

Azides from Hydrazides
$\cdot CONHNH_2 \rightarrow \cdot CON_3$

60. 5,8-Dichloro-2-naphthoyl hydrazide (prepn., see 308) is treated with an aq. $NaNO_2$ soln. in glacial AcOH → 5,8-dichloro-2-naphthazide (s.m. 358). Y = 98%. H. Goldstein and P. Viaud, *Helv. Chim. Acta 27*, 883 (1944); *C.A. 1945*, 926.

Hydrazinecarboxylic Acids $\cdot NH_2 \rightarrow \cdot NHNH_2$

261. Anthranilic acid is diazotized in HCl; the diazonium salt soln. is poured into a satd. aq. SO_2 soln., while SO_2 is introduced and concd. HCl is added → o-hydrazinebenzoic acid · HCl. Y = 84%. Comp. 396. F.e.s. K. Pfannstiel and J. Janecke, *Ber.* **75**, 1096 (1942); *C.A. 1943*, 4392.

Indazole   O
See 321.

Cinnoline
See 322.

Triazole

262.

o-$C_6H_4(NH_2)_2$ in AcOH is treated with a conc. aq. $NaNO_2$ soln. at 5°; the temp. must rise to 80° → 1,2,4-benzotriazole. Y = 75–81%. R. E. Damschroder and W. D. Peterson, *Organic Syntheses* **20**, 16 (1940); *C.A. 1940*, 5082.

263.

2-Amino-4-acetyldiphenylamine is diazotized in hot glacial AcOH → 5-acetyl-1-phenyl-1,2,3-benzotriazole (s.m. 614). Y = 62%. F.e.s. R. W. G. Preston, S. H. Tucker and J. M. L. Cameron, *J. Chem. Soc. 1942*, 500; *C.A. 1943*, 642.

264. 2-Bromo-6-aminodiphenylamine-4-carboxylic acid is diazotized in a H_2SO_4 soln. → 7-bromo-1-phenylbenzotriazole-5-carboxylic acid. Y = nearly quant. N. Campbell and J. A. R. MacLean, *J. Chem. Soc. 1942*, 504; *C.A. 1943*, 643.

Glacial acetic acid CH_3COOH

Azo Compounds

265.

o-Aminoazobenzene is shaken with PhNO in glacial AcOH → o-disazobenzene. Y = 83%. P. Ruggli and J. Rohner, *Helv. Chim. Acta 25,* 1533 (1943); *C.A. 1943*, 5947.

Nitrogen ⚡   NN ⚡ N

Iodine   *I*

Symmetrical Hydrazides

66.

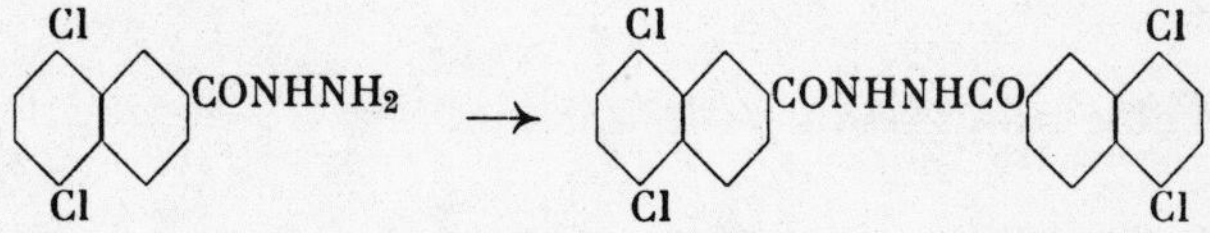

5,8-Dichloro-2-naphthoylhydrazine (prepn., see 308) is refluxed for 1 hr. with iodine in alc. → 1,2-bis-(5,8-dichloro-2-naphthoyl)hydrazine. Y = 53%. H. Goldstein and P. Viaud, *Helv. Chim. Acta 27*, 883 (1944); *C.A. 1945*, 926.

Formation of N—Hal Bond by:

Exchange

Hydrogen ⋏   **NHal ⥮ H**

Quinonechlorimide from *p*-Nitrophenols

267. 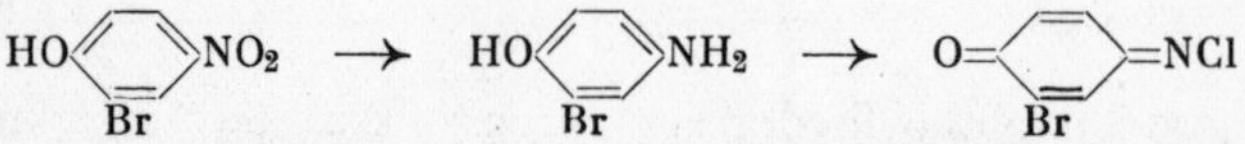   HO⟨⟩NO₂ → HO⟨⟩NH₂ → O=⟨⟩=NCl
              Br   Br   Br

2-Bromo-4-nitrophenol is reduced to 2-bromo-4-aminophenol chloro-
stannate with Sn and HCl and then oxidized with NaOCl → 2-bromo-
quinonechlorimide. Y = 87–90%. G. Mickhailov, *Trans. Inst. Pure
Chem. Reagents (U.S.S.R.), No. 16*, 83–8 (1939); *C.A. 1940*, 3707.

Formation of N—S Bond by:

Exchange

Oxygen ⚹   **NS ⫯⫰ O**

Acetic Anhydride   *(CH₃CO)₂O*

Sulfonylimines $> SO \rightarrow > S = NSO_2 \cdot$

68. $\underset{CH_2CH_2}{\overset{CH_2CH_2}{|}} \Big\rangle SO + H_2NSO_2C_6H_4CH_3 \longrightarrow \underset{CH_2CH_2}{\overset{CH_2CH_2}{|}} \Big\rangle S = NSO_2C_6H_4CH_3$

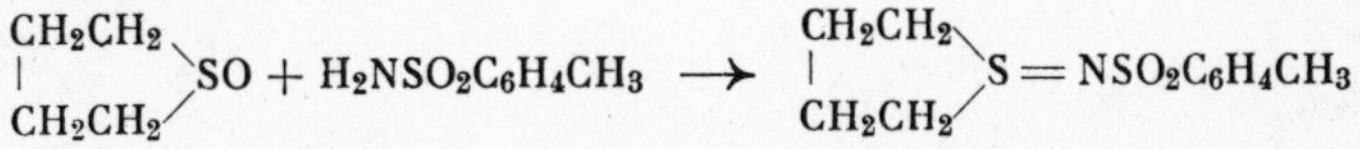

Tetramethylene sulfoxide (prepn., see 116) is heated with p-MeC₆H₄-
SONH₂ in Ac₂O on a water bath → tetramethylenesulfin-p-tolylsul-
fonylimine. Y = 66%. F.e.s. D. S. Tarbell and C. Weaver, *J. Am.
Chem. Soc. 63*, 2939 (1941); *C.A. 1942, 470.*

Halogen ⚹   **NS ⫯⫰ Hal**

Without additional reagents

269. **Sulfonamide Compounds
from Sulfinic Acids** $\cdot NH_2 \rightarrow \cdot NHSO_2 \cdot$

$\underset{S}{\overset{N}{\bigcup}}NH_2 + ClSO\langle\ \rangle NO_2 \rightarrow \underset{S}{\overset{N}{\bigcup}}NHSO\langle\ \rangle NO_2 \rightarrow \underset{S}{\overset{N}{\bigcup}}NHSO_2\langle\ \rangle NO_2$

2-Aminothiazole is treated with p-O₂NC₆H₄SOCl in ether → 2-(4-
nitrophenylsulfinamido)thiazole (crude Y = 72%), which is oxidized
with alkaline KMnO₄ → 2-(4-nitrophenylsulfonamido)thiazole. Y =
70%. H. Morren and R. Lehmann, *J. Pharm. Belg. 1*, 127 (1942); *C.A.
1944, 3263.*

Sulfonylimino Ethers $-C\underset{OR}{\overset{NH}{\langle}} \rightarrow -C\underset{OR}{\overset{NSO_2-}{\langle}}$

270. $\langle\ \rangle C\underset{OC_2H_5}{\overset{NH}{\langle}} + ClSO_2\langle\ \rangle NO_2 \rightarrow \langle\ \rangle \underset{\underset{OC_2H_5}{|}}{C} = NSO_2\langle\ \rangle NO_2$

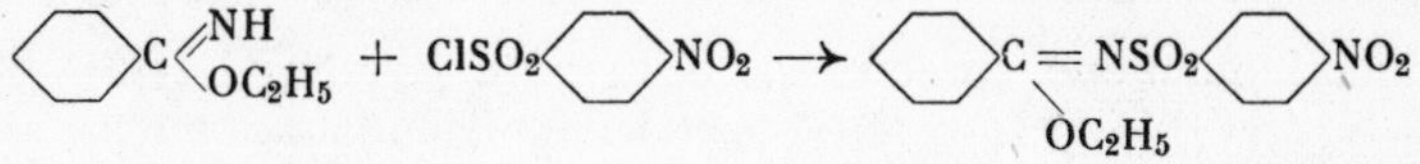

PhC(OEt) : NH and $4\text{-}O_2NC_6H_4SO_2Cl$ in Me_2CO are allowed to stand at 30–35° → Et N-(4-nitrophenylsulfonyl)benzimidate. Y = 55–60%. H. J. Barber, *J. Chem. Soc. 1943*, 101; *C.A. 1943*, 4374.

Sodium hydroxide   *NaOH*

Sulfonylamines $\cdot NH_2 \rightarrow \cdot NHSO_2-$

271. Glycine is treated with 2-chloropyridine-5-sulfonic acid chloride in the presence of NaOH and acetone → 2-chloropyridine-5-sulfonilamide. Y = 96%. F.e.s. C. Naegeli, W. Kündig and H. Suter, *Helv. Chim. Acta 25*, 1485 (1942); *C.A. 1943*, 5949.

Sulfonylamidines $\cdot C{<}^{NH}_{NH_2} \rightarrow \cdot C{<}^{NSO_2}_{NH_2}$

272.

$$\langle\ \rangle C{<}^{NH}_{NH_2} + ClSO_2{<}\rangle NO_2 \rightarrow \langle\ \rangle C = N \cdot SO_2{<}\rangle NO_2$$

A suspension of PhC(: NH)NH_2 · HCl in Me_2CO and aq. NaOH is shaken with $4\text{-}O_2NC_6H_4SO_2Cl$ → N-(4-nitrophenylsulfonyl)benz-amidine. Y = 88%. H. J. Barber, *J. Chem. Soc. 1943*, 101; *C.A. 1943*, 4374.

Bis-(alkylsulfonyl)imides $2\ RSO_2Cl - \rightarrow {}^{RSO_2}_{RSO_2}{>}NH$

273. The disulfonylimides are prepd. from alkylsulfonyl chlorides with NH_3 in a weakly alkaline soln., while the mixed derivs. are obtained from alkylsulfonyl chloride and alkylsulfonilamide. Ex: $MeSO_2Cl$ and $MeSO_2NH_2$ in the presence of NaOH in H_2O → $(MeSO_2)_2NH$. Y = 90%. Bis-(ethanesulfonyl)imide. Y = 90%. Bis-(butanesulfonyl)-imide. Y = 42%. B. Helferich and H. Flechsig, *Ber. 75*, 532 (1942); *C.A. 1943*, 3399.

Pyridine

Sulfanilylamines $\cdot NH_2 \rightarrow \cdot NHSO_2 \cdot$

274. Acetylsulfanilylamines are obtained from amines and acetylsulfanilic acid chloride in pyridine. Ex: 2-Amino-5-pyridinesulfonic acid → acetylsulfanilyl-2-aminopyridine-5-sulfonic acid (s.m. 31). Y = 88%. 2-Aminopyridine-5-sulfonic acid amide → 2-acetylsulfanilylaminopyri-dine-5-sulfonic acid amide. Y = 88%. F.e.s. C. Naegeli, W. Kündig and H. Suter, *Helv. Chim. Acta 25*, 1485 (1942); *C.A. 1943*, 5949.

275. 4-Aminoisoquinoline (prepn., see 381) with $p\text{-}AcNHC_6H_4SO_2Cl$ in C_5H_5N and Me_2CO → $4\text{-}N^4\text{-}$acetylsulfanilamidoisoquinoline (s.m.

36). Y = 80–90%. J. J. Craig and W. E. Cass, *J. Am. Chem. Soc. 64,* 783 (1942); *C.A. 1942,* 3175.

6.

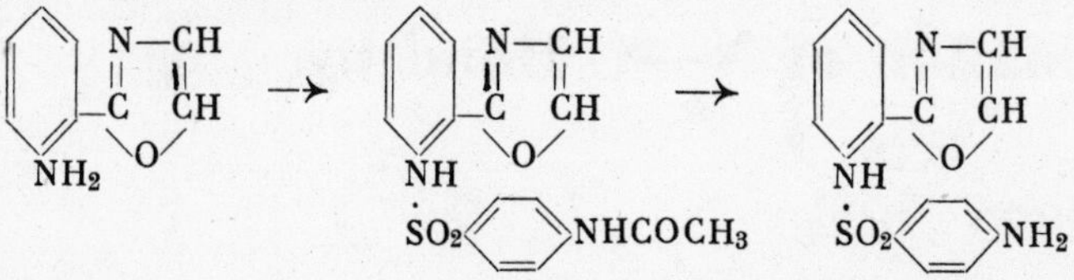

2-(*o*-Aminophenyl)oxazole is treated with an equimol. amt. of acetyl-sulfanyl chloride in C_5H_5N → 2-[*o*-(N^4-acetylsulfanilamido)phenyl]oxazole (Y = 90%), which is refluxed with 12% HCl → 2-(*o*-sulfanil-amidophenyl)oxazole. Y = 80%. W. E. Cass, *J. Am. Chem. Soc. 64,* 785 (1942).

Formation of N—C Bond by:

Addition

Addition to Oxygen and Carbon   NC ⇓ OC

Without additional reagents

2-Hydroxyalkylamines

277. $CH_3C(CH_3)CH_2$ + $H_2NCH_2CH_2NH_2$ → $CH_3C(CH_3)CHNHCH_2CH_2NH_2$
                \O/   OH

Good yields are obtained in the monoalkylation of ethylene diamines with $RCH \cdot CH_2 \cdot O$ when an excess of the diamine is used. Ex: $Me_2C \cdot CH_2 \cdot O$ is added dropwise over a period of 2 hrs. at 70–80° to a 70% soln. of $(CH_2NH_2)_2$ in MeOH → N-(2-hydroxy-2-methyl-propyl)ethylenediamine. Y = 87%. F.e.s. L. J. Kitchen and C. B. Pollard, *J. Org. Chem.* **8**, 342 (1943); *C.A.* *1943*, 5945.

278.

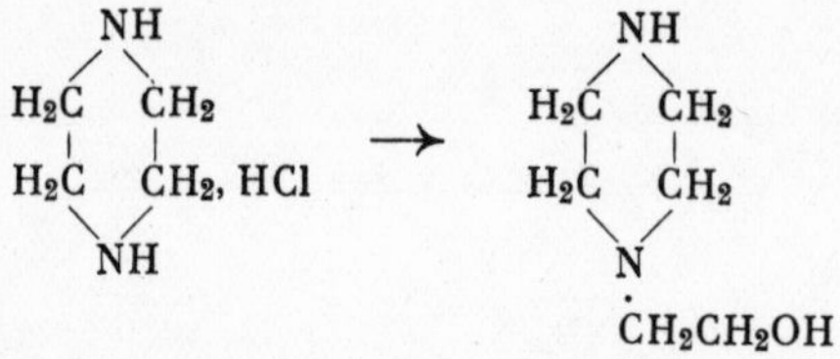

Piperazine monochlorohydrate is treated with ethylene oxide → 1-(2-hydroxyethyl)piperazine. Y = 44%. O. Hromatka and E. Engel, *Ber.* **76**, 712 (1943); *C.A.* *1944*, 2627.

Sodium ethoxide   *NaOR*

Barbituric Acids

    See 315.

Phosphoric acid H_3PO_4

Acylation of Amines   · NH → · NCOR

79.

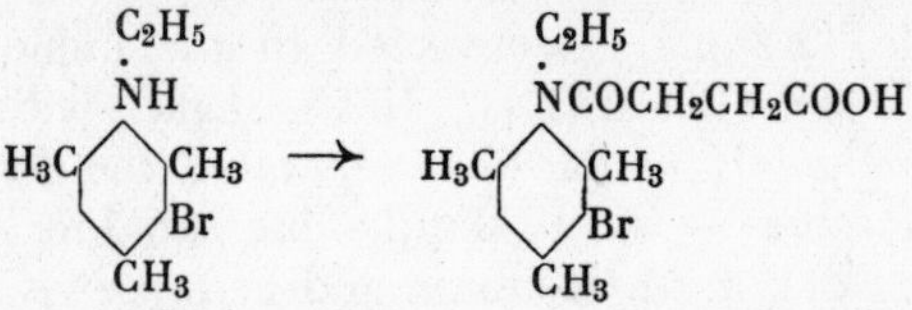

$$C_2H_5$$

H_3C — NH — CH_3 → H_3C — $NCOCH_2CH_2COOH$ — CH_3

N-ethyl-3-bromomesidine and succinic anhydride with a drop of 85% H_3PO_4 in benzene are refluxed for 4 hrs. → N-succinyl-N-ethyl-3-bromomesidine. Y = 96%. F.e.s. R. Adams and H. W. Stewart, *J. Am. Chem. Soc. 63*, 2859 (1941); *C.A. 1942*, 421.

Addition to Nitrogen   NC ⇓ NN

Without additional reagents

Triazole *o*-Dialdehydes   O
  See 290.

Addition to Nitrogen and Carbon   NC ⇓ NC

Without additional reagents

**Secondary Acid Amides from Nitriles
and Carboxylic Acids**   · CN → · CONHCOR

80.
$$CCl_3COOH + ClCH_2CN \longrightarrow CCl_3CONHCONH_2Cl$$

Chlorinated acetic acids when heated with $ClCH_2CN$ yield chlorinated acetylacetamides. Ex: Cl_3CCO_2H and $ClCH_2CN$ are heated at 135° for 2 hrs. → chloroacetyltrichloroacetamide. Y = 95%. W. Steinkopf and M. Kühnel, *Ber. 75*, 1326 (1942); *C.A. 1943*, 4687.

Isatin Ring Opening   C

81.

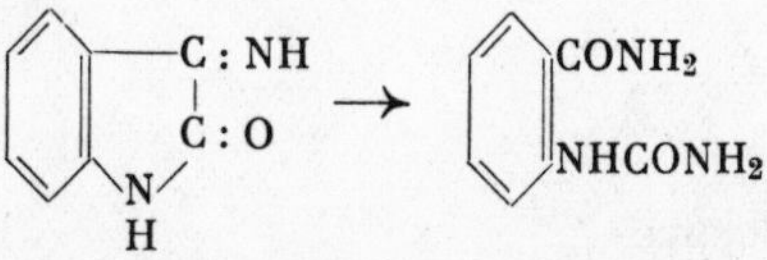

β-Isatinimide is treated with H_2O_2 in a 20% NH_3 soln. → *o*-carbamylphenylurea in good yields when a maximum of 5 g. starting material is used. G. Jacini, *Gazz. chim. ital. 72*, 510 (1942); *C.A. 1944*, 4592.

Amidines from Nitriles   · CN → · C$\langle$NH NH$_2$

82.

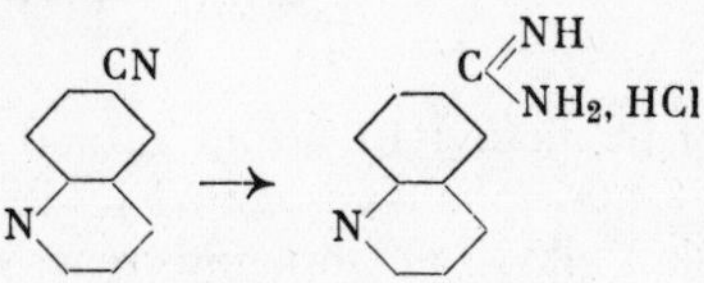

2-Cyanoquinoline (2.2 g.) is converted to the imino ether hydrochloride with alc. and HCl in C_6H_6; this is shaken with 15% alc. NH_3 for 4 days. After the NH_4Cl has been separated, the product is evapd. and pptd. with ether → 1 g. 2-quinoline amidine · HCl. F.e.s. H. Coates, A. H. Cook, I. M. Heilbron and F. B. Lewis, *J. Chem. Soc.* 1943, 419; *C.A.* 1944, 106.

Biurets

283.

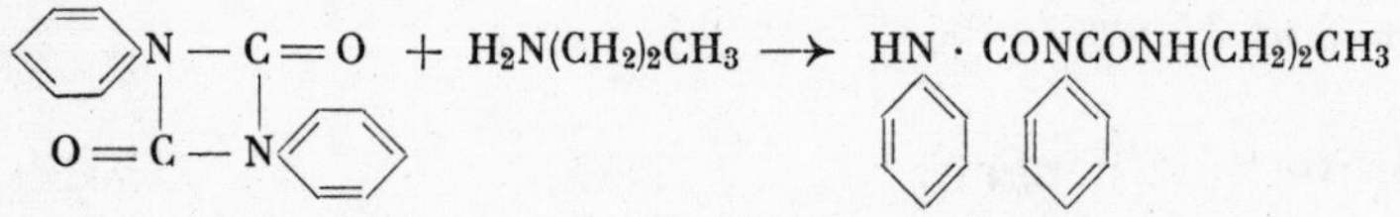

$$\text{(ring)}N-C=O + H_2N(CH_2)_2CH_3 \rightarrow HN \cdot CONCONH(CH_2)_2CH_3$$
$$O=C-N\text{(ring)}$$

Uretediones (prepn., see 286) yield 1,3,5-subst. biuret derivs. when they are refluxed with about 2 moles of the required amine in EtOH. Ex: 1,3-Diphenyluretedione and Pr amine → 1,3-diphenyl-5-*n*-propylbiuret. Y = 96%. L. C. Raiford and H. B. Freyermuth, *J. Org. Chem.* 8, 230 (1943); *C.A.* 1943, 5057.

General Method for Preparation
of Thiourea Compounds $\cdot N=C=S \rightarrow \cdot NHC\overset{S}{\underset{NH_2}{}}$

284. $CH_3N=C=S + NH_3 \rightarrow CH_3NHC\overset{S}{\underset{NH_2}{}}$

Addition of MeNCS to concd. NH_4OH → $MeNHCSNH_2$. Y = 74–81%. M. L. Moore and F. S. Crossley, *Organic Syntheses* 21, 83 (1941); *C.A.* 1941, 6241.

Hydrazones from Azines $=N-N= \rightarrow =N \cdot NH_2$
See 615.

Thiazoline Ring   O
See 490.

Lithium   *Li*

Triazine Ring Closure   O

$$CH_3Li + 3 C_6H_5CN \rightarrow$$

285.

$$\begin{array}{c} C_6H_5 \diagdown \diagup CH_3 \\ C \\ N \quad NH \\ \| \quad | \\ C_6H_5C \quad CC_6H_5 \\ \diagdown N \diagup \end{array}$$

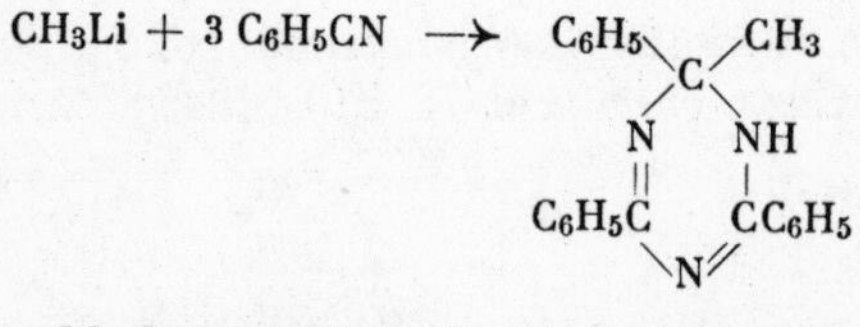

Benzonitrile is added to methyl Li (from Li and methyl iodide) in ether in the cold → 2,4,6-triphenyl-2-methyl-1,2-dihydro-1,3,5-triazine (s.m. 765). Homologous alkyl Li compounds react similarly; benzyl Li

reacts differently. F.e.s. R. M. Anker and A. H. Cook, *J. Chem. Soc.*
1941, 323; *C.A. 1941*, 6260.

Sodium ethoxide   NaOR

Purines
   See 398.

Pyrimidine Ring
   See 360, 605.

Triethylphosphine   P(C₂H₅)₃

Uretediones from Isocyanates

286.

The uretediones are prepd. from the corresponding isocyanates either
without solvents or in dioxane in the presence of a few drops of
P(C₂H₅)₃. Ex: Ph isocyanate → 1,3-diphenyluretedione (s.m. 283);
Y = 80%. 4-Tolyl- and an equimol. amt. of 4-chlorophenyl isocyanate
→ 1-[4-chlorophenyl-3-(4-tolyl)]uretedione; Y = 88%. F.e.s. L. C.
Raiford and H. B. Freyermuth, *J. Org. Chem. 8*, 230 (1943); *C.A. 1943*,
5057.

Chlorosulfonic acid   ClSO₃H

Triazine Ring Synthesis   O

287.

Benzonitrile (25 g.) is allowed to stand overnight with chlorosulfonic
acid at 0° → 17 g. cyaphenine. A. H. Cook and D. G. Jones, *J. Chem.*
Soc. 1941, 278; *C.A. 1941*, 5897.

Hydrochloric acid   HCl

Quinazolines

288.

o-Aminobenzonitrile is heated as the mineral acid salt with cyanamide or dicyanamide in aq. HCl for 2 hrs. at 90–95° → 2,4-diaminoquinazoline. Y = 75–80%. Also: 4-methyl-2-aminobenzonitrile → 7-methyl-2,4-diaminoquinazoline. W. Zerweck and W. Kunze (to I. G. Farbenindustrie A.-G.), *German Pat.* 737,931; *French Pat.* 877,071; *Swiss Pat.* 222,250; *C.A. 1944,* 3993.

Addition to Carbon   NC ⇓ CC

Without additional reagents

Chloronitro Compounds   C = C → CCl · CNO₂

289. To $CH_2 : CHBr$ is introduced NO_2Cl cooled with CO_2 → 1-chloro-1-bromo-2-nitroethane. Y = 85%. (NO_2Cl is easily prepd. from chlorosulfonic acid and HNO_3 according to I. G. Farbenindustrie A.-G., *German Pat.* 509,405). For further reactions with NO_2Cl, see W. Steinkopf and M. Kühnel, *Ber.* 75, 1323 (1942); *C.A. 1943,* 4687.

Substituted Aspartic Acids
from Aromatic Oximes and Maleic Anhydride
See 153.

Triazole o-Dialdehydes   O

290.

Acetylenedialdehyde bis-(di-Et acetal) (prepn., see 532) is heated for 24 hrs. in a sealed tube at 90° with PhN_3 and alc. → 1-benzyl-1,2,3-triazole-4,5-dicarboxyaldehyde bis-(di-Et acetal) (Y = 78%) which is heated with 1 N H_2SO_4 and alc. for 20 min. on a water bath → 1-benzyltriazoledialdehyde (s.m. 515). Y = 95%. F.e.s. K. Henkel and F. Weygand, *Ber.* 76, 812 (1943); *C.A. 1944,* 1742.

Sodium   *Na*

Amines   · CH : CH ·→ CH₂ · CHN <

291. $CH_3NHCH_2COOH + CH_2 = CHCH_2OH → HOCH_2CH_2CH_2NCH_2COOH$
                                                                                    CH_3

The corresponding amino acids add onto allyl alcohol to form aminopropanols just like secondary amines. Ex: Sarcosine is heated in the presence of $CH_2 : CHCH_2OH$ and Na for 70 hrs. at 108° and esterified with MeOH–HCl $\rightarrow$ Me[methyl-(3-hydroxypropyl)amino]acetate. Y = 48.6%. For further ex., also with prim. amines and allyl alc. homologues, see O. Hromatka, *Ber.* 75B, 379 (1942); *C.A. 1943*, 3401-2.

Sulfuric acid $\qquad\qquad\qquad\qquad\qquad\qquad\qquad\qquad$ H_2SO_4

Pseudonitrosites

α-**Amino Alcohols**
from Ethylene Derivatives $\qquad\qquad$ $C = C \rightarrow C(NH_2) \cdot C(OH)$

292.

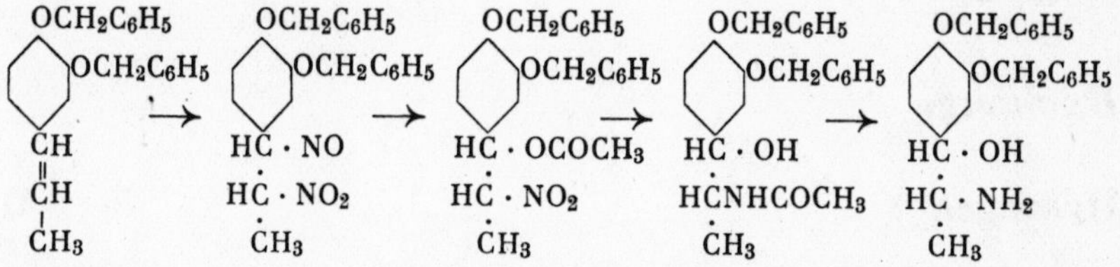

3,4-Dibenzyloxypropenylbenzene (prepn., see 242) is dissolved in ether, poured on aq. $NaNO_2$, and 20% H_2SO_4 is added $\rightarrow$ 3,4-dibenzyloxypropenylbenzene-χ-nitrosite (s.m. 766) (Y = 81%), which is suspended in Ac_2O and an $AcOH-H_2SO_4$ (10 : 1) mixture is slowly stirred into it $\rightarrow$ 1-(3,4-dibenzyloxyphenyl)-2-nitropropyl acetate (s.m. 741) (Y = 67-70%). This is reduced electrolytically with a Hg cathode $\rightarrow$ 1-(3,4-dibenzyloxyphenyl)-2-acetamido-1-propanol (Y = 67%). (For other reduction methods, see original.) Heating the propanol for 1.5 hrs. with 2.1% HCl on a water bath and pptg. with 0.5 N NaOH $\rightarrow$ 1-(3,4-dibenzyloxyphenyl)-2-amino-1-propanol (s.m. 13). Y = 83%. V. Bruckner and G. v. Fodor, *Ber.* 76, 466 (1943); *C.A. 1943*, 6656.

Rearrangement $\qquad\qquad\qquad\qquad\qquad\qquad\qquad\qquad$ NC $\curvearrowright$

Sodium hydroxide–hydrogen peroxide $\qquad\qquad\qquad$ $NaOH-H_2O_2$

Quinazoline Ring from Isatin Ring

293.

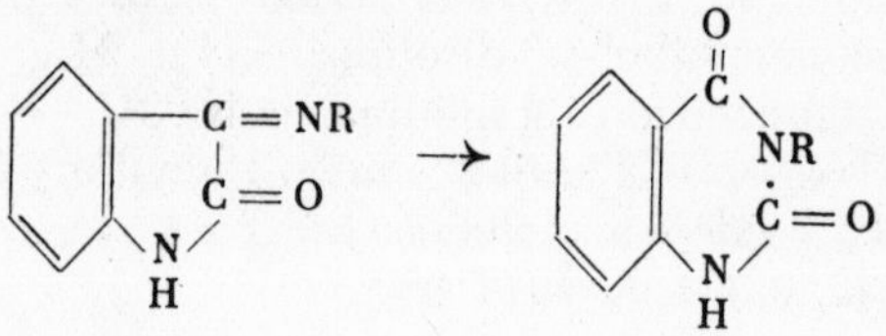

Substituted β-isatinimides yield substd. diketotetrahydroquinazolines on oxidn. with H_2O_2 in the presence of NaOH and NH_3. Ex: Phenylisatinimide → 3-phenyl-2,4-diketotetrahydroquinazoline; Y = 85%. p-Anisylisatinimide → 3-(p-anisyl)-2,4-diketotetrahydroquinazoline; Y = 91%. (1-Naphthyl)isatinimide → 3-(1-naphthyl)-2,4-diketotetrahydroquinazoline; Y = 47%. F.e.s. G. Jacini, *Gazz. chim. ital.* 73, 85 (1943); *C.A. 1944*, 5825.

Glacial acetic acid CH_3COOH

Urea Derivatives from Azides
See 334.

Exchange

Hydrogen ↟   NC ↟↡ **H**

Without additional reagents

Reaction of Nitroso Compounds with Active Methylene Groups
See 298.

Sodium   *Na*

Tertiary from Secondary Amines $\begin{matrix} R \\ R' \end{matrix}{>}NH \rightarrow \begin{matrix} R \\ R' \end{matrix}{>}NR''$

294. Diphenylamine is treated with an equiv. amt. of Na in liq. NH_3 in the presence of some $Fe(NO_3)_3$ → Na diphenylamide to which 2 moles of $PhNO_2$ are added → p-nitrotriphenylamine, $C_{18}H_{14}O_2N_2$. Y = 45%. F. W. Bergstrom, I. M. Granara and V. Erickson, *J. Org. Chem.* 7, 98 (1942); *C.A. 1942*, 1913.

Sodium hydroxide   *NaOH*

Azo Dyes by Coupling

295. 5-Iodo-o-toluidine · HCl (26 g.) in HCl is diazotized below 0° and, after 30 min. of fast stirring, an ice-cold soln. of NaH-1-amino-8-naphthol-3,6-disulfonate in NaOH is added → 25 g. Na-2-(5-iodo-o-tolylazo)-1-amino-8-naphthol-3,6-disulfonate (I). 24 g. of (I) in HCl is coupled with tetrazotized o-toluidine in NaOH → 17 g. Na-3,3'-dimethylbiphenyl-4,4'-bis-[2''-azo-8''-amino-1''-hydroxy-3'', 6''-disulfonaphthalene-7''-(5'''-iodo-o-azotoluene)]. F.e.s. A. A. Goldberg, *J. Chem. Soc. 1942*, 713; *C.A. 1943*, 880.

Ammonium polysulfide $(NH_4)_2S_x$

Acid Amides from Methyl Ketones   · $COCH_3$ → · CH_2CONH_2
See 151–152.

Ferric nitrate $Fe(NO_3)_3$
See 294.

Oxygen ⚡   NC ⚡ O

Without additional reagents

Amines with Formaldehyde
See 599, 767.

Secondary Amines from Ethers   ROR → RNHR

296. 3-Nitro-4-methoxypyridine is boiled for several hrs. with propylamine in alc. → 3-nitro-4-propylaminopyridine. Y = nearly quant. R. Weidenhagen, G. Train, H. Wegner and L. Nordström, *Ber.* 75, 1936 (1943); *C.A. 1944*, 1235.

Ketimines   C : NH

297.

PhAc and AcOEt are condensed with Na → $BzCH_2CMe$: NH which is heated with $EtOH–NH_3$ at 110° for 12 hrs. in a sealed tube → allylmethylphenacylcarbinamine. Y = 90–95%. C. E. Rehberg and H. R. Henze, *J. Am. Chem. Soc.* 63, 2785 (1941); *C.A. 1942*, 420.

Azomethines   R = N · R

Reaction of Nitroso Compounds with Active Methyl Groups

298.

Acid anilides can be prepd. by the action of nitroso derivs. upon active methylene groups, in addition to nitrones and azomethines. Ex: 4-Methyl-3-nitrobenzophenone and *p*-nitrosodimethylaniline → the *p*-dimethylaminoanilide of 2-nitro-4-(benzoyl)-benzaldehyde and of 3-nitrobenzophenone-4-carboxylic acid. L. Chardonnes and P. Heinrich, *Helv. Chim. Acta* 27, 321 (1944); *C.A. 1944*, 4581.

N-Alkylbenzimidazoles   O
See 391.

Hydrazones   CO → C: NNHR

299. The identification of carbonyl compounds by the use of 1-methyl-3-carbohydrazidopyridinium-p-toluene sulfonate.

By the use of the methyl-p-toluene sulfonate addn. product of nicotinic acid hydrazide it is possible to secure derivatives of aliphatic aldehydes with melting points appr. 40° higher than those of both the 2,4-dinitrophenylhydrazones and semicarbazones. The CO compounds can be regenerated easily from these derivs. or they can be transformed into other derivs. Prepn: The CO compound is boiled for 15 min. with the reagent (prepn., see original) in EtOH. The derivative crystallizes from this soln. upon cooling. The melting points of a series of derivs. are given, including some cases in which the reaction failed. C. F. H. Allen and I. W. Gates, Jr., *J. Org. Chem. 6*, 596 (1941).

300. 5,8-Dichloro-2-naphthoylhydrazine (prepn., see 308) is refluxed in acetone for 1 hr. → acetone 5,8-dichloro-2-naphthoylhydrazone. Y = 90%. F.e.s. H. Goldstein and P. Viaud, *Helv. Chim. Acta 27*, 883 (1944); *C.A. 1945*, 926.

See 615.

Azines   R : N · N : R
See 615.

Isonitroso Compounds   R : NOH
See 360.

Nitration   RH → RNO₂

301. **Higher Paraffin Hydrocarbons.** "Atomized" superheated HNO_3 (d. 1.15–1.54) or NO_2 is passed through the liquid hydrocarbon which has been preheated to 160–80° (linear hydrocarbons C_{10}–C_{18} and hydrocarbon mixts. from the Fischer-Tropsch synthesis). When 1–2 moles HNO_3 per mole hydrocarbon is used, the nitration is finished in 1–2 hrs. under the conditions and in the apparatus described in the original. Under the most favorable conditions, 25–55% starting material, 28–44% mononitro hydrocarbons, 11–40% di- and polynitro derivs., and 1–9% fatty acids are obtained. C. Grundmann, *Chemie 56*, 159 (1943); *Ber. 77*, 82 (1943); *C.A. 1945*, 906.

302. **Composition of Nitration Products of Higher Aliphatic Hydrocarbons.** In contrast to Grundmann [*Chemie 56*, 159 (1943); *C.A.*

37, 6640] it was found that in the nitration of the higher aliphatic hydrocarbons the substituent does not enter preferably and exclusively in the 2-position, the present work indicates that in the nitration of dodecane at 160–180° all the theoretically possible secondary mono-nitro substituted derivs. are produced simultaneously in about equi-molecular proportions. The same statistical substitution regularities prevail as with the halogenations.

Ex: Dodecane (1130 g.) is nitrated according to Fr. Pat. 874,721 in 500-g. portions and is isolated and purified by being dissolved first in aq. MeOH-KOH; repptn. by CO_2 saturation and rectification → 440 g. mononitrododecane mixt. (s.m. 193). F. Asinger, *Ber. 77B*, 73 (1944); *C.A. 1945*, 906.

See also 192.

Acid Amides from Carboxylic Acids   · COOH → · CONH₂

303. **General Method for Preparation of Amides of α-Hydroxy Acids.** Mandelic acid is condensed with acetone in presence of conc. H_2SO_4 at −10° and the condensate is reacted with liquid NH_3 to give → mandelamide. Y = 62%. L. F. Audrieth and M. Sveda, *Organic Syntheses 20*, 62 (1940); *C.A. 1940*, 5069.

304. **Preparation of Larger Amounts of Amides of Nonvolatile Acids.** NH_3 is passed into molten *m*-methoxyphenoxyacetic acid and the H_2O formed is distilled off → *m*-methoxyphenoxyacetamide. Y = nearly 100%. P. Pfeiffer and H. Simons, *J. prakt. Chem. 160*, 83 (1942); *C.A. 1943*, 4067.

Substituted Acid Amides   · COOH → · CONHR

305. CH₃   CH₃
HOCH₂ĊCH(OH)COONa+H₂NCH₂CH₂COOH → HOCH₂ĊCH(OH)CONHCH₂CH₂COOH
        CH₃   CH₃

Racemic Na α,β-dihydroxy-β,β-dimethylbutyrate is fused with alanine at 175° → racemic Na pantothenate. Y = 91%. For other methods see H. C. Parke and E. J. Lawson, *J. Am. Chem. Soc. 63*, 2869 (1941); *C.A. 1942*, 406.

Acid Amides from Esters   · COOR → CONH₂

306. General Method: Me lactate is treated with liq. NH_3 at room temp. in an autoclave → lactamide. Y = 70–74%. Many esters have to be kept at 200–250° for several hrs. J. Kleinberg and L. F. Audrieth, *Organic Syntheses 21*, 71 (1941); *C.A. 1941*, 6238.

307. Me-*n*-butyl propiolate with liq. NH_3 in abs. MeOH → *n*-butylpropiol-amide. Y = quant. F.e.s. A. O. Zoss and G. F. Hennion, *J. Am. Chem. Soc. 63*, 1151 (1941); *C.A. 1941*, 3601.

Acid Hydrazides from Esters   · COOR → · CONHNH₂

308.   The Me ester of 5,8-dichloro-2-naphthoic acid is refluxed for 2 hrs. on an oil bath with $H_2NNH_2 \cdot H_2O$ → 5,8-dichloro-2-naphthoyl-hydrazine (s.m. 260, 266, 300). Y = 85%. H. Goldstein and P. Viaud, *Helv. Chim. Acta* 27, 883 (1944); *C.A. 1945*, 926.

See also 110.

Dicarbobenzoxyamino Compounds   = C(NHCOOR)₂
See 353.

Synthesis of the Pyridine Ring   O
See 531, 542.

Pyridones
See 574.

Naphthyridines
See 543.

Hydantoins

309.

$Me_2C(OH)CN$ and $(NH_4)_2CO_3$ at 68–80° → 5,5-dimethylhydantoin. Y = 51–56%. E. C. Wagner and M. Baizer, *Organic Syntheses* 20, 42 (1940); *C.A. 1940*, 5053.

Cyclohydrazides

310.

Di-Me 2,3-coumaronedicarboxylate is heated with 42% $N_2H_4H_2O$ in a sealed tube at 100° → 2,3-coumaronedicarboxylic acid cyclo-hydrazide. Y = 94%. F.e.s. E. H. Huntress and W. M. Hearon, *J. Am. Chem. Soc.* 63, 2762 (1941); *C.A. 1942*, 466.

Diketopiperazines

311.   2 CH₃CH(NH₂)COOH →

Diketopiperazines are obtained by refluxing the amino acids with $(CH_2OH)_2$ until there is no reaction with $Cu(OH)_2$. Ex: Alanine → 2,5-diketo-3,6-dimethylpiperazine. $Y = 70.2\%$. Valine → 2,5-diketo-3,6-diisopropylpiperazine. $Y = 56.8\%$. F.e.s. C. Sannié, *Bull. soc. chim.* 9, 487 (1942); *C.A. 1943*, 5065.

Quinazoline Ring Synthesis

312.

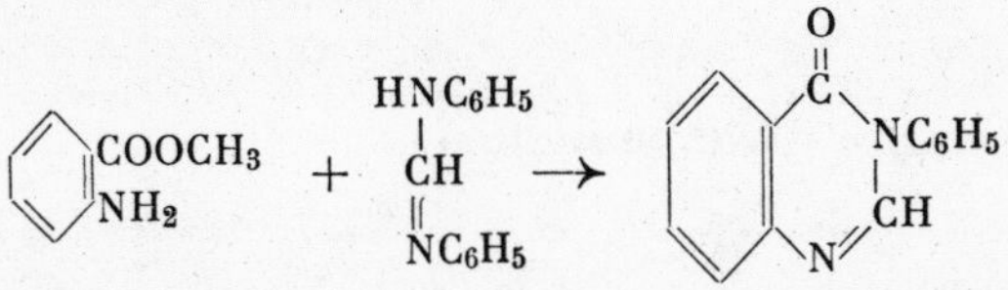

PhNH : CHNHPh and Me anthranilate are heated for 3 hrs. at 200–230° → 3-phenyl-4-keto-3,4-dihydroquinazoline. $Y = 88.7\%$. F.e.s. J. F. Meyer and E. C. Wagner, *J. Org. Chem.* 8, 239 (1943); *C.A. 1943*, 5066.

Quinoxaline Ring
See 350.

Thiazole Ring Closure
See SC ⅄ Hal.

Alkali

Azomethines   C = NR
See 244.

Hydrazones, Wolff-Kishner Reduction   C = N · NHR
See 80–82.

Sodium hydroxide   *NaOH*

Quinoline Syntheses   O
See 610.

Oxazolone Ring Synthesis

313.

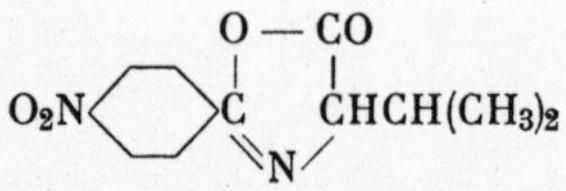

dl-PhCH$_2$CH(NH$_2$)CO$_2$H (5 g.) in NaOH is shaken for 2 hrs. with *p*-nitrobenzoyl chloride in diethyl ether → 1.9 g. 2-(*p*-nitrophenyl)-4-isopropyl-5-oxazolone. As this class of compounds is unstable under the conditions of synthesis, the yields are low. F.e.s. P. Karrer and C. Christoffel, *Helv. Chim. Acta* 27, 622 (1944); *C.A. 1945*, 300.

Potassium hydroxide   *KOH*

Nitrosites
   See 193.

2-Substituted Quinolines   O
   See 555.

Sodium ethylate   *NaOR*

Pyrimidine Synthesis with Amidines

314.

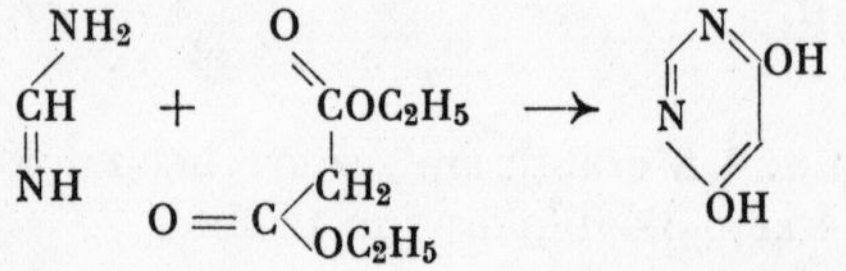

1. HN : CHNH$_2$ · HCl is treated with Na in EtOH at 0° and, after the NaCl has been filtered off, the filtrate is treated with CH$_2$-(CO$_2$Et)$_2$ in EtOH; after 12 hrs. it is worked up → 4,6-dihydroxypyrimidine. Y = 80%.

2. 2-Furylamidine · HCl is boiled for 2 hrs. with CH$_2$(CO$_2$Et)$_2$ and EtONa and worked up after 12 hrs. → 4,6-dihydroxy-2-(2-furyl)-pyrimidine. Y = 42%. G. W. Kenner, B. Lythgoe, A. R. Todd and A. Topham, *J. Chem. Soc. 1943*, 388; *C.A. 1943*, 6668.

Barbituric Acids

315.

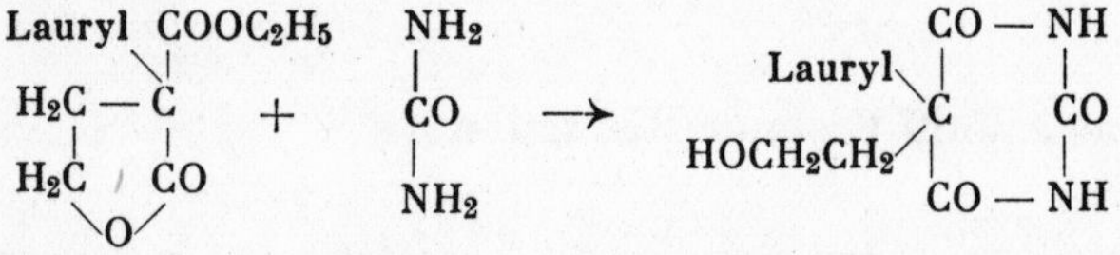

α-Lauryl-α-carbethoxy-γ-butyric lactone treated with urea in the presence of Na ethylate → 5-lauryl-5-(2-hydroxyethyl)-barbituric acid. Y = 82%. F.e.s. G. S. Skinner and A. P. Stuart, *J. Am. Chem. Soc. 63*, 2993 (1941); *C.A. 1942*, 411.

Uric Acids
   See 360.

Oxazolidine Diones

316.

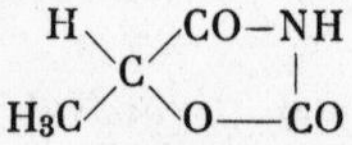

Ethyl lactate and urea are refluxed for 15 hrs. in EtOH with the calcd. amt. of EtONa → 5-methyl-2,4-oxazolidinedione. Y = 81%. F.e.s. R. W. Stoughton, *J. Am. Chem. Soc. 63*, 2376 (1941); *C.A. 1941*, 7402.

Potassium alcoholate   KOR

α-Isonitroso Ketones $- CO \cdot CH_2 \rightarrow - COC : NOH$

317.

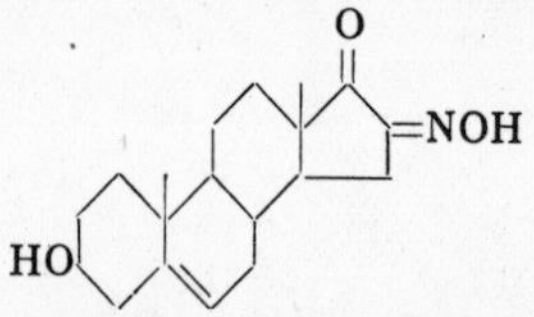

To a mixt. of dehydroisoandrosterone and Me_3COK, AmONO is added in a N_2 atm. → isonitrosodehydroisoandrosterone. Y = 65.5%. F. H. Stodola, E. C. Kendall and B. F. McKenzie, *J. Org. Chem.* **6**, 841 (1941); *C.A. 1942*, 778.

Potassium cyanide   KCN

α-Amino Acids from Ketones $CO \rightarrow C \begin{smallmatrix} NH_2 \\ COOH \end{smallmatrix}$
See 568.

Potassium acetate

Oximes from Ketones $CO \rightarrow C : NOH$

318.

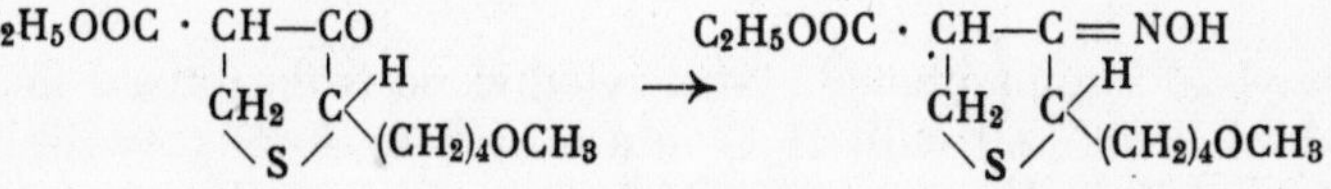

2-(4-Methoxybutyl)-4-hydroxy-3-thiophenone is heated with NH_2-OH $\cdot$ HCl and KOAc in H_2O–alc. on a water bath → oxime deriv. Y = 80%. H. Schmid, *Helv. Chim. Acta* **27**, 127 (1944); *C.A. 1944*, 4589.

Semicarbazones $CO \rightarrow C : N \cdot NHCONH_2$

319. 2-Dodecanone is treated with semicarbazide $\cdot$ HCl and Na acetate in H_2O–alc. → semicarbazone deriv. Y = 93%. F. Asinger, *Ber.* **77**, 73 (1944); *C.A. 1945*, 906.

Sodium nitrite $NaNO_2$

α-Isonitroso Ketones $CH_2 \rightarrow C : NOH$

320.

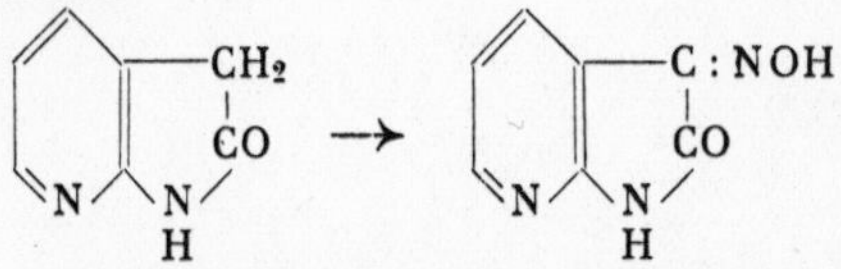

7-Pyroxindole is treated with $NaNO_2$ and 2 N AcOH → 1-pyrisatin-3-oxime. Y = 94%. H. Kägi, *Helv. Chim. Acta* **24**, 141E (1941); *C.A. 1942*, 5176.

Nitration   · H → · NO₂
   See 330.

Pseudonitrols
   See 193.

Indazoles

321.

2,5-$H_2N(O_2N)C_6H_3$Me in glacial AcOH is treated with an aq. NaNO₂
soln. at 15–20° → 5-nitroindazole. Y = 72–80%. o-$H_2NC_6H_4$Me gives
only 3–5% indazole. H. D. Porter and W. D. Peterson, *Organic Syntheses 20*, 73 (1940); *C.A. 1940*, 5080.

**Influence of Substituents on Widman-Stoermer
Cinnoline Synthesis**

322.

1-Phenyl-1-(2-aminophenyl)-2-benzylethylene is diazotized in AcOH–
concd. HCl, diluted with H₂O and heated to 40–50° → 4-phenyl-3-
benzylcinnoline. Y = nearly quant. F.e.s. J. C. E. Simpson, *J. Chem.
Soc. 1943*, 447; *C.A. 1944*, 361.

Pyridine C_5H_5N

Semicarbazones   CO → C : N · NHCONH₂

323. 5,7-Dimethyl-2-octanone (2 g.) and semicarbazide · HCl are dissolved
   in C_5H_5N on a water bath with a few drops H₂O → 1.9 g. pure
   (3.1 g. crude) 5,7-dimethyl-2-octanonesemicarbazone. W. Dirscherl
   and H. Nahm, *Ber. 76*, 709 (1943); *C.A. 1944*, 1748.

Quinoline Syntheses   O
   See 610.

Piperidine   See 609.

Barium oxide   *BaO*

Hydrazones   CO → C : N · NH₂

324.

Propionylanisole is treated with $N_2H_4 \cdot H_2O$ and BaO in abs. EtOH → p-MeOC$_6$H$_4$C(: NNH$_2$)Et. Y = 80%. L. v. Vargha and E. Kovács, *Ber. 75*, 794 (1942); *C.A. 1943*, 3424.

Magnesium methylate $Mg(OR)_2$

Barbituric Acids   O

325. Prepn.: The Mg methylate soln. is boiled for a short time after addition of urea and ester and then kept at a temp. of 105–115° for a considerable time. Ex: Malonic ester and phenylurea, heated for 16.5 hrs. → 1-phenylbarbituric acid. Y = 82%. Diallylmalonic ester and urea heated for 26 hrs. → 5,5-diallylbarbituric acid. Y = 68%. F.e.s. H. Aspelund and L. Lindh, *Acta Acad. Aboensis, Math. et Phys. 12*, 10 (1939); *C.A. 1939*, 6802.

326. (2-Methoxyethyl)phenyldiethyl malonate and urea are refluxed with MeOMg (from Mg and abs. MeOH) → 5-(2-methoxyethyl)-5-phenyl-barbituric acid. Y = 73%. F.e.s. F. F. Blicke and M. F. Zienty, *J. Am. Chem. Soc. 63*, 2991 (1941); *C.A. 1942*, 403. Methods, see Lund, *Ber. 69, 1621* (1936).

Zinc chloride $ZnCl_2$

2,3-Substituted Quinolines and Acridines
   See 620.

Aluminum oxide Al_2O_3

Pyrrolidines

327. Tetrahydrofuran (furanidin) with NH_3 at 400° passed over Al_2O_3 → pyrrolidine. Y = 43.5%. J. K. Yur'ev and W. A. Tronowa, *J. Gen. Chem. U.S.S.R. 11*, 344 (1941); *C.A. 1941*, 5893; *C.A. 1940*, 4733.

328. Tetrahydrofuran and 2-aminopyridine are passed over Al_2O_3 in a N_2 stream at 390° → N-(2-pyridyl)pyrrolidine. Y = 17%. Also: Tetrahydrofuran and o-aminoquinoline → N-(o-quinolyl)pyrrolidine. Y = 9.5%. F.e.s. J. K. Yur'ev and co-worker, *J. Gen. Chem. U.S.S.R. 10*, 1839 (1940); *C.A. 1941*, 4377.

Ammonium formate NH_4OOCH

Azadipyrromethines   O

$O_2N \cdot C_6H_5 \cdot CH \cdot CH_2COC_6H_5$

329. $\overset{\cdot}{C}H_2NO_2$ →

γ-Nitro-β-(m-nitrophenyl)-butyrophenone (10 g.) is heated for 0.5 hr. at 180–190° with HCO_2NH_4 → 2.8 g. 2,2′,4,4′-diphenyl-bis-(m-nitrophenyl)-azadipyrromethine. M. A. T. Rogers, *J. Chem. Soc. 1943*, 590; *C.A. 1944, 1495.* Also, *J. Chem. Soc. 1943*, 596.

Phenol C_6H_5OH

Quinoxaline Ring Closure   O
   See 350.

Acetic acid CH_3COOH

Nitration $\cdot H \to \cdot NO_2$
330. Dimethylaniline is treated with HNO_3 and a trace of $NaNO_2$ in AcOH at 15° → 2,4-dinitrodimethylaniline (s.m. 24). Y = 77%. E. E. Ayling, J. H. Gorvin and L. E. Hinkel, *J. Chem. Soc. 1942*, 755; *C.A. 1943*, 1398 (*C.A. 1942*, 419).

C- and N-Nitro Compounds $\cdot H \to \cdot NO_2$
                                                 $\cdot NH_2 \to \cdot NHNO_2$
331. 1. 2,3,5,6-Cl_4C_6HNHAc is heated to 50° with Ac_2O and HNO_3 → 2,3,5,6-tetrachloro-N-nitroacetanilide. Y = 100%.
   2. 2,3,5,6-$Cl_4C_6HNH_2$ is heated to 60° with HNO_3 (d. 1.5) and AcOH → 2,3,5,6-tetrachloro-4-nitroaniline (Y = 31.6%) and 2,3,5,6-tetra-chloro-N-nitroaniline (Y = 57.8%).
   3. 2,3,5,6-$Cl_4C_6HNH_2$ is slowly heated to 50° with excess HNO_3 and AcOH → 2,3,5,6-tetrachloro-4-nitro-N-nitroaniline. Y = 93.3%. A. T. Peters, F. M. Rowe and D. M. Stead, *J. Chem. Soc. 1943*, 372; *C.A. 1943*, 6651.

Phthalyl Derivatives of Amines. Phthalimides

332. Amines or their salts are transformed to the phthalyl derivatives by treatment with 1.5–2 moles of phthalic anhydride per amino group and 30–60 moles of glacial AcOH per mole of amine. When the salts are used NaOAc must be added. When the reaction is finished (no color with bindone) the mixt. is poured into H_2O, boiled, and filtered while hot. The phthalimide remains on the filter in most cases. Ex: o-Phenylenediamine → N,N'-o-phenylenediphthalimide. Ethylenediamine → 1,2-diphthalimidoethane. Leucofuchsin → 4,4′,4″-triphthalimido-3-methyltriphenylmethane (triphthalylleucofuchsin). F.e.s. G. Vanags, *Ber. 75,* 719 (1942); *C.A. 1943*, 102.

333. The ability of primary aromatic and aliphatic amino compds. which possess another functional group in addition to the NH_2 group, to condense with phthalic anhydride has been studied. In nearly all cases phthalimides are obtained which are uniform and suitable for the identification of the amines. The examples which give negative results are, for the greater part, acid amides such as thiourea and guanidine. Schiff bases also yield phthalimides, while the aldehyde is set free. F.e.s. G. Vanags and A. Veinbergs, *Ber. 75*, 1558 (1943); *C.A. 1944*, 1221.

Urea Derivatives from Azides $\cdot CON_3 \rightarrow \cdot NHCONH \cdot$

334.

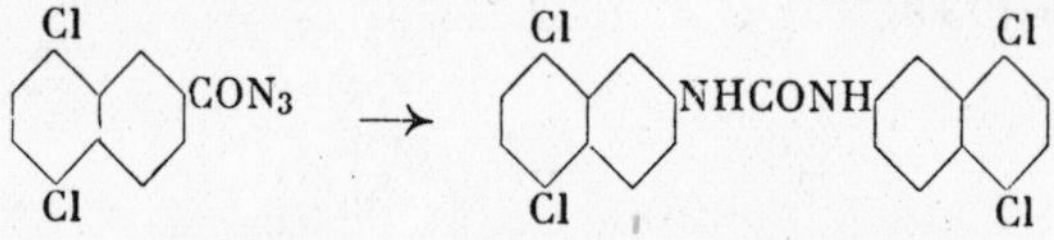

5,8-Dichloro-2-naphthazide is boiled in glacial AcOH → N,N'-bis-(5,8-dichloro-2-naphthyl)urea. Y = 72%. H. Goldstein and P. Viaud, *Helv. Chim. Acta 27*, 883 (1944); *C.A. 1945*, 926.

Syntheses of Pyrrole Rings

335.

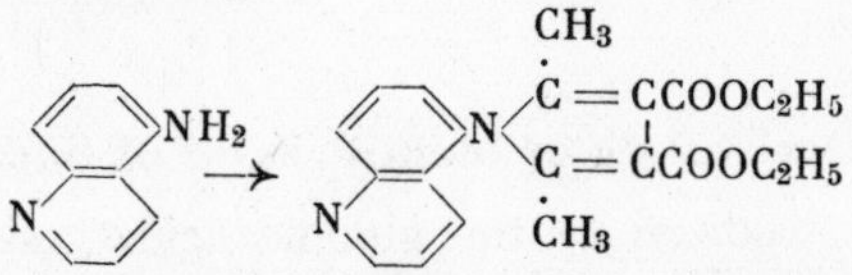

5-Aminoquinoline is boiled for 24 hrs. with $(AcCHCO_2Et)_2$ in di-EtOH and glacial AcOH → di-Et 1-(5-quinolyl)-2,5-dimethyl-3,4-pyrroledicarboxylate. Y = 50%. F.e.s. H. Coates, A. H. Cook, I. M. Heilbron and F. B. Lewis, *J. Chem. Soc. 1943*, 419; *C.A. 1944*, 106.

336.

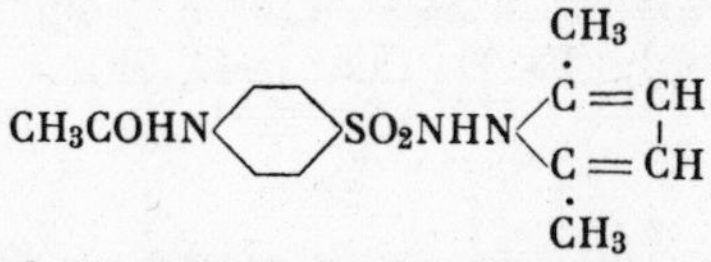

Acetonylacetone and p-$AcNHC_6H_4SO_2NHNH_2$ are reacted in boiling glacial AcOH → Ac deriv. of 1-p-aminophenylsulfonamido-2,5-dimethylpyrrole. Y = quant. E. O'Farell Walsh, *J. Chem. Soc. 1942*, 726; *C.A. 1943*, 874.

Glyoxalin Ring Synthesis

337.

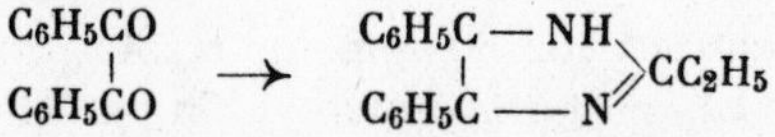

Benzil, EtCHO, and $AcONH_4$ in glacial AcOH are refluxed for 1 hr. → 4,5-diphenyl-2-ethylglyoxaline. Y = excellent. A. H. Cook and D. G. Jones, *J. Chem. Soc. 1941*, 278; *C.A. 1941*, 5897.

Hydrazoic acid HN_3

Degradation of Carboxylic Acids to Amines $\cdot COOH \rightarrow \cdot NH_2$

338. The degradation of carboxylic acids to amines depends little on steric influences. From podocarbic acid whose carboxyl group is adjacent to a tertiary C-atom, the corresponding amine is obtained in good yields. $CHCl_3$ is a good solvent, and in some cases C_6H_6. In substd. benzoic acids the position of the substituents greatly influences the yields. Thus *o*-, *m*-, and *p*-toluyl acids when treated with a 50% excess of HN_3 yield 46, 24, and 70% toluidine, respectively. Ex: Stearic acid → $C_{17}H_{35}NH_2$. Y = 96%. L. H. Briggs, G. C. De Ath and S. R. Ellis, *J. Chem. Soc. 1942,* 61; *C.A. 1942,* 3496.

339. Bicyclo[2.2.2]octanecarboxylic acid is stirred in concd. H_2SO_4 with HN_3 in $CHCl_3$ at 35–40° → bicyclo[2.2.2]octylamine. Y = 87.5%. R. Seka and O. Tramposch, *Ber. 75,* 1379 (1942); *C.A. 1943,* 4723.

Phosphoric acid H_3PO_4

Benzimidazol Derivatives in Identification of Sugars   O

340. The sugars are oxidized to the aldonic acids and condensed with *o*-phenylenediamine. Ex: D-Ribonic acid is heated with o-$C_6H_4(NH_2)_2$ and H_3PO_4 at 130–40° → D-ribobenzimidazole. J. M. Gulland and G. R. Barker, *J. Chem. Soc. 1943,* 625; *C.A. 1944,* 1512. Methods, see Moore and K. P. Link; see also R. J. Dimler and K. P. Link, *J. Biol. Chem. 150,* 345 (1943); *C.A. 1944,* 719; R. Lohmar and K. P. Link, *J. Biol. Chem. 150,* 351 (1943); *C.A. 1944,* 721.

Sulfurous acid H_2SO_3

Amines $\cdot OH \rightarrow \cdot NHR$

341.

8-HOC_9H_6N is refluxed for 30 min. in H_2SO_3 soln. with H_2NCH-$MeCH_2CH_2CH_2NEt_2$ → 8-[(α-methyl-8-diethylaminobutyl)amino]-quinoline. Y, based on reacted hydroxyquinoline = 97%; based on starting material, 64.8%. G. V. Chelintsev and B. M. Dubinin, *J. Gen. Chem. U.S.S.R. 10,* 1395 (1940); *C.A. 1941,* 3641.

Sulfuric acid H_2SO_4

Hydrazones $CO \rightarrow C : N \cdot NHR$

2. $2,4\text{-}(HO)_2C_6H_3CHO$ in 95% EtOH and $2,4\text{-}(O_2N)_2C_6H_3NHNH_2$ dissolved in the smallest possible quantity of dil. $H_2SO_4 \rightarrow 2,4$-dihydroxybenzaldehyde-2,4-dinitrophenylhydrazone. Y = 87%. A. W. Scott and J. M. Burns, *J. Am. Chem. Soc. 62*, 3522 (1940); *C.A. 1941*, 1038.

Nitration $\cdot H \rightarrow \cdot NO_2$

3. An emulsion of *p*-cymene in a mixt. of concd. H_2SO_4 and glacial AcOH is nitrated at $-15°$ to $-10°$ (by the addn. of solid CO_2) with HNO_3 (d. 1.42) and H_2SO_4 (1 : 2.7) $\rightarrow$ 2-nitro-*p*-cymene. Y = 78–82%. K. A. Kobe and T. F. Doumani, *Organic Syntheses 21*, 96 (1941); *C.A. 1941*, 6246.

Skraup's Quinoline Synthesis   See 572.

Pyrimidine Ring

4.

$$ClHC\left\langle \begin{array}{c} CHO \\ CHO \end{array} \right. + \left. \begin{array}{c} HN \\ H_2N \end{array} \right\rangle CNH_2 \rightarrow Cl\text{—}\langle \begin{array}{c} N \\ N \end{array} \rangle\text{—}NH_2$$

$ClCH(CHO)_2$ and guanidine carbonate is condensed in a mixt. of 95% H_2SO_4 and 20% fuming $H_2SO_4 \rightarrow$ 2-amino-5-chloropyrimidine. Y = 74%. R. O. Roblin, Jr., P. S. Winnek and J. P. English, *J. Am. Chem. Soc. 64*, 567 (1942); *C.A. 1942*, 2532.

Pyrazine Ring

5.

$$\begin{array}{c} OH \\ N{=}C{-}CNH_2 \\ HN{:}C{-}N{-}CNH_2 \\ H \end{array} + \begin{array}{c} O:COH \\ O:CH \end{array} \rightarrow \begin{array}{c} OH \\ N{=}C{-}C{-}N{-}COH \\ HN{:}C{-}C{-}N{-}CH \\ H \end{array}$$

2,4,5-Triamino-6-hydroxypyrimidine sulfate is treated with the $BaHSO_3$ deriv. of glyoxylic acid in 78% $H_2SO_4 \rightarrow$ xanthopterine. Y = 78%. W. Koschara, *Z. physiol. Chem. 277*, 159 (1943); *C.A. 1943*, 5743.

Hydrochlorides of organic bases

Amines $\cdot NH_2$
See 599.

Tetrahydropyridine Ring   O
See 600.

2,3-Substituted Quinolines   See 620.

Quinoxaline Ring
See 350.

Glacial acetic acid–hydrochloric acid $CH_3COOH–HCl$

Nitration $\cdot H \rightarrow \cdot NO_2$

Nitroso Amines $\cdot N(CH_3)_2 \rightarrow \cdot N\underset{NO}{\overset{CH_3}{<}}$

346. When dimethylanilines are nitrated in AcOH, one methyl group is replaced by a nitroso group, the nitroso amines being formed; when nitration is done in HCl no exchange takes place. 2-Nitro-4-acetamido-dimethylaniline (I) (2 g.) is treated with HNO₃ (d. 1.42) in glacial AcOH at 15° → 2 g. 2,6-dinitro-N-nitroso-4-acetamidomethylaniline. 2.2 g. (I) is treated with HNO₃ (d. 1.42) in concd. HCl at 15° → 1.6 g. 2,6-dinitro-4-acetamidodimethylaniline. F.e.s. E. E. Ayling, J. H Gorvin and L. E. Hinkel, *J. Chem. Soc. 1942*, 755; *C.A. 1943*, 1398 (*C.A 1942*, 419).

Hydrochloric acid   *HCl*

Hydrazones $CO \rightarrow C : N \cdot NHR$

347. 5,7-Dimethyl-2-octanone (2 g.) is treated with 2,4-dinitrophenylhydra-zine and a few drops concd. HCl in MeOH → 2.25 g. pure 5,6-di-methyl-2-octanone-2,4-dinitrophenylhydrazone. W. Dirscherl and H. Nahm, *Ber. 76*, 709 (1943); *C.A. 1944*, 1748.

348. 2-Dodecanone is added to a boiling soln. of 2,4-dinitrophenylhydrazine and concd. HCl in EtOH → phenylhydrazone deriv. Y = 94%. F. Asinger, *Ber. 77*, 73 (1944); *C.A. 1945*, 906.

Nitroso Compounds $\cdot H \rightarrow \cdot NO$

349. 2,4-Diphenylpyrrole (5 g.) (prepn., see 397) is treated with NaNO₂ and concd. HCl in EtOH → 5.8 g. of the 5-NO deriv. F.e.s. M. A. T. Rogers, *J. Chem. Soc. 1943*, 590; *C.A. 1944*, 1495.

α-Isonitroso Ketones $CO \cdot C = NOH$
See 783.

Quinoxaline Ring Closure

350.

Et ester of 2-keto-1-methyl-1,2-dihydro-3-quinoxalinepyruvic acid is treated with o-$C_6H_4(NH_4)_2$ in 50% EtOH and excess 32% HCl, or the Et ester is heated for 40 min. at 150–170° without solvents, or in phenol at 100° → 3-(2-keto-1-methyldihydroquinoxalinyl)-3-(2-ketodihydro-quinoxalinyl)methane. Y = quant. Attempts to convert such compounds into monomethinecyanines failed. F.e.s. A. H. Cook and R. F. Naylor, *J. Chem. Soc. 1943*, 397; *C.A. 1944*, 363.

Via halogen compounds

Amines   · NH₂
    See 429.

Amidines

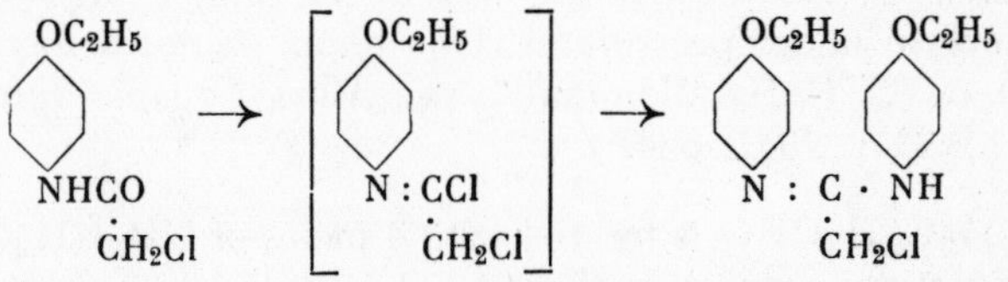

p-$H_2NC_6H_4OEt$ and p-$EtOC_6H_4NHOCCH_2Cl$ are treated with PCl_5 in C_6H_6 → [N,N'-bis-(4-ethoxyphenyl)guanyl]chloromethane (s.m. 367, 641, 658). Y = 80%. H. P. Kaufmann, J. Budwig and K. Mohnke, *Ber. 75*, 1585 (1943); *C.A. 1944*, 1215.

Acid Amides   · COOH → · CONH ·

2,7-Diaminofluorene is powdered together with 2,3-hydroxynaphthoic acid and p-dichlorobenzene; the mixt. is fused at 65–70°, PCl_3 is added over a period of 15 min. and heated for 2 hrs. to boiling (170–180°) → 2,7-(3'-hydroxynaphthoyl-2')diaminofluorene. Y = 75–80%. F.e.s. B. Porai-Koschitz and W. Perekalin, *Org. Chem. Ind. (U.S.S.R.) 4*, 165 (1937); *C.A. 1938*, 1935, 9505.

Primary Amines from Aldehydes   CHO → CH₂NH₂

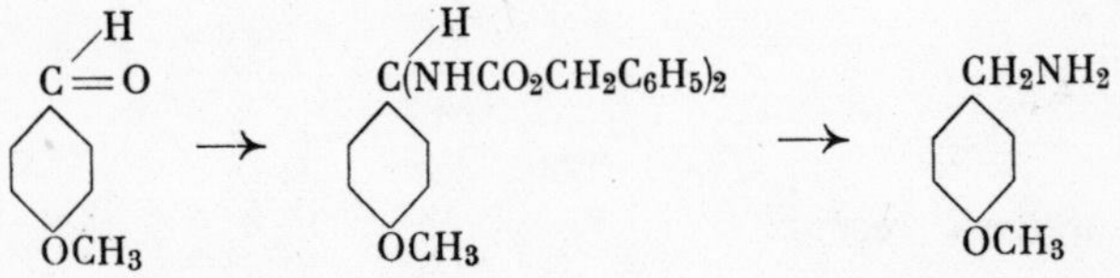

1–2 moles of aldehyde or α-keto acid is condensed with benzyl carbamate and the reaction product is split off by catalytic hydrogenation. Method: The carbonyl compound is heated for several hours at 10–15 mm. pressure with benzyl carbamate at 70–135° and the condensation product is hydrogenated with H_2–Pd in EtOH. Ex: Anisaldehyde and benzyl carbamate → dicarbobenzoxy-p-methoxybenzylidenediamine

(Y = 65%) → anisylamino · HCl (Y = 89%). Pyruvic acid and benzyl carbamate → α,α-dicarbobenzoxyaminopropionic acid (Y = 85%) → alanine (Y = 60%). F.e.s. A. E. Martell and R. M. Herbst, *J. Org. Chem. 6*, 878 (1941); *C.A. 1942*, 753.

Secondary Amines from Oxo Compounds via Schiff Bases

354.

General Method. *m*-Toluidine and benzaldehyde are condensed in di-Et ether. The Schiff base formed is reduced catalytically (Raney Ni) in an autoclave under pressure at room temp. → *m*-tolylbenzylamine. Y = 89–94%. C. F. H. Allen and J. van Allen, *Organic Syntheses 21*, 108 (1941); *C.A. 1941*, 6247.

355. 3,4-(MeO)$_2$C$_6$H$_3$CHO is treated with 4 moles of NH$_2$CH$_2$CH$_2$NH$_2$ · H$_2$O and rapidly reduced with Na → 1-(3,4-dimethoxybenzylamino)-2-aminoethane. Y = 75%. A. Funke and J. P. Fourneau, *Bull. soc. chim. 9*, 806 (1942); *C.A. 1944*, 3262.

356. **4-Monoalkylated Aminoantipyrines.** The catalytic alkylation of 4-amino-, 4-nitroso-, or 4-nitroantipyrines in the presence of carbonyl compds. (except HCHO) yields pure 4-monoalkylated aminoantipyrines. Ex: 4-Aminoantipyrine in di-Et ether is treated with EtCHO and a Pt–BaSO$_4$ catalyst at 3 atm. and room temp. → 4-propylaminoantipyrine. Y = nearly 100%; 4-aminoantipyrine and Me$_2$CO with Pt–BaSO$_4$ at 3 atm. and room temp.; or 4-nitrosoantipyrine and Me$_2$CO with Pt–BaSO$_4$ at 3.4 atm. and 60° or 4-aminoantipyrine and Me$_2$CO with Ni at 50 atm. and 90° → 4-isopropylaminoantipyrine, C$_{14}$H$_{19}$ON$_3$. Y = nearly 100%. F.e.s. A. Skita, F. Keil and W. Stühmer *et al.*, *Ber. 75*, 1696 (1943); *C.A. 1944*, 1233.

Nitrogen ⅄   NC ⅄ N

Without additional reagents

Phenylhydrazones from Anils   · C = NR → · C = N · NHR

357. 2-Hydroxy-1,4-dihydro-3-quinoxaldehydeanil (prepn., see 386) is heated to boiling with 10 times the amt. of phenylhydrazine for 5 min. → 2-hydroxy-3-quinoxaldehyde-phenylhydrazone. Y = 80%. H. Ohle, M. Hielscher, G. Noetzel and A. Wolter, *Ber. 76*, 1051 (1943); *C.A. 1944*, 3654.

Urethans from Azides
$\cdot CON_3 \rightarrow \cdot NHCOOCH_3$

8.

5,8-Dichloro-2-naphthazide (prepn., see 260) is refluxed for 4 hrs. with MeOH → Me 5,8-dichloro-2-naphthalene carbamate. Y = 80%. H. Goldstein and P. Viaud, *Helv. Chim. Acta 27*, 883 (1944); *C.A. 1945*, 926.

See also 389.

Substituted Acid Amides
from Hydrazides via Azides
$\cdot CONHNH_2 \rightarrow \cdot CONHR$

9. Partial Synthesis of Ergobasine Type Alkaloids. Condensation of the pure, optically active isolysergic and lysergic acid hydrazides or azides with α-aminopropanol provides a superior method for the synthesis of ergobasine and its isomers. Ex: 2.82 g. of *d*-isolysergic acid hydrazide is treated with $NaNO_2$ in HCl → *d*-isolysergic acid azide which is kept for 24 hrs. in the dark with *l*(+)-2-amino-1-propanol in ether → 2.4 g. crude *d*-isolysergic acid *l*-2-propanolamide (*d*-ergobasinine). F.e.s. A. Stoll and A. Hofmann, *Helv. Chim. Acta 26*, 944 (1943); *C.A. 1944*, 1501.

Quinazoline Ring Synthesis
O
See 312.

Sodium ethylate
NaOR

Uric Acids

0.

$HOCH_2CH_2NHCONH_2$ and $NCCH_2CO_2Et$ are refluxed with EtONa in EtOH for 14 hrs. → 3-(2-hydroxyethyl)-4-iminobarbituric acid, Y = 71%; this is treated with iso-AmNO$_2$ in 45% EtOH → 3-(2-hydroxyethyl)-4-iminovioluric acid, Y = 90%. This is reduced with $Na_2S_2O_4$ in NH_3 → 3-(2-hydroxyethyl)-4,5-diaminouracil (Y = 87%), which is fused with urea at 170–180° → 3-(2-hydroxyethyl)uric acid.

Y = quant. A. H. Nathan and M. T. Bogert, *J. Am. Chem. Soc. 63*, 2567 (1941); *C.A. 1942*, 479.

Pyrimidine Ring   See 605.

Organic bases

Oxindoles

361.

2-Amino-3-diazoacetylpyridine (I) is heated with PhNMe₂ at 120–180° until the nitrogen evolution ceases → 7-pyroxindole. Y = 61.5%. An Arndt-Eistert reaction (see CC ⅄ Hal without additional reagents) with (I) failed. (Compare Miescher and Kägi, *Helv. Chim. Acta 24*, 1471 (1941); *C.A. 1942*, 4820.) H. Kägi, *Helv. Chim. Acta 24*, 141E (1941); *C.A. 1942*, 5176.

Silver oxide   Ag₂O

Acid Amides   COCl → CH₂CONHR
   See 631.

Sulfuric acid   H₂SO₄

Acid Amides from Ketones   RCOR′ → RCONHR′

362.   CH₃COCH₂CH₂C₆H₅ $\xrightarrow{N_3H}$ CH₃CONHCH₂CH₂C₆H₅

PhCH₂CH₂Ac is dissolved in CHCl₃, treated dropwise with 5.6% N₃H in CHCl₃ and concd. H₂SO₄ while cooling with an ice–salt mixture and then heated at 60° for 45 min. after N₂ evoln. has ceased after which it is decomposed by H₂O → PhCH₂CH₂NHAc. Y = 62.5%. F.e.s. L. H. Briggs, G. C. De Ath and S. R. Ellis, *J. Chem. Soc. 1942*, 61; *C.A. 1942*, 3496.

Hydrochloric acid   HCl

Substituted Urea Compounds   · NH₂ → · NHC⟨S / NH₂

363.

o-Anisidine is heated to cloudiness with a H₂O-dilute NH₄SCN soln. in dil. HCl → *o*-methoxyphenylthiourea (s.m. 465). Y = 90%. H. Erlenmeyer and H. Ueberwasser, *Helv. Chim. Acta 25*, 515 (1942); *C.A. 1942*, 7021.

Halogen $\wedge$ NC $\psi\wedge$ Hal

Without additional reagents

Primary Amines $\cdot$ Hal $\to$ $\cdot$ NH$_2$

4. α-Me$_2$CHCHBrCO$_2$H is treated with an aq. NH$_3$ soln. After several days $\to$ dl-valine. Y $= 47$–48%. Also: α-bromoisocaproic acid $\to$ dl-leucine. Y $= 43$–45%. α-Bromo-β-methylvaleric acid $\to$ dl-isoleucine. Y $= 49\%$. C. S. Marvel, *Organic Syntheses* **20**, 106 (1940); *21*, 60, 74 (1941); *C.A. 1940*, 5052.

5. Dry NH$_3$ is introduced at 180° into a PhOH soln. of 4-chloroquinaldines $\to$ 4-aminoquinaldines. Y $=$ almost quant. 2-Chlorolepidines yield only 10% according to this method. Prepn. of 2-aminolepidines, see 382. O. G. Backeberg and J. L. C. Marais, *J. Chem. Soc. 1942*, 381; *C.A. 1942*, 5821.

See 429.

Tertiary Amines $\dfrac{R'}{R''}$N $\cdot$ H $\longrightarrow$ $\dfrac{R'}{R''}$NR

6. (PhCh$_2$)$_2$NH and ClCH$_2$CO$_2$H are mixed in dioxane $\to$ N,N-dibenzylglycocoll. Y $= 82\%$. L. Birkofer, *Ber. 75*, 429 (1942); *C.A. 1943*, 3067.

OC$_2$H$_5$ OC$_2$H$_5$ OC$_2$H$_5$ OC$_2$H$_5$

$\to$

N $=$ C $-$ NH   N $=$ C $-$ NH

CH$_2$Cl   CH$_2$N(C$_2$H$_5$)$_2$

[N,N'-Bis-(4-ethoxyphenyl)-guanyl] chloromethane (prepn., see 351) is treated with Et$_2$NH in MeOH $\to$ [bis-N,N'-(4-ethoxyphenyl)-guanyl]-(diethylamino)-methane. Y $=75\%$. H. P. Kaufmann, J. Budwig and K. Mohnke, *Ber. 75*, 1585 (1943); *C.A. 1944*, 1215.

Benzoylation of Amines $\cdot$ NH$_2$ $\to$ $\cdot$ NHCOC$_6$H$_5$
See 447.

Hydrazinocarboxylic Acids $\cdot$ Cl $\to$ $\cdot$ NHNH$_2$

8. 2-Chloro-5-nitrobenzoic acid is boiled with N$_2$H$_4$ $\cdot$ H$_2$O in abs. alc. $\to$ 5-nitro-o-hydrazinobenzoic acid (s.m. 396). Y $=$ nearly quant. F.e.s. K. Pfannstiel and J. Janecke, *Ber. 75*, 1096 (1942); *C.A. 1943*, 4392.

Thiocarbimides
See 464.

Potassium carbonate K_2CO_3

Isoquinolines   O

369. (structure) CH_2CH_2Br / CH_2Br $+ H_2NSO_2C_6H_4NHCOCH_3 \rightarrow$ (structure) $NSO_2C_6H_4NHCOCH_3$

o-BrCH$_2$CH$_2$C$_6$H$_4$CH$_2$Br (2.8 g.) (prepn., see 425) and *p*-MeC$_6$H$_4$-SO$_2$NH$_2$ are refluxed with K_2CO_3 in EtOH for 5 hrs. → 3.3 g. 2-*p*-acetaminobenzenesulfonyl-1,2,3,4-tetrahydroisoquinoline. F.e.s. F. G. Hollimann and F. G. Mann, *J. Chem. Soc. 1942*, 737; *C.A. 1943*, 1396.

Acridines
     See 755–756.

Sodium acetate–iodine $NaOOCCH_3$–I_2

Tertiary Amines $\cdot NH_2 \rightarrow \cdot N(R)_2$

370. Aniline and benzyl chloride are heated with anhyd. NaAc and a little I_2 for 5–6 hrs. at 104°. The soln. is stirred and kept moisture free → *N,N*-dibenzylaniline. Y = 94%. F.e.s. L. Birkofer, *Ber. 75*, 429 (1942); *C.A. 1943*, 3067.

Sodium azide NaN_3

Azides $\cdot I \rightarrow \cdot N_3$

371. Iodododecane is heated at 90° in a pressure tube for 8 hrs. with NaN_3 in MeOH $\cdot H_2O$ → dodecylazide. Y = 80%. F.e.s. K. Henkel and F. Weygand, *Ber. 76*, 812 (1943); *C.A. 1944*, 1742.

Sodium nitrite $NaNO_2$

Cinnoline Synthesis   O
     See 322.

Silver nitrite $AgNO_2$

Aliphatic Nitro Compounds $\cdot I \rightarrow \cdot NO_2$

372. $ICH_2(CH_2)_3OC_6H_7O(O_2CCH_3)_4 \longrightarrow O_2NCH_2(CH_2)_3OC_6H_7O(O_2CCH_3)_4$

(4-Iodobutyl)-1-tetraacetyl-β-D-glucoside is refluxed with $AgNO_2$ in C_6H_6 on a water bath → 4-nitro deriv. Y = 59%. B. Helferich and M. Hase, *Ann. 554*, 261 (1943); *C.A. 1943*, 6246.

Organic bases

Benzoylation $\cdot NH_2 \rightarrow \cdot NHCOC_6H_5$

. *o*-Nitroaniline is treated with benzoyl chloride in $PhNEt_2 \rightarrow$ benzoyl-*o*-nitroaniline. Y = 93%. P. Ruggli and J. Rohner, *Helv. Chim. Acta* 25, 1533 (1942); *C.A. 1943*, 5947.

. 5,8-Dichloro-2-naphthylamine with benzoyl chloride in $C_5H_5N \rightarrow$ *N*-benzoyl-5,8-dichloro-2-naphthylamine. Y = nearly quant. H. Goldstein and P. Viaud, *Helv. Chim. Acta* 27, 883 (1944); *C.A. 1945*, 926.

. 2-(*o*-Aminophenyl)oxazole is treated with benzoyl chloride in $C_5H_5N \rightarrow$ 2-(*o*-benzoylaminophenyl)oxazole, $C_{16}H_{12}O_2N_2$. Y = almost quant. W. E. Cass, *J. Am. Chem. Soc.* 64, 785 (1942); *C.A. 1942*, 3174.

Copper compounds–alkali carbonate

Secondary Amines $\cdot NH_2 \rightarrow \cdot NHR$

. 4-Bromo-3-nitroanisole and $o\text{-}H_2NC_6H_4CO_2H$ are treated with Cu and Na_2CO_3 in *p*-methylcyclohexanol $\rightarrow$ 6'-nitro-4'-methoxydiphenyl-amine-2-carboxylic acid. Y = 70–82%. $C_{14}H_{12}O_5N_2$. F.e.s. B. V. Samant, *Ber.* 75, 1008 (1942); *C.A. 1943*, 4400.

Sulfonic Acid Amides $\cdot Br \rightarrow \cdot NHSO_2R$

. 2,5-Dibromoterephthalaldehyde (prepn., see 226) is treated with Cu powder, CuBr, K_2CO_3, and $p\text{-}MeC_6H_4SO_2NH_2$ in $PhNO_2$, while K_2CO_3 is added gradually at 150–155° $\rightarrow$ 2,5-di-*p*-tolylsulfonamido-terephthaldehyde (s.m. 400). Y = 53–54%. P. Ruggli and F. Brandt, *Helv. Chim. Acta* 27, 274 (1944); *C.A. 1944*, 6288.

Copper compounds–ammonia

Amine $\cdot Hal \rightarrow \cdot NH_2$

. 4-Bromo-*o*-xylene is treated with concd. NH_3, Cu wire, and CuCl at 195° and 900–1100 lb. pressure $\rightarrow 3,4\text{-}Me_2C_6H_3NH_2$. Y = 79%. W. A. Wisansky and S. Ansbacher, *J. Am. Chem. Soc.* 63, 2532 (1941); *C.A. 1941*, 7380. Methods, see Groggins and Stirton, *Ind. Eng. Chem.* 28, 1051 (1936); *C.A. 1936*, 7977.

. 2,4-Dichlorobenzoic acid is heated in a pressure tube at 120° with 37% NH_4OH and freshly reduced Cu $\rightarrow 2,4\text{-}Cl(H_2N)C_6H_3CO_2H$. Y = 77%. B. V. Samant, *Ber.* 75, 1008 (1942); *C.A. 1943*, 4400. Methods, see Bad. Anilin- und Sodafabrik, *German Pat.* 224,207; *C. 1910*, II, 525.

. Aminopyridines are obtained from chloropyridines by heating for 4–7 hrs. with 20% to concd. NH_3, and if necessary with some $CuSO_4$, in a sealed tube at 130–160°. Ex: (1) Without $CuSO_4$: 2-Chloropyridine-

5-sulfonic acid *n*-butylamide → 2-amino deriv. (Y = 87%.) 2-Chloro-
pyridine-5-sulfoaminoacetic acid → 2-aminopyridine deriv. (Y = 84%.)
(2) With $CuSO_4$: 2-Chloropyridine-5-sulfonic acid dimethylamide →
2-aminopyridine deriv. (Y = 87.5%.) 2-Chloropyridine-5-sulfonic acid
allylamide → 2-aminopyridine deriv. (Y = 78%.) F.e.s. C. Naegeli,
W. Kündig and H. Suter, *Helv. Chim. Acta* 25, 1485 (1942); *C.A. 1943*,
5949.

381. 4-Bromoisoquinoline is heated with a concd. NH_3 soln. and $CuSO_4$ in
an autoclave at 165–170° → 4-aminoisoquinoline (s.m. 275). Y = 70%.
J. J. Craig and W. E. Cass, *J. Am. Chem. Soc.* 64, 783 (1942); *C.A.
1942*, 3175.

Zinc chloride $ZnCl_2$

382. 2-Chlorolepidines are heated in a sealed tube at 210–220° with $ZnCl_2$–
$2 NH_3$ and NH_4Cl → 2-aminolepidines. Ex: 2-Amino-6-methoxylepi-
dine; Y = 70%. 2-Amino-6-ethoxylepidine; Y = 50%. O. G. Backeberg
and J. L. C. Marais, *J. Chem. Soc. 1942*, 381; *C.A. 1942*, 5821.

Phenol C_6H_5OH

Secondary from Primary Amines $\cdot NH_2 \rightarrow \cdot NHR$

383. Dodecylamine, 5-chloroacridine, and phenol heated for 0.5 hr. at 160°
→ 5-dodecylaminoacridine. F.e.s. A. Albert, R. Goldacre and E. Heymann, *J. Chem. Soc. 1943*, 651; *C.A. 1944*, 1506.

Glacial acetic acid CH_3COOH

384.

2-Chlorolepidine is heated for 2–3 hrs. with sulfanilimide in glacial
AcOH → N^4-(2′-lepidyl)-sulfanilamide. Y = 70–80%. F.e.s. O. G.
Backeberg and J. L. C. Marais, *J. Chem. Soc. 1942*, 758; *C.A. 1943*,
1403.

Hydrochlorides of organic bases

Isocyanates $\cdot NH_2 \rightarrow \cdot N = C = O$

385.

4-Aminoazobenzene · HCl is treated with $COCl_2$ in toluene → 4-
(phenylazo)-phenylisocyanate (Y = 90%) in addition to 4-phenylazo-
phenylurea. L. C. Raiford and H. B. Freyermuth, *J. Org. Chem.* 8,
230 (1943); *C.A. 1943*, 5057.

Iodine   *I*
See 370.

Carbon ⚡   NC ⚡ C

Without additional reagents

Cleavage of Hexoses via Tetrahydroxybutylquinoxalines

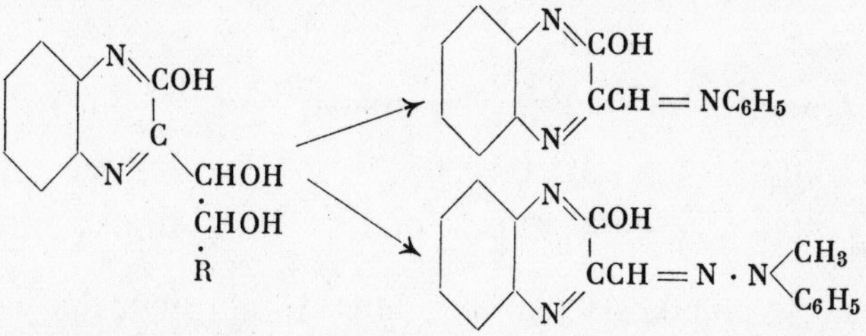

The quantitative decompn. of a hexose in compounds of the C_3-series is made possible under conditions where free hexoses can otherwise be split only in small amounts or not at all. This method leads, for example, from the fructose via the fructuronic acid to the 2-hydroxy-3-(D-arabotetrahydroxybutyl)-quinoxaline (I) which is then split in the following manner: 1. With *asym*-methylphenylhydrazone (II): (I) and (II) are refluxed in 50% alc. for 40 hrs. in a current of CO_2 → 2-hydroxy-3-quinoxaldehyde methylphenylhydrazone. Y = 80%. 2. With aniline: (I) is refluxed with aniline in H_2O for 20 hrs. at 110° on an oil bath → 2-hydroxy-1,4-dihydro-3-quinoxaldehyde anil (s.m. 357). Y = 96%. H. Ohle, M. Hielscher, G. Noetzel and A. Wolter, *Ber. 76B*, 1051 (1943); *C.A. 1944*, 3654.

Pyrimidine Ring Synthesis   O

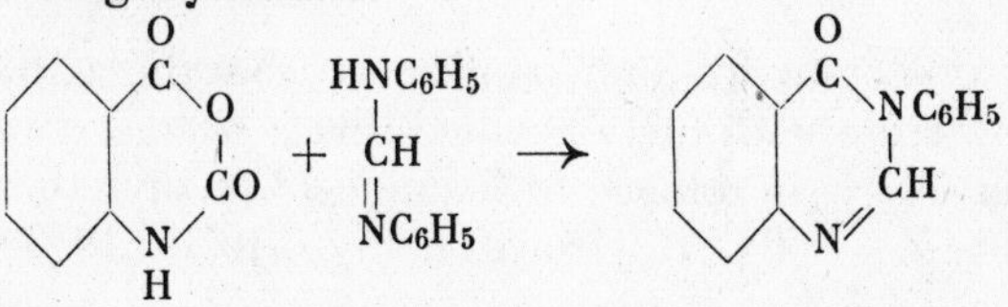

PhN : CHNHPh is heated with an equimolar amt. of isatoic anhydride at 136° → 3-phenyl-4-keto-3,4-dihydroquinazoline. Y = 86.3%. F.e.s. J. F. Meyer and E. C. Wagner, *J. Org. Chem. 8*, 239 (1943); *C.A. 1943*, 5066.

Glacial acetic acid   *CH₃COOH*

Urea Derivatives from Azides

$$\cdot \text{CON}_3 \rightarrow \cdot \overset{\diagup \text{NHR}}{\underset{\diagdown \text{NHR}}{\text{CO}}}$$

388.

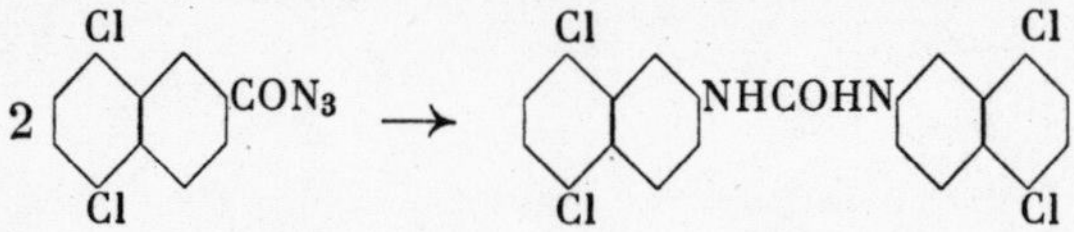

5,8-Dichloro-2-naphthazide is heated in glacial AcOH → bis-(5,8-dichloro-2-naphthyl)urea. Y = 72%. H. Goldstein and P. Viaud, *Helv. Chim. Acta 27*, 883 (1944); *C.A. 1945*, 926.

Via intermediates

Amines from Azides via Benzylurethans   · CON₃ → · NH₂

Amines from Azides via Benzylurethans $\cdot CON_3 \rightarrow \cdot NH_2$

389.

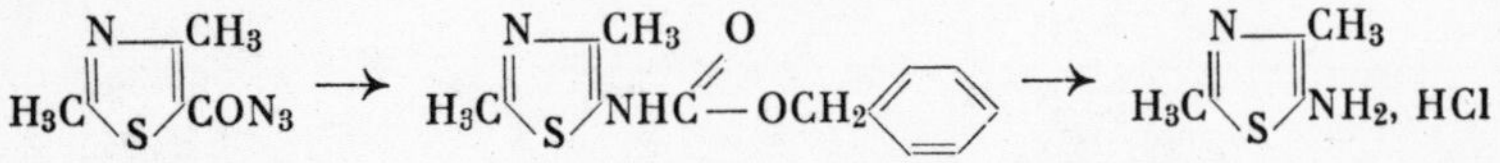

The amine is prepd. via the benzylurethan although the yields are small, because the ethyl urethan cannot be saponified. Ex: Et-2,4-dimethyl-5-thiazole carbamate is refluxed with benzyl alc. in xylene → benzyl ester deriv. which is boiled in 33% HCl → 2,4-dimethyl-5-amino-thiazole · HCl. K. A. Jensen and O. R. Hansen, *Dansk. Tids. Farm. 17*, 189 (1943); *C.A. 1944*, 4571.

See also 358.

Shortened Curtius Degradation   · COOH → · NH₂

Shortened Curtius Degradation $\cdot COOH \rightarrow \cdot NH_2$

390.

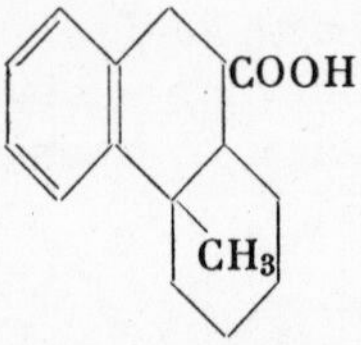

13-Methyl-*asym*-octahydro-9-phenanthrenecarboxylic acid is converted to the acid chloride with $SOCl_2$; when this is heated on a water bath with activated NaN_3 in toluene → 9-amino-13-methyl-*asym*-octahydrophenanthrene. Y = 60%. R. Grewe, *Ber. 76*, 1076 (1943); *C.A. 1944*, 4936.

Elimination

Hydrogen ⚹   NC ⇑ H

Copper acetate $Cu(CH_3COO)_2$

N-Alkylbenzimidazoles   O

1.

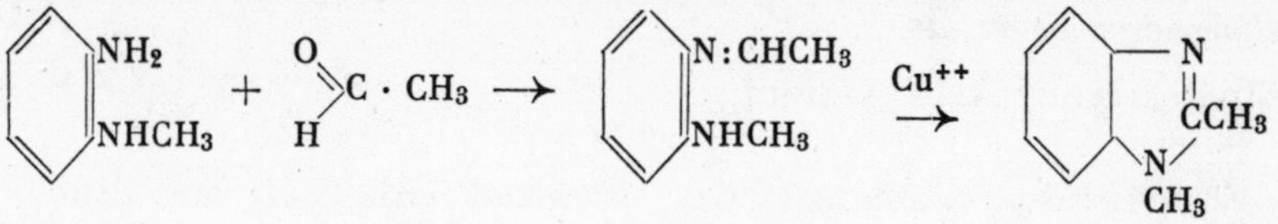

N-Substituted o-phenylenediamines are subject to the influence of $Cu(OAc)_2$ in the presence of aldehydes. Ex: N-Methyl-o-phenylenediamine $\cdot$ 2HCl (I) and AcH in 50% alc. $\rightarrow$ N-methyl-2-methylbenzimidazole. Y = 83%. The N-ethyl deriv. of (I) and anisaldehyde $\rightarrow$ N-ethyl-2-(p-methoxyphenyl)-benzimidazole. Y = 90%. 3-Amino-4-(ethylamino)pyridine is heated for 4.5 hrs. at 150° in a sealed tube with furfurole $\rightarrow$ N-ethyl-2'-furylimidazolo-4',5',3,4-pyridine. Y = 68%. F.e.s. R. Weidenhagen, G. Train, H. Wegner and L. Nordstrom, *Ber.* 75, 1936 (1943); *C.A. 1944*, 1235.

Nitric acid HNO_3

Hantzsch's Pyridine Synthesis   See 542.

Hydrochloric acid HCl

Cinnoline Synthesis   See 322.

Oxygen ⋏   NC ⇑ O

Sodium hydroxide $NaOH$

Synthesis of Indoline   ⧫   O

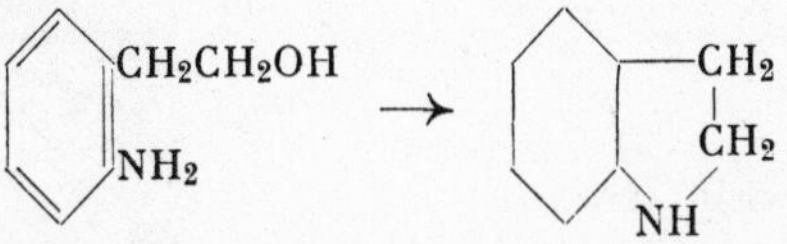

o-$H_2NC_6H_4CH_2CH_2OH$ is shaken with $PhSO_2Cl$ in aq. NaOH $\rightarrow$ indoline. Y = good. G. M. Bennett and M. M. Hafez, *J. Chem. Soc.* 1941, 287; *C.A. 1941*, 5890.

Acetic anhydride $(CH_3CO)_2O$

Carboxylic Acids
from Oximes via Nitriles $C\overset{NOH}{\underset{H}{\diagdown}}$ $\rightarrow$ CN $\rightarrow$ COOH

Δ^3-Tetrahydrobenzaldoxime is treated with Ac_2O $\rightarrow$ Δ^3-tetrahydrobenzonitrile (Y = 78%), which in turn is treated with alc. NaOH $\rightarrow$ Δ^3-tetrahydrobenzoic acid. Y = 73%. H. Fiesselmann, *Ber.* 75, 881 (1942); *C.A. 1943*, 3417.

Phosphorus pentoxide   P$_2$O$_5$

Nitriles from Acid Amides $C\underset{NH_2}{\overset{O}{\diagdown}}$ → CN

394. α-Et-myristic acid amide (20 g.) is mixed with P$_2$O$_5$ and distd. *in vacuo* → 14 g. α-Et-myristic acid nitrile. N. P. Buu-Hoi and P. Cagniant, *Ber. 76*, 689 (1943).

Thionyl chloride   SOCl$_2$

395. 3,4-Dinitrobenzamide is refluxed with SOCl$_2$ → 3,4-dinitrobenzonitrile. Y = 91%. H. Goldstein and R. Voegeli, *Helv. Chim. Acta 26*, 1125 (1943); *C.A. 1944*, 78. Methods, see Michaelis and Siebert, *Ann. 274*, 312 (1893).

Sulfurous acid and hydrochloric acid   SO$_2$–HCl

Indazolones

396. 1. *o*-HO$_2$CC$_6$H$_4$NH$_2$ or its hydrochloride is boiled with H$_2$O and a little HCl for 30 min. Ex: 5-Nitro-*o*-hydrazinobenzoic acid · HCl (prepn., see 368) → 5-nitroindazolone. Y = 95%.

2. 6-Nitroanthranilic acid is diazotized, poured into a SO$_2$ soln. and finally gently boiled for 15 min. → 4-nitroindazolone. Y = 79%. Compare 261. F.e.s. K. Pfannstiel and J. Janecke, *Ber. 75*, 1096 (1942);*C.A. 1943*, 4392.

Nickel   Ni

Synthesis of Pyrrole Ring

397. C$_6$H$_5$COCH$_2$CHC$_6$H$_5$ →   C$_6$H$_5$⬮⬮   →   C$_6$H$_5$⬮⬮
              ĊN $\diagdown_{N}\diagup$C$_6$H$_5$ $\diagdown_{N}\diagup$C$_6$H$_5$
                                                    H   H

PhCOCH$_2$CHPhCN is reduced catalytically (Raney Ni) in MeOH or AcOEt at room temp. and atm. pressure → 2,4-diphenylpyrroline. Y = 95%. This is treated at 250° with Se (Y = 55%) or Raney Ni (Y = 50%) at 350° or in the vapor phase with a Ni–pumice catalyst (Y = 83%) (prepn., see original) → 2,4-diphenylpyrrole (s.m. 349). F.e.s. M. A. T. Rogers, *J. Chem. Soc. 1943*, 590; *C.A. 1944*, 1495.

Sulfur ↗   NC ⇑ S

Organic bases

Purines from Pyrimidines

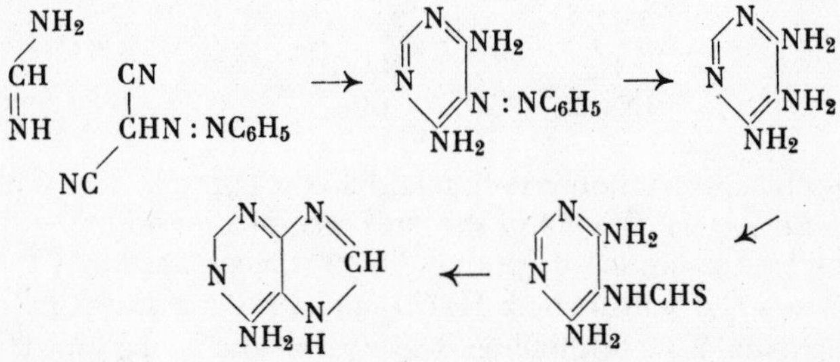

PhN : NCH(CN)$_2$ and HN : CHNH$_2$ are treated with EtONa in EtOH; after 1 hr. at room temp. the mixture is refluxed for 0.75 hr. → 4,6-diamino-5-phenylazopyrimidine (Y = 75%); hydrogenated with Raney Ni → 4,5,6-triaminopyrimidine (Y = 90%). 1 gram of this is treated with HCS$_2$Na and worked up in the usual manner after 12 hrs. → 1 g. 4,6-diamino-5-thioformamidopyrimidine which is refluxed for 12 hrs. in H$_2$O → adenine. Y = almost quant. The rearrangement to adenine proceeds faster on boiling in pyridine or quinoline than on boiling in H$_2$O. For the condensation of malonitrile with CH$_2$(CN)$_2$, see 605. J. Baddiley, B. Lythgoe and A. R. Todd, *J. Chem. Soc. 1943*, 386; *C.A. 1943*, 6667.

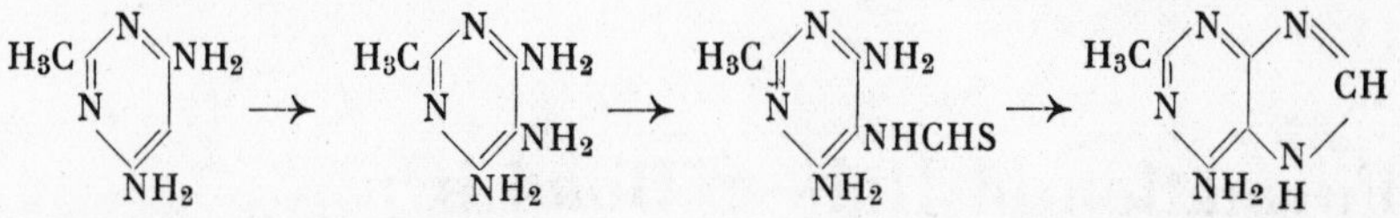

1. 4,5-Diamino-6-hydroxy-2-methylpyrimidine is dissolved in H$_2$O at 65° and treated with HCS$_2$Na · 6 H$_2$O; the soln. is cooled rapidly and allowed to stand overnight → 4-amino-5-thioformamido-6-hydroxy-2-methylpyrimidine. Y = quant. 3 grams of this is refluxed with 30 cc. quinoline → 2.7 g. 6-hydroxy-2-methylpurine.

2. 4,6-Diamino-2-methylpyrimidine (prepn., see 429) is diazotized with NaNO$_2$ in 3 N HCl at 0° → 4,6-diamino-5-nitroso deriv. which is reduced with (NH$_4$)$_2$S, evapd., extrd. with H$_2$O, and treated with HCS$_2$Na → 4,6-diamino-5-thioformamido-2-methylpyrimidine. Y = 35%. This is boiled with quinoline → 2-methyladenine. Y = 75%. F.e.s. J. Baddiley, B. Lythgoe, D. McNeil and A. R. Todd, *J. Chem. Soc. 1943*, 383; *C.A. 1943*, 6667.

Sulfuric acid H_2SO_4

Quinoline Ring Closure

400.

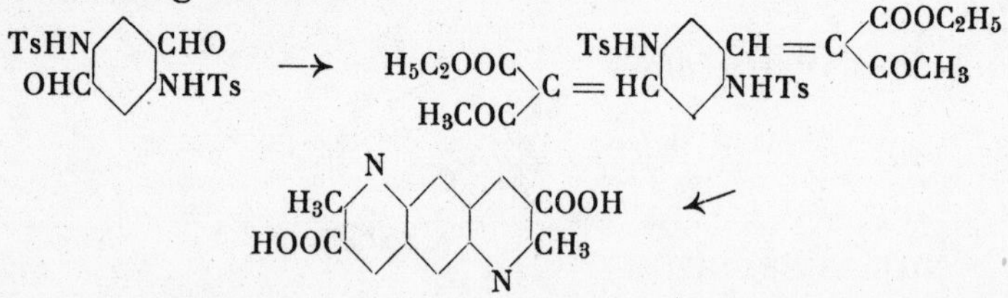

$$TsHN\begin{array}{c}CHO\\NHTs\end{array} \rightarrow H_5C_2OOC\begin{array}{c}\\C=HC\end{array} TsHN\begin{array}{c}CH=C\\NHTs\end{array}\begin{array}{c}COOC_2H_5\\COCH_3\end{array}$$

$$H_3C\begin{array}{c}N\\\\HOOC\end{array}\begin{array}{c}COOH\\CH_3\end{array}\begin{array}{c}\\N\end{array} \leftarrow$$

2,5-Di-*p*-tolylsulfonamidoterephthalaldehyde (prepn., see 377) is condensed with $AcCH_2CO_2Et$ in the presence of piperidine → di-Et-2,5-bis-(*p*-tolylsulfonamido)terephthalylidene diacetoacetate (Y = 90%), which is warmed with concd. H_2SO_4 on a boiling water bath → 2,7-dimethylpyrido[2,3-g]-quinoline-3,8-dicarboxylic acid (s.m. 112). Y = 65%. P. Ruggli and F. Brandt, *Helv. Chim. Acta* 27, 274 (1944); *C.A. 1944*, 6288.

Via intermediates

General Method for Preparation of Alkyl Isothiocyanates

401.
$$CH_3NH_2 \rightarrow CH_3NHC\begin{array}{c}S\\SNa\end{array} \rightarrow CH_3NHC\begin{array}{c}S\\SCO_2C_2H_5\end{array} \rightarrow CH_3N=C=S$$

CS_2 and NaOH are treated with $MeNH_2$ → Na salt of methyldithiocarbamic acid treated with $ClCO_2Et$ → MeNCS. Y = 65–76%. Also: EtNCS. Y = 60–70%. M. L. Moore and F. S. Crossley, *Organic Syntheses 21*, 81 (1941); *C.A. 1941*, 6241.

Formation of Hal—S Bond by:

Exchange

Oxygen ⬆   **HalS ⇅ O**

Phosphorus pentachloride PCl_5

Sulfonic Acid Chlorides   · SO_2Cl

402. NaO-carbethoxy-2,6-dimethylphenol-4-sulfonate with PCl_5 → O-carbethoxy-2,6-dimethylphenol-4-sulfonate. Crude Y = 93%. F.e.s. P. Karrer and P. Leiser, *Helv. Chim. Acta* 27, 678 (1944); *C.A. 1945*, 519.

Formation of Hal—C Bond by:

Addition

Addition to Carbon   HalC ⇓ CC

Without additional reagents

Addition of HBr to the Double Bond   C = C → CH · CBr

CH : CHCOOCH₃ → BrCH₂CH₂COOCH₃

Me acrylate is treated with HBr in ether → Me β-bromopropionate.
Y = 80–84%. R. M. Mozingo and L. A. Patterson, *Organic Syntheses*
20, 64 (1940); *C.A. 1940*, 5049.

Dry HBr is passed through benzyl allyl thioether (prepn., see 481) at
95–100° → 1-benzylthio-2-bromopropane (s.m. 639). Y = 73%. F. Kögl,
J. H. Verbeek, H. Erxleben and W. A. J. Borg, Z. *physiol. Chem. 279*,
121 (1943); *C.A. 1944*, 3978.

Chloronitro Compounds   C = C → CCl · CNO₂
  See 289.

Bromoacetamide

α-Hydroxyhalogen Compounds
from Ethylene Derivatives   C = C → CBr · C(OH)

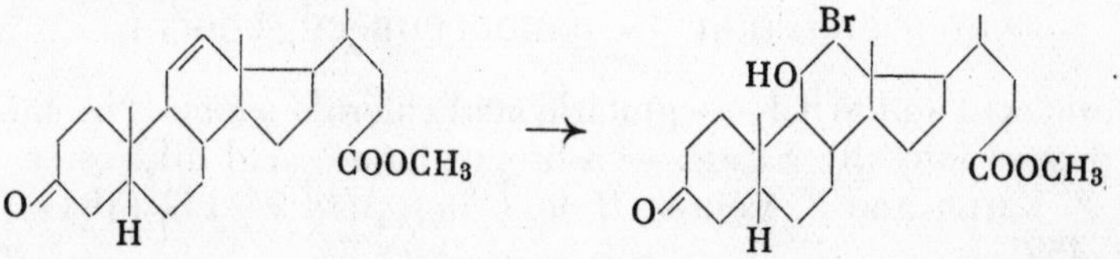

Me 3-keto-11-cholenate (500 mg.) is allowed to stand for 15 hrs. at
18° with BrCH₂CONH₂ and AcONa · 3 H₂O in H₂O–Me₂CO → 160
mg. Me 3-keto-11(α)-hydroxy-12-bromocholanate. F.e.s. G. H. Ott and
T. Reichstein, *Helv. Chim. Acta 26*, 1799 (1943); *C.A. 1944*, 4611.

Cuprous chloride   Cu₂Cl₂

Addition of Hydrogen Chloride
to the Triple Bond
                                                C ≡ C → CH = CCl

406. $$CH_2 = C(CH_3)C \equiv CH \longrightarrow CH_2 = C(CH_3)CCl = CH_2$$

2-Methyl-1-buten-3-yne is treated with concd. HCl, CuCl, NH$_4$Cl, and pyrogallol at room temp. → 2-chloro-3-methyl-1,3-butadiene. Y = 75% (s.m. 713). H. J. Backer and T. A. H. Blass, *Rec. trav. chim. 61*, 785 (1942); *C.A. 1944*, 3646.

Bauxite Al_2O_3

**Catalytic Addition of Cl
to the Ethylene Linkage** $C = C \rightarrow CCl \cdot CCl$

407. Ethylene and Cl are heated in the presence of bauxite at 55–65° → dichloroethane. Y = 90–5%. Also: Propylene at 100–155° → dichloropropane. Y = 90%. F.e.s. J. Gavat, *Ber. 76*, 1115 (1943); *C.A. 1944*, 4901.

Exchange

Hydrogen ⋏   **HalC ⋎⋏ H**

Without additional reagents

Chlorination in the Gas Phase $\cdot H \rightarrow \cdot Cl$

408. AcCH$_2$CO$_2$Et is chlorinated in the gas phase at 76–102° at 7 mm. pressure → α-chloroacetoacetic ester. Y = 68%. For the refluxing app., see original. J. Ubaldini and A. Fiorenza, *Chimica e industria (Italy) 25*, 113 (1943); *C.A. 1944*, 5799.

α-Halogendicarboxylic Acid Esters from Dicarboxylic Acids

409. $$HOOC(CH_2)_3COOH \longrightarrow C_2H_5OOCCHBr(CH_2)_2COOC_2H_5$$

Glutaric acid and SOCl$_2$ → glutaric acid chloride which is brominated and poured into abs. Et alc. → α-bromoglutaric acid diEt ester. Y = 58%. P. Karrer and F. Kehrer, *Helv. Chim. Acta 27*, 142 (1944); *C.A. 1944*, 4591.

Aldehydes from Hydrocarbons via Alkyl Bromides $\cdot CH_3 \rightarrow \cdot CHO$

410. Boiling p-C$_6$H$_4$Me$_2$ and Br with sunlight or corresponding artificial light → α,α,α',α',-tetrabromo-p-xylene. Y = 51–55%. Heating this with 95% H$_2$SO$_4$ at 70–110° while air is passed through → terephthalaldehyde. (Y = 81–84%). J. M. Snell and A. Weissberger, *Organic Syntheses 20*, 92 (1940); *C.A. 1940*, 5065.

See also 418.

Bromination
    See 645.

Chlorination   · H → · Cl

11. Cl_2 is passed through a soln. of p-nitrodimethylaniline in $CHCl_3$ at
    room temp. until one mole has been added → 2-chloro-4-nitrodimethyl-
    aniline. Y = 75% (prepn., see also 442). F.e.s. E. E. Ayling, J. H.
    Gorvin and L. E. Henkel, *J. Chem. Soc. 1942*, 755; *C.A. 1943*, 1398.

Sodium bicarbonate $NaHCO_3$

Iodation   · H → · I

12. Anthranilic acid is stirred with iodine in H_2O in the presence of
    $NaHCO_3$ → 5-iodoanthranilic acid. Y = 85%. A. Chichibabin and
    M. Vialatout, *Bull. soc. chim. Mém. 9*, 631 (1942); *C.A. 1944*, 733.

Mercuric acetate $Hg(OOCCH_3)_2$
    See 668.

Calcium carbonate $CaCO_3$
    See 419.

N-bromosuccinimide

Halogenation of Unsaturated Compounds
in the Allyl Position   : C = CH · CH₂ · → : C = CH · CHBr ·

13. $(CH_2CO)_2NBr$ is very suitable for the bromination of the allyl posi-
    tion. It possesses all the necessary properties: the bromine carrier can
    easily be recovered while the reaction time is short (for simple olefins,
    15–60 min.) when a slight excess of olefin is used. No addition ten-
    dency exists while monosubstitution predominates. Y = up to 80%.
    Methylene groups react faster, in general, than methyl groups.
    Method: The compound is boiled with $(CH_2CO)_2NBr$ in CCl_4 until
    the heavy particles have all risen to the surface of the CCl_4 and no
    more active Br is present. After cooling, the reaction product is
    filtered from the succinimide and fractionated. Ex: Cyclohexene →
    1-bromocyclohexene; Y = 87%. Amylene → monobromoamylene;
    Y = 40.3%. 2-Methylhexene → bromo-2-methylhexene (s.m. 773);
    Y = 40%. 1-Ph-1-propylene → cinnamylbromide; Y = 75.5%. Pinene
    → monobromopinene; Y = 55%. 1-Bromo-2-cyclohexene → dibromo-
    cyclohexene; Y = 31.3%. 1-Dodecylene → dibromododecylene; Y =
    33%. Cyclohexenyl acetate → bromo deriv.; Y = 58%. Me crotonate
    → Me γ-bromocrotonate; Y = 81–86%. F.e.s. K. Ziegler and co-workers,
    Ann. 551, 80 (1942); *C.A. 1943*, 5032.

Dichloramine-T

Chlorination   · H → · Cl

414.

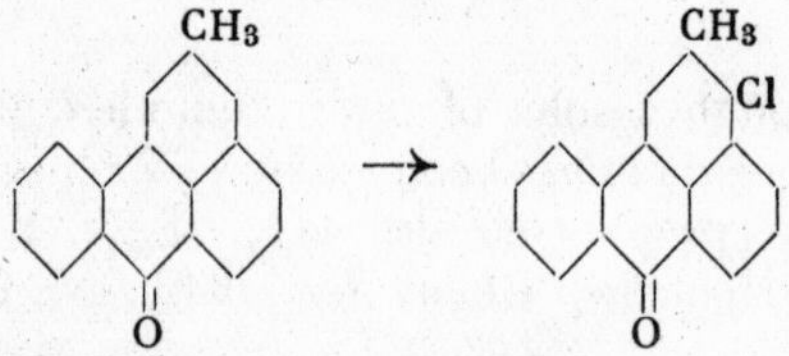

2-Methyl-*meso*-benzanthrone (5 g.) (prepn., see 589) is warmed in
HCl · glacial AcOH with dichloramine-T → 4 g. 3-chloro-2-methyl-
meso-benzanthrone (s.m. 652). D. H. Hey, R. J. Nicholls and C. W.
Pritchett, *J. Chem. Soc. 1944*, 97; *C.A. 1944*, 3644.

Glacial acetic acid CH_3COOH

Bromination   · H → · Br

415. Acetyl-*m*-toluidine is stirred with Br in glacial AcOH in the cold →
5-acetamido-2-bromotoluene. Y = 94%. H. Goldstein and G. Preitner,
Helv. Chim. Acta 27, 888 (1944); *C.A. 1945*, 918.

Phosphorus P
   See 451.

Phosphorus trichloride PCl_3

416. Isovaleric acid is heated for several hrs. with Br_2 and PCl_3 at 70-80°
→ α-bromoisovaleric acid. Y = 87.5-88.6%. C. S. Marvel, *Organic
Syntheses 20*, 106 (1940); *C.A. 1940*, 5052. Also: Isocaproic acid →
α-bromoisocaproic acid. Y = 63-66%. C. S. Marvel, *Organic Syntheses
21*, 74 (1941); *C.A. 1941*, 6238.

Sulfuryl chloride SO_2Cl_2

Chlorination   · H → · Cl
417.
$$CH_3COCH(CH_3)_2 \longrightarrow CH_3COCCl(CH_3)_2$$

Methyl isopropyl ketone is added dropwise to SO_2Cl_2 → 3-methyl-
3-chloro-2-butanone. Y = 84%. P. Delbaere, *Bull. soc. chim. Belg. 51*,
1 (1942); *C.A. 1943*, 5018.

Iodine I

Bromination   · H → · Br

$$\underset{\text{CH}_3}{\overset{\text{CH}_3}{\bigcirc}} \rightarrow \underset{\text{CH}_3}{\overset{\text{CH}_3}{Br\bigcirc Br}} \rightarrow \underset{\text{CHBr}_2}{\overset{\text{CHBr}_2}{Br\bigcirc Br}}$$

p-Xylene (20 g.) is brominated (10% excess Br) at 10–15% over a period of 0.5 hr., in the presence of some iodine. The reaction product is allowed to stand for 3 days at room temp. → 44 g. 2,5-dibromo-*p*-xylene. The side chain is brominated with 10% excess dry Br and 1000-watt illumination at 120–170° and anhyd. conditions → $\alpha,\alpha,\alpha',\alpha',2,5$-hexabromo-*p*-xylene (s.m. 226). Y = 71–74%. P. Ruggli and F. Brandt, *Helv. Chim. Acta* 27, 274 (1944); *C.A. 1944*, 6288.

Potassium iodide–potassium iodate and chloroiodide
(calcium carbonate)   *KI–KIO₃-ICl*

Iodation   • H → • I

1. *o*-Toluidine (30 g.) is refluxed with occasional shaking for 4 hrs. with I_2 and $CaCO_3$ in ether · H_2O and worked up with HCl → 42 g. 5-iodo-*o*-toluidine hydrochloride [compare, Wheeler and Liddle, *J. Am. Chem. Soc.* 42, 498 (1909)].

2. Arsinilic acid (11 g.) is treated with KI and KIO_3 in dil. H_2SO_4 → 12 g. 2,6-diiodoarsanilic acid [compare, Bertheim, *Ber.* 43, 535 (1910); *C.A. 1910*, 1299].

3. Na sulfanilate (19.5 g.) is treated with ICl in dil. HCl at 60–80° → 36 g. 2,6-diiodosulfanilic acid (compare, Germ. Pat. 129,808). F.e.s. A. A. Goldberg, *J. Chem. Soc. 1942*, 713; *C.A. 1943*, 880.

Oxygen ↑   HalC ↓↑ O

Without additional reagents

Replacement of Hydroxyl Group by Bromine   • OH → • Br
General Method for Aliphatic Compounds

HBr passed into decamethylene glycol at 100–135° → decamethylene bromide. Y = 90%. F.e.s. W. L. McEwen, *Organic Syntheses* 20, 24 (1940); *C.A. 1940*, 5047.

See also 489.

Replacement of Hydroxyl Group by Chlorine   • OH → • Cl

o-$H_2NC_6H_4CH_2OH$ is heated for a short time at 100° with 6 M HCl (d. 1.195) in a pressure bottle → *o*-aminobenzyl chloride · HCl. Crude Y = 56%. B. Beilenson and F. M. Hamer, *J. Chem. Soc. 1942*, 98; *C.A. 1942*, 3442.

Sodium iodide   *NaI*

**Replacement of Hydroxyl Group
by Iodine via Tolyl Compounds**   · OH → · I

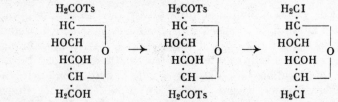

422.

1-*p*-Tolylsulfonyl-2,5-anhydro-L-iditol is converted in pyridine with tolylsulfonyl chloride → bis(*p*-tolylsulfonyl)-2,5-anhydro-L-iditol (Y = 65%), which is heated for 5 hrs. at the temp. of a water bath with NaI in abs. acetone in a sealed tube → diiodo-2,5-anhydro-L-iditol. Y = 70%. Iodine can replace only such tolylsulfonyl groups which have been esterified with a primary OH group. L. Vargha and T. Puskás, *Ber. 76*, 859 (1943); *C.A. 1944*, 2930. Oldham and Rutherford, *J. Am. Chem. Soc. 54*, 366 (1932); *C.A. 1932*, 968.

Pyridine

Alkyl Halides   · OH → · Hal
See 437.

Acid Chlorides   COOH → COCl
See 626.

Copper chloride   *CuCl*
See 424.

Zinc chloride–phthaloyl chloride

Low-Boiling Acid Chlorides $\dfrac{CO}{CO}$>O → 2 · COCl

423. Maleic anhydride with a slight excess of phthaloyl chloride and some ZnCl$_2$ (not always needed) → fumaryl chloride. Y = 82–95%. L. P. Kyrides, *Organic Syntheses 20*, 51 (1940); *C.A. 1940*, 5053.
See also 437.

Zinc chloride–thionyl chloride

Acid Chlorides $\dfrac{CO}{CO}$>O → 2 COCl

424. 1. Succinyl anhydride is treated with SOCl$_2$ in the presence of a small amount of anhyd. ZnCl$_2$ → succinyl chloride. Y = 74%.

COOH ← COCl

2. Succinic acid is treated with a large excess of $SOCl_2$ in the presence of a little CuCl and anhyd. $ZnCl_2$ → succinyl chloride. Y = 57–68%. P. Ruggli and A. Maeder, *Helv. Chim. Acta* 26, 1476 (1943); *C.A. 1944*, 2934. Methods, see P. Kyrides, *J. Am. Chem. Soc.* 59, 206 (1937); *C.A. 1937*, 1383.

Aluminum chloride $AlCl_3$
   See 427.

Acetic acid CH_3COOH

Replacement of Hydroxyl Group by Bromine   · OH → · Br

25. o-HOCH$_2$CH$_2$C$_6$H$_4$CH$_2$O Et is heated on a boiling water bath for 24 hrs. with HBr in AcOH → o-BrCH$_2$CH$_2$C$_6$H$_4$CH$_2$Br (s.m. 369). Y = 90%. F. G. Holliman and F. G. Mann, *J. Chem. Soc. 1942*, 737; *C.A. 1943*, 1396.
   See also 427.

Phosphorus   P

Replacement of Hydroxyl Group by Iodine   · OH → · I

26. 2-Ethyl-2-isopropylethyl alcohol is refluxed with red P and I → 2-ethyl-2-isopropylethyl iodide. Y = 79%. W. Dirscherl and H. Nahm, *Ber. 76*, 635 (1943); *C.A. 1944*, 1747.
   See also 437.

Phosphorus tribromide

Replacement of Hydroxyl Group by Bromine
   See 437.

Phosphorus pentachloride PCl_5

Aceto Halogen Sugars

27.   C$_7$H$_8$O(OOC · CH$_3$)$_6$ → C$_7$H$_8$O(OOC · CH$_3$)$_5$Hal

β-Hexaacetyl-D-manno-D-galaheptose (I) is refluxed with PCl$_5$ and AlCl$_3$ in CHCl$_3$ → α-acetochloro-D-manno-D-galaheptose. Y = 65%. (I) with HBr and glacial AcOH → α-acetobromo deriv. Y = 84%. E. M. Montgomery and C. S. Hudson, *J. Am. Chem. Soc. 64*, 247 (1942); *C.A. 1942*, 1906.

Acid Chlorides   COOH → COCl
   See 100, 435.

Phosphorus oxychloride $POCl_3$

Replacement of Hydroxyl Group by Chlorine $\cdot OH \rightarrow \cdot Cl$

428.

2-Hydroxylepidine and $POCl_3$ are heated at 70–80° until the mixt.
liquefies → 2-chlorolepidine. Y = 95%. S. E. Krahler and A. Burger,
J. Am. Chem. Soc. 63, 2367 (1941); *C.A. 1941*, 7406.

Aminopyrimidines from Hydroxypyrimidines
via Chloropyrimidines $\cdot OH \rightarrow \cdot Cl \rightarrow \cdot NH_2$

429.

4,6-Dihydroxy-2-methylpyrimidine is refluxed with $POCl_3$ until HCl
evoln. ceases → 4,6-dichloro deriv. (Y = 75%), which is heated for
4 hrs. at 200° with NH_3 in MeOH in a sealed tube → 4,6-diamino-
2-methylpyrimidine (s.m. 399). Y = 75%. 1 g. of the 4,6-dichloro
deriv. is heated for 3 hrs. in a sealed tube at 130° → 0.5 g. 4-chloro-
6-amino-2-methylpyrimidine. J. Baddiley, B. Lythgoe, D. McNeil and
A. R. Todd, *J. Chem. Soc. 1943*, 383; *C.A. 1943*, 6667.

Thionyl chloride $SOCl_2$

Alkyl Chlorides $\cdot OH \rightarrow \cdot Cl$

430. m-$MeOC_6H_4CH_2OH$ in C_5H_5N is stirred with $SOCl_2$ at a temp.
below 30° for 2.5 hrs. → m-$MeOC_6H_4CH_2Cl$ (s.m. 668). Y = 91%.
J. W. Cornforth and R. Robinson, *J. Chem. Soc. 1942*, 684; *C.A. 1943*,
881.

431. α-(p-Bromophenyl)-EtOH is treated with $SOCl_2$ on a water bath
→ α-(p-bromophenyl)-ethyl chloride. Y = 81%. H. J. Barber, R. Slack
and A. M. Woolman, *J. Chem. Soc. 1943*, 99; *C.A. 1943*, 4385.

432. 1-(2-Hydroxyethyl)-piperazine $\cdot$ 2 HCl is refluxed for 3 hrs. with
$SOCl_2$ → 1-(2-chloroethyl)-piperazine $\cdot$ 2 HCl. Y = 82%. O. Hromatka
and E. Engel, *Ber. 76*, 712 (1943); *C.A. 1944*, 2627.

See also 437.

Acid Chlorides   COOH → COCl
See 424.

3. Oleic acid, freed of satd. acids by Bertram's HgOAc method (*C.A.* *21*, 2662), and further purified via the Li salt, is treated with $SOCl_2$ → oleoyl chloride. Y = 90%. P. E. Verkade, *Rec. trav. chim.* *62*, 393 (1943); *C.A. 1944*, 3250.

4. Mesitoic (β-isodurylic) acid is treated with $SOCl_2$ → mesitoyl chloride. Y = 90–97%. R. P. Barnes, *Organic Syntheses 21*, 77 (1941); *C.A. 1941*, 6249.

See also 203, 204.

5. 5,8-Dichloro-2-naphthoic acid is refluxed for 1 hr. with $SOCl_2$; the excess $SOCl_2$ is evaporated or triturated with PCl_5 and melted on an oil bath → 5,8-dichloro-2-naphthoic acid chloride. Y = 90%. H. Goldstein and P. Viaud, *Helv. Chim. Acta 27*, 883 (1944); *C.A. 1945*, 926.

See also 626, 629.

Sulfuric acid H_2SO_4

Replacement of Hydroxyl Groups by Bromine   OH → Br
See 437.

Hydrochloric acid   HCl

Opening of the Pyran Ring   Ɔ

6.

4-Aminotetrahydropyran · HCl is heated in a sealed tube with concd. HCl at 120–130° → 1,5-dichloro-3-aminopentane · HCl. Y = 81%. F.e.s. V. Hahn, E. Cerkovnikov and V. Prelog, *Helv. Chim. Acta 26*, 1132 (1943); *C.A. 1944*, 100.

Iodine   *I*

Alkyl Halides from Alcohols
Alkyl Chlorides   · OH → · Hal

7. 1. The alcohol is refluxed over a free flame with $ZnCl_2$ and concd. HCl for 4 hrs. Ex: *sec*-BuCl. Y = 78%.

2. A mixt. of alc. and C_5H_5N is treated with freshly distd. $SOCl_2$ over a period of 3–4 hrs. and refluxed for 0.75 hr. Ex: 0.5 g.-mole sec-BuOH → 22 g. sec-BuCl.

3. As in method 2, but without C_5H_5N. Ex: n-Octyl·Cl. Y = 80%.

Alkyl Bromides

1. Refluxed with 47.5% HBr and H_2SO_4 for 6–12 hrs.

2. With 47.5% HBr only; poor yields are obtained with n-amyl and higher homologues. Ex: iso-PrBr. Y = 75%.

3. With PBr_3; good yields with iso-Pr and iso-BuOH at −10 to 0°. Less suitable for higher alcohols.

4. With HBr gas (purification, see Organic Syntheses, Coll. Vol. II, 338) at 100–20°. Best method for higher alcohols such as n-heptyl alc. Emulsions are prevented by adding some anhyd. $CaCl_2$.

Alkyl Iodides

1. Slow distillation of the alc. with constant boiling HI. Ex: 58 g. heptyl alcohol → 110 g. heptyl iodide.

2. With I and red P, or a mixt. of white and red P. F.e.s. A. I. Vogel, J. Chem. Soc. 1943, 636.

Nitrogen ⋏   HalC ⫏ N

Potassium iodide   KI

Replacement of Amino Group by Iodine   · NH_2 → · I

438. 3-Methyl-4-aminobenzophenone is diazotized and then treated with a KI soln. → 3-methyl-4-iodobenzophenone (s.m. 662) Y = 54%. E. Müller and E. Hertel, Ann. 555, 157 (1944).

Copper   Cu

Replacement of Amino Group by Halogen in Compounds Which Are Difficult to Diazotize   · NH_2 → · Hal

439. 2-Amino-4-methoxybenzothiazole (I) (prepn., see 465) is diazotized with aq. $NaNO_2$ in a mixt. of 84% H_3PO_4 and HNO_3 (d. 1.4) at −12 to −8°; the diazonium salt is decomposed with concd. HCl and Gatterman Cu in the cold → 2-chloro-4-methoxybenzothiazole; Y = 80–90%. (I) with 48% HBr → 2-bromo-4-methoxybenzothiazole; Y = 80–90%. H. Erlenmeyer and H. Ueberwasser, Helv. Chim. Acta 25, 515 (1942); C.A. 1942, 7021.

440. Et 2-amino-4-thiazolecarboxylate (prepn., see 476) is diazotized as

above and HBr is added → Et 2-bromo-4-thiazolecarboxylate, $C_6H_6O_2NBr$. Y = 70%. H. Erlenmeyer and C. J. Morel, *Helv. Chim. Acta* 25, 1073 (1942); *C.A. 1943*, 1702.

Copper compounds

Replacement of Amino Nitrogen by Chlorine $\cdot NH_2 \rightarrow \cdot Cl$

. 2,4-Dinitroaniline in concd. H_2SO_4 is diazotized with nitrosylsulfuric acid and H_3PO_4 and then treated with CuCl (prepd. from NaOH, $Na_2S_2O_5$, $CuSO_4$, and NaCl in concd. HCl) → 2,4-dinitrochlorobenzene. Y = 66%. F.e.s. L. H. Welsh, *J. Am. Chem. Soc.* 63, 3276 (1941); *C.A. 1942*, 1021.

. 2-Amino-4-nitrodimethylaniline is diazotized with $NaNO_2$ in HCl and then poured into a 10% CuCl soln. → 2-chloro-4-nitrodimethylaniline (prepn., see also 411). Y = 70%. F.e.s. E. E. Ayling, J. H. Gorvin and L. E. Hinkel, *J. Chem. Soc. 1942*, 755; *C.A. 1943*, 1398.

. 5-Chloro-2-amino-4'-hydroxybenzophenone is diazotized with glacial AcOH and concd. HCl and treated with CuCl → 2,5-dichloro-4'-hydroxybenzophenone. Y = 80%. J. C. E. Simpson and O. Stephenson, *J. Chem. Soc. 1942*, 353; *C.A. 1942*, 5179.

Replacement of Amino Group by Bromine $\cdot NH_2 \rightarrow \cdot Br$

. 3,4-$O_2N(H_2N)C_6H_3OMe$ in H_2SO_4 is diazotized and treated with $CuSO_4$, H_2SO_4, NaBr, and Cu wool → 4-bromo-3-nitroanisole. Y = 75%. B. V. Samant, *Ber.* 75, 1008 (1942); *C.A. 1943*, 4400.

. 2,4-Dibromo-3-nitro-1-naphthylamine (3.5 g.) is diazotized according to the method of Hodgson and Walker (*J. Chem. Soc. 1933*, 1620; *C.A. 1933*, 1335), and $CuBr_2$ in HBr (d. 1.7) is added to the diazonium salt soln. → 4 g. 1,3,4-tribromo-2-nitronaphthalene. F.e.s. H. H. Hodgson and D. E. Hathway, *J. Chem. Soc. 1944*, 21; *C.A. 1944*, 2030.

Mercuric bromide $HgBr_2$

. Diazotized 2-naphthylamine is converted with some $HgBr_2$, forming a complex corresponding to $(C_{10}H_7N_2Br)_2HgBr_2$; the dry complex salt is decomposed → 2-bromonaphthalene. Y = 53–59%. Doubling the amount of $HgBr_2$ increases the yield to 61–65%, but further increase of $HgBr_2$ has no more effect upon the yield. M. S. Newman and P. H. Wise, *J. Am. Chem. Soc.* 63, 2847 (1943).

Phosphorus Halides

Replacement of Amino Group by Halogen in Experiments on Larger Scale $\cdot NH_2 \rightarrow \cdot Hal$

447. Tridecylamine · HCl (prepn., see 51) is heated for 85 hrs. at 110°
     with BzCl in C_6H_6 in a current of CO_2 → benzoyltridecylamine
     (Y = 90%), which is treated with PCl_5 (PBr_5) → tridecyl chloride
     (Y = 67%), and tridecyl bromide (Y = 52.5%). H. Suida and
     F. Drahowzal, *Ber.* 75, 991 (1942); *C.A. 1943*, 4683.

Via intermediates

**Via Imide Bromides in the Case of
Aliphatic Compounds**   · NH_2 → · Br

$$C_{15}H_{31}CH_2NH_2 \longrightarrow C_{15}H_{31}CH_2NHCOC_6H_5 \longrightarrow$$

448.
$$C_{15}H_{31}CH_2Br \longleftarrow C_{15}H_{31}CH_2N : C \cdot C_6H_5 \longleftarrow$$
$$Br$$

4,8,12-Trimethyltridecylamine is shaken for 0.5 hr. with benzoyl
chloride and 2 N NaOH in ether → benzoyl-4,8,12-trimethyltridecyla-
mine which is converted to the imide bromide with PBr_5. Heating at
180–200° at 0.3 mm. pressure causes cleavage → 4,8,12-trimethyl-
tridecyl bromide. Y = ca. 60%. F.e.s. W. John and H. Pini, *Z. physiol.
Chem.* 273, 225 (1942); *C.A. 1943*, 5722. Methods, see v. Braun and
Sobecki, *Ber.* 43, 2844 (1910); 44, 1464, 2867 (1911); *C.A. 1911*, 3067.

Via Diazonium Perbromides in the Case of Aromatic Compounds

449.

2,5-Dichlorophenylazo-2-naphthylamine is diazotized in glacial
AcOH · HCl below 20° and the filtered soln. is treated with Br in
glacial AcOH → 2,5-dichlorophenylazo-2-naphthalenediazonium per-
bromide (Y = good), which is heated with glacial AcOH → 2-bromo-
1-(2,5-dichlorophenylazo)naphthalene. Y = 95%. F.e.s. H. H. Hodgson
and C. K. Foster, *J. Chem. Soc. 1942*, 435; *C.A. 1942*, 6524.

Halogen ⚓   **HalC ⚓ Hal**

Alkali halides

Replacement of Bromine by Iodine   · Br → · I

450. 2-Bromoheptane is boiled with NaI in MeOH → 2-iodoheptane. Y =
     75%. M. Schirm and H. Besendorf, *Arch. Pharm.* 280, 64 (1942); *C.A.
     1943*, 5015.

α-Hydroxycarboxylic Acids from Carboxylic Acids

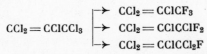

51. Dihydrochaulmoogric acid is treated with red P and Br → α-bromo deriv. (Y = almost quant.), which is treated with KI in EtOH → α-iodo deriv. This is heated for 12 hrs. at 100° with KOH in H_2O → α-hydroxydihydrochaulmoogric acid. Y = 90%. F.e.s. N. P. Buu-Hoi and P. Cagniant, *Ber. 75B*, 1181 (1942); *C.A. 1943*, 4706.

Antimony trifluoride SbF_3

Alkyl Fluorides $\cdot Cl \rightarrow \cdot F$

52.
$$CCl_2 = CClCCl_3 \begin{cases} \rightarrow & CCl_2 = CClCF_3 \\ \rightarrow & CCl_2 = CClCClF_2 \\ \rightarrow & CCl_2 = CClCCl_2F \end{cases}$$

$Cl_2C : CClCCl_3$ and SbF_3 are heated on an oil bath at 150° → 43% $Cl_2C : CClCF_3$; 28% $Cl_2C : CClCClF_2$; and 13% $Cl_2C : CClCCl_2F$. The reaction proceeds only when halogen atoms are attached to the double bond. F.e.s. A. L. Henne, A. M. Whaley and J. K. Stevenson, *J. Am. Chem. Soc. 63*, 3478 (1941); *C.A. 1942*, 1009.

Carbon ⋏   HalC ⥮ C

Without additional reagents

Silver Salt Degradation $R \cdot COOH \rightarrow RHal$

53. By heating Ag salts of carboxylic acids with excess I, the corresponding alkyl iodides are formed in yields of approx. 80%. J. W. H. Oldham and A. R. Ubbelohde, *J. Chem. Soc. 1941*, 368; *C.A. 1941*, 6926.

54. $AgOOC(CH_2)_4COOAg \longrightarrow BrCH_2(CH_2)_2CH_2Br$

The Ag deriv. of adipic acid is passed into a soln. of Br in abs. CCl_4 for a period of 7 hrs. at 50° under anhyd. conditions → 1,4-dibromobutane. Y = 58%. H. Schmid, *Helv. Chim. Acta 27*, 127 (1944); *C.A. 1944*, 4589.

Formation of S—S Bond by:

Elimination

Hydrogen ⚡   SS ⇑ H

Hydrogen peroxide H_2O_2
Disulfides from Mercaptans $2\,RSH \rightarrow R \cdot S \cdot S \cdot R$

455.

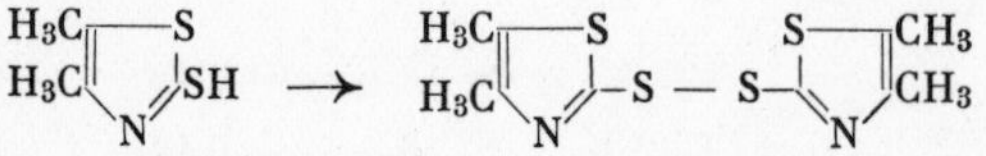

$$\underset{N}{\overset{H_3C}{\underset{H_3C}{\bigsqcup}}}\!\!{\overset{S}{\diagdown}}SH \rightarrow \underset{H_3C}{\overset{H_3C}{\bigsqcup}}\!\!S-S\!\!\underset{N}{\overset{CH_3}{\bigsqcup}}CH_3$$

2-Mercapto-4,5-dimethylthiazole is treated with H_2O_2 in a neutralized aq. soln. at 65–70° → 4,5-dimethyl-2-thiazolyl disulfide. Y = 76%. E. R. Buchman, A. O. Reims and H. Sargent, *J. Org. Chem.* 6, 764 (1941); *C.A. 1942, 1606.*

Formation of S—Remaining Elements Bond by:

Exchange

Oxygen ⚡   SR ⇅ O

Without additional reagents
Organomercury Compounds $RHgBr \rightarrow RHgSR$

456.

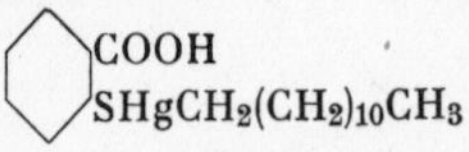

$$\bigcirc\!\!\begin{array}{l}COOH\\ SHgCH_2(CH_2)_{10}CH_3\end{array}$$

Dodecylmercury bromide is treated with NaOH in $H_2O \cdot$ alc. and the resulting soln. of the dodecylmercury hydroxide is heated with mercaptosalicylic acid → dodecylmercurymercaptosalicylic acid. Y = 84%. P. Rumpf, *Bull. soc. chim. Mém.* 9, 661 (1942); *C.A. 1944, 2951.*

Formation of S—C Bond by:

Addition

Addition to Carbon   SC ⇓ CC

Without additional reagents

Mercaptans from Ethylene Derivatives   C = C → CH · CSH

57.
$$\underset{CH_3}{\overset{CH_3}{>}}CHC(COOH) = CH_2 \;\longrightarrow\; \underset{CH_3}{\overset{CH_3}{>}}CHCH(COOH)CH_2SCOCH_3 \;\longrightarrow$$

$$\underset{CH_3}{\overset{CH_3}{>}}CHCH(COOH)CH_2SH \;\longleftarrow$$

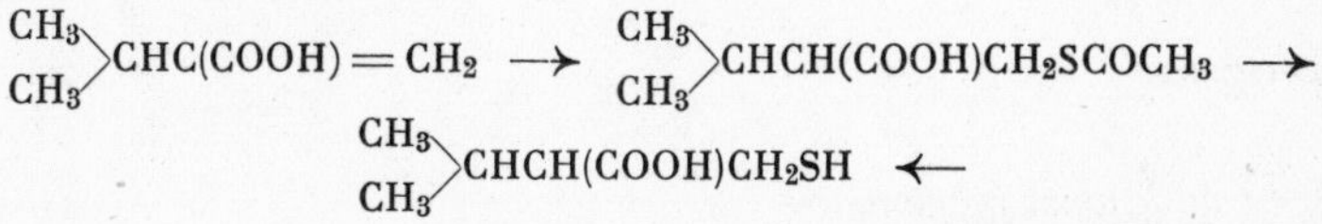

α-Isopropylacrylic acid (prepn., see 767) and AcSH are warmed for a short time and allowed to stand at room temp. for 1 day → α-isopropyl-β-acetylmercaptopropionic acid, which is hydrolyzed with the calcd. amt. of 10% NaOH in the cold → α-isopropyl-β-mercaptopropionic acid. F. Kögl, J. H. Verbeek, H. Erxleben and W. A. J. Borg, *Z. physiol. Chem.* 279, 121 (1943); *C.A. 1944*, 3978. Methods, see B. Holmberg and E. Schjanberg, *Arkiv. Kemi. Mineral. Geol.* A14, 1 (1940); *C.A. 1941*, 2113; E. Schjanberg, *Ber.* 74, 1751 (1941); *C.A. 1942*, 1902.

Barium hydroxide and   Ba(OH)$_2$
Thioacetic acid

Hydroxy Mercaptans from Ethylene Oxides

58.
$$\begin{array}{l} CH_2 \\ | \quad\;\; \rangle O \\ CH \\ | \\ CH_2OH \end{array} \longrightarrow \begin{array}{l} CH_2SH \\ | \\ CHOH \\ | \\ CH_2OH \end{array}$$

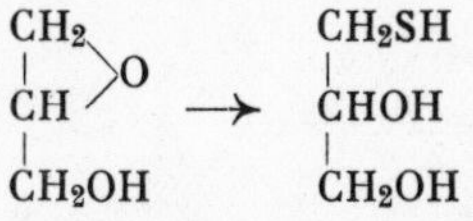

1. H$_2$S is passed into an aq. soln. containing Ba(OH)$_2$ and satd. with H$_2$S while O · CH$_2$ · CHCH$_2$OH (I) is added over a period of 1.5 hrs. → α-thioglycerol. Y = 61%.

2. (I) is heated with AcSH at 40° for 4 hrs. → α-Ac-thioglycerol. The mixture of isomers is hydrolyzed with 1% MeOH · HCl → α-thioglycerol. Y = 71%. F.e.s. B. Sjöberg, *Ber.* 75B, 13 (1942); *C.A. 1942*, 6138.

Pyrogallol

Sulfones from Dienes

459.

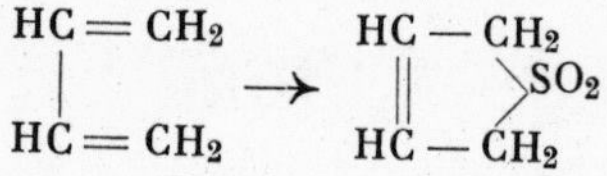

$$
\begin{array}{ccc}
HC = CH_2 & & HC - CH_2 \\
| & \rightarrow & \| \quad \rangle SO_2 \\
HC = CH_2 & & HC - CH_2
\end{array}
$$

Butadiene is allowed to stand for several weeks with SO_2 and pyrogallol in ether → 1-thio-3-cyclopentene-1-dioxide. Y = 70%. H. J. Backer and T. A. H. Blass, *Rec. trav. chim. 61*, 785 (1942); *C.A. 1944*, 3646.

See also 713.

Exchange

Hydrogen   SC ⫯↟ H

Without additional reagents

Sulfonic Acids   · H → · SO₃H

460.　β,β-Dimethylacrylic acid is treated with H_2SO_4 and SO_3 for 2 hrs. at 90° → α-sulfo-β,β-dimethylacrylic acid. Y = 72% (isolated as Ba salt). F.e.s. H. J. Backer and R. D. Mulder, *Rec. trav. chim. 62*, 46 (1943); *C.A. 1945*, 1623.

461.　　　　　　$(C_2H_5O)_2SO_2 \rightarrow OHCH_2CH_2SO_3Ca$

Et_2SO_4 (100 g.) is treated with fuming H_2SO_4 (60% SO_3) over a period of 2.5 hrs. below 10°. The mixture is allowed to stand overnight, poured into H_2O, refluxed for 10–12 hrs., and the H_2SO_4 is separated with $CaCO_3$ → 118 g. Ca isethionate (Na salt, s.m. 202). A. A. Goldberg, *J. Chem. Soc. 1942*, 716; *C.A. 1943*, 868.

Sulfur monochloride S_2Cl_2

Mercaptans   · H → · SH

462.

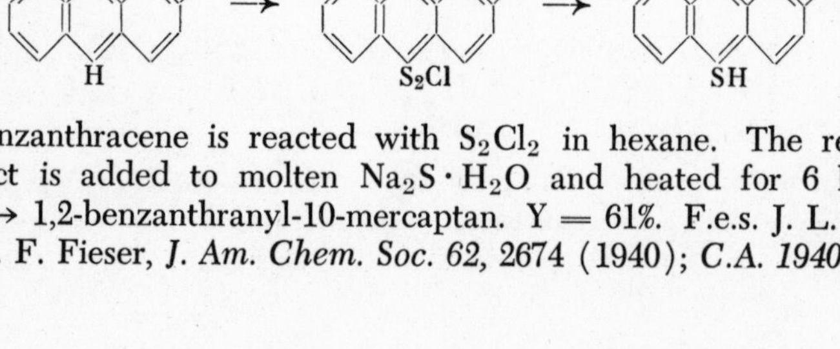

1,2-Benzanthracene is reacted with S_2Cl_2 in hexane. The reaction product is added to molten $Na_2S \cdot H_2O$ and heated for 6 hrs. at 130° → 1,2-benzanthranyl-10-mercaptan. Y = 61%. F.e.s. J. L. Wood and L. F. Fieser, *J. Am. Chem. Soc. 62*, 2674 (1940); *C.A. 1940*, 7901.

Chlorine–sulfur dioxide and sulfuryl chloride

Aliphatic Sulfonic Acids from Hydrocarbons $\cdot H \rightarrow \cdot SO_3H$

63. A survey in regard to the present state of sulfochlorination, *i.e.*, direct introduction of the sulfo group into aliphatic compounds by means of Cl–SO_2 mixtures and sulfuryl chloride. The sulfochlorination of paraffin hydrocarbons, aliphatic cyclic hydrocarbons, and satd. carboxylic acids is discussed. J. H. Helberger, *Chemie 55*, 172 (1942); *C.A. 1943*, 79.

Chlorine Cl_2

Thiazoles   O

64.

$1\text{-}C_{10}H_7NH_2$ (145 g.) in $CHCl_3$ is added to $CSCl_2 \rightarrow$ 100 g. $1\text{-}C_{10}H_7NCS$ (I); 50 g. (I) in $CHCl_3$ is treated with $Cl \rightarrow$ 30 g. bis-(1-naphthylthiocarbimide) oxide. G. M. Dyson and T. Harrington, *J. Chem. Soc. 1942*, 374; *C.A. 1942*, 5170.

Bromine Br_2

65.

o-Methoxyphenylthiourea (prepn., see 363) is treated with Br in $CHCl_3 \rightarrow$ 2-amino-4-methoxybenzothiazole (s.m. 439). Y = almost quant. H. Erlenmeyer and H. Ueberwasser, *Helv. Chim. Acta 25*, 515 (1942); *C.A. 1942*, 7021. Methods, see Hugershoff, *Ber. 36*, 3121 (1903).

Oxygen ⋏   SC ⫯⋏ O

Sodium Sulfite Na_2SO_3

Aliphatic Sulfonic Acids from Sulfates $\cdot CH_2OSO_3H \rightarrow \cdot CH_2SO_3H$

66. $H_2NCH_2CH_2OSO_3H \longrightarrow H_2NCH_2CH_2SO_3H$

A mixture of $H_2NC_2H_4SO_4H$ and Na_2SO_3 in water is heated at 106–108° for 32 hrs. under slight pressure or for 20 hrs. at 140° under a stronger pressure of 50 lbs. ($\frown$25 atm.) $\rightarrow$ taurine. Y = 62–63%. A. A. Goldberg, *J. Chem. Soc. 1943*, 4; *C.A. 1943*, 1990.

Aluminum oxide Al_2O_3

Replacement of Ring Oxygen by Ring Sulfur   —O— → —S—

467. Tetrahydrofuran (furanidine) and H_2S are passed over Al_2O_3 at 400° → thiophane. Y = up to 90%. Also: furan → thiophene. Y = maximum 37%. Yu. K. Yer'ev and V. A. Tronova, *J. Gen. Chem. (U.S.S.R.) 10*, 31 (1940); *C.A. 1940*, 4733. Compare: *J. Gen. Chem. (U.S.S.R.) 11*, 344 (1941); *C.A. 1941*, 5893.

Phosphorus pentoxide P_2O_5

Isopropylidene Compounds

468.

$HOCH_2CH_2CH_2SH$ and acetone with P_2O_5 are mixed with sand and neutralized with K_2CO_3 → acetone-3-hydroxy-1-propanethiol. Y = 41%. F.e.s. B. Sjöberg, *Ber. 75*, 13 (1942); *C.A. 1942*, 6138.

Hydrochloric acid HCl

Acyclic Sugar Derivatives. Mercaptals   : $C(SR)_2$

469. D-Lyxose (10 g.) in conc. HCl (d. 1.19) at 0° is stirred with EtSH → 13.4 g. D-lyxose di-Et-mercaptal, $C_5H_{10}O_4(SC_2H_5)_2$. M. L. Wolfrom and F. B. Moody, *J. Am. Chem. Soc. 62*, 3465 (1940); *C.A. 1941*, 1033.

Nitrogen ⚹   SC ⚹ N

Sodium disulfide Na_2S_2

Thioindoxyls   O
See 717.

Cuprous thiocyanate $CuSCN$

Rhodanates   · NH_2 → · SCN

470.

3-Nitro-6-aminotoluene is diazotized and then treated with potassium thiocyanate and cuprous thiocyanate prepared from $CuSO_4$, KSCN, and $FeSO_4$ → 3,6-$O_2N(NCS)C_6H_3Me$. Y = 65%. P. Pfeiffer and H. Jäger, *Ber. 75*, 1885 (1943); *C.A. 1944*, 1218.

Halogen ⚹   SC ⚹ Hal

Without additional reagents

Thio Ethers from Alkyl Iodides

1. 2-Mercapto-4,5-dimethylthiazole (prepn., see 478) is treated with CH_3I → 2-methylmercapto-4-methylthiazole. Y = 91%. E. R. Buchmann, A. O. Rheims and H. Sargent, *J. Org. Chem. 6*, 764 (1941); *C.A. 1942*, 1606.

Thiazole Ring Closure   O
With Thio Amides

2.
$$HC\underset{SH}{\overset{NH}{<}} + \underset{ClC \cdot CO \cdot CH_3}{\overset{HOC \cdot CH_3}{|}} \rightarrow HC\underset{S-C \cdot CO \cdot CH_3}{\overset{N-C \cdot CH_3}{<}}$$

MeC(OH) : CClAc is gradually added to thioformamide in EtOH (via the HCl salt) → 4-methyl-5-acetylthiazole. Y = 55%. P. Baumgarten, A. Dornow, K. Gutschmidt and H. Krehl, *Ber. 75*, 442 (1942); *C.A. 1943*, 3091.

3.
$$\text{[quinoline-C(S)NH}_2\text{]} + \underset{CH_3}{\overset{BrCH_2}{\underset{|}{\overset{|}{OC}}}} \rightarrow \text{[quinoline-thiazolyl]}$$

2-Quinolinecarbothionamide is heated with $BrCH_2Ac$ in EtOH → 2-(5-methyl-2-thiazolyl)quinoline. Y = 100%. F.e.s. H. Coates, A. H. Cook, I. M. Heilbron and F. B. Lewis, *J. Chem. Soc. 1943*, 419; *C.A. 1944*, 106.

With Thiourea

4.
$$BrH_2C-CO-CH \cdot COOC_2H_5$$
$$+ \quad (CH_2)_5$$
$$HS \quad NH \quad CH_3$$
$$\underset{NH_2}{\overset{|}{\underset{|}{C}}}$$
$$\rightarrow$$
$$HC=C \cdot CH \cdot COOC_2H_5$$
$$| \quad | \quad (CH_2)_5$$
$$S \quad N \quad CH_3$$
$$\overset{C}{\underset{NH_2}{|}}$$
$$\rightarrow$$
$$HC=C(CH_2)_5CH_3$$
$$| \quad |$$
$$S \quad N$$
$$\overset{C}{\underset{NH_2}{|}}$$

Synthesis of 2-Amino-4-Alkylthiazoles. The monobromo derivatives of $AcCHRCO_2Et$ are converted with thiourea to the esters of the corresponding 2-aminothiazolyl-4-acetic acids from which, by saponification and decarboxylation, the 2-amino-4-alkylthiazoles are prepared. Ex: $AcCH(C_6H_{13})CO_2Et$ is shaken with $CS(NH_2)_2$ and ice water → Et α-(2-amino-4-thiazolyl)caprylate (Y = 45%), which is hydrolyzed with NaOH in 95% EtOH and decarboxylated in HCl soln. at 60° → 2-amino-4-heptylthiazole. Y = 85%. F.e.s. W. M. Ziegler, *J. Am. Chem. Soc. 63*, 2946 (1941); *C.A. 1942*, 470.

475. AcOCHClCH$_2$Cl is refluxed with thiourea in MeOH → 2-aminothiazole. Y = 50%. H. Morren and R. Dupont, *J. pharm. Belg. 1*, 126 (1942); *C.A. 1944*, 3284.

476. BrCH$_2$COCO$_2$Et is condensed with H$_2$NCSNH$_2$ in abs. alc. → Et 2-amino-4-thiazolecarboxylate (s.m. 440). Y = 66%. H. Erlenmeyer and C. J. Morel, *Helv. Chim. Acta 25*, 1073 (1942); *C.A. 1943*, 1702.

477. Equimolar amounts of CS(NH$_2$)$_2$ and HCOCHClCO$_2$Et are boiled in abs. EtOH → Et 2-amino-5-thiazolecarboxylate · HCl, C$_6$H$_9$O$_2$N$_2$-ClS. Y = 84%. O. Dann, *Ber. 76*, 419 (1943); *C.A. 1943*, 6260.

With Dithiocarbamate. 2-Mercaptothiazoles

478.   CH$_3$COCH$_2$Cl + NH$_2$CSSNH$_4$ →

MeCOCH$_2$Cl is treated with NH$_2$CS$_2$NH$_4$ in EtOH with ice cooling and the mixture is allowed to stand for several hrs. at room temp. → 2-mercapto-4-methylthiazole (s.m. 471). Y = 85%. F.e.s. E. R. Buchman, A. O. Rheims and H. Sargent, *J. Org. Chem. 6*, 764 (1941); *C.A. 1942*, 1606.

Alkali hydroxide

Thio Ethers   R · S · R

479.   ClCH$_2$CH$_2$COOH → HOOC · CH$_2$SCH$_2$CH$_2$COOH

β-Chloropropionic acid via the Na salt with thioglycollic acid and KOH → thioacetic-β-propionic acid. Y = quant. P. Karrer and H. Schmid, *Helv. Chim. Acta 27*, 116 (1944).

See also 717.

Alkali alcoholates

Thio Ethers from Mercaptans   R · S · H → R · S · R

480.

α-Bromo-α-carboxypimelic acid di-Et ester and HSCH$_2$CH$_2$CO$_2$Et are treated with NaOEt in abs. EtOH at −20° in a N$_2$ atm. → 2-carbethoxyethyl 1,5-dicarbethoxyamyl sulfide (s.m. 558). Y = 83%. F.e.s. P. Karrer, R. Keller and E. Usteri, *Helv. Chim. Acta 27*, 237 (1944); *C.A. 1944*, 4941. P. Karrer and H. Schmid, *Helv. Chim. Acta 27*, 124 (1944); *C.A. 1944*, 4588. H. Schmid, *Helv. Chim. Acta 27*, 127 (1944); *C. A. 1944*, 4589.

481. Benzyl mercaptan is dissolved in C_6H_6 and Na in EtOH is added. Now allyl bromide is added → benzyl allyl thioether. Y = 70% (s.m. 404). F. Kögl, J. H. Verbeek, H. Erxleben and W. A. J. Borg, Z. *physiol. Chem. 279*, 121 (1943); *C.A. 1944*, 3978.

482. **Alkyl Phenacyl Sulfides.** Methyl mercaptide and ω-chloroacetonphenone is added to a soln. of Na in MeOH. This soln. is heated to boiling for 2 hrs. and worked up after standing overnight → Me phenacyl sulfide (s.m. 44). Y = 88%. Also **Thioalcohols:** Ethyl mercaptide and β-bromo-α-phenyl ethanol with Na methylate → ethyl-(β-hydroxy-β-phenylethyl) sulfide. Y = 81%. F.e.s. V. Prelog, V. Hahn, H. Brauchli and H. C. Beyermann, *Helv. Chim. Acta 27*, 1209 (1944); *C.A. 1946*, 848.

483. 2-Amino-6-chloro-4-methylpyrimidine is treated with excess abs. MeSH and Na in abs. MeOH → 2-amino-6-methylmercapto-4-methylpyrimidine. Y = 59%. H. J. Backer and A. B. Grevenstuk, *Rec. Trav. Chim. 61*, 291 (1942); *C.A. 1944*, 2326.

Sodium sulfide Na_2S

Thio Ether   R · S · R

484. Tetramethylene bromide is treated with Na_2S in EtOH → tetramethylene sulfide (s.m. 116, 117). Y = 64%. F.e.s. D. S. Tarbell and C. Weaver, *J. Am. Chem. Soc. 63*, 2939 (1941); *C.A. 1942*, 470.

Sodium disulfide Na_2S_2

Sulfonic Acids from Halogenides via Disulfides   · Hal → · SO_3H

485.

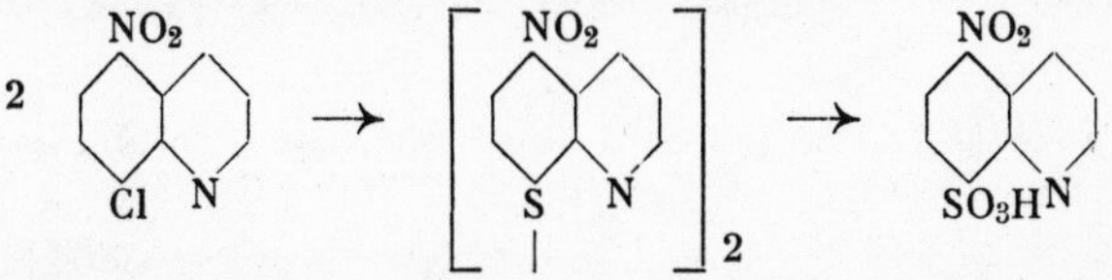

5-Nitro-8-chloroquinoline and Na_2S_2 → bis(5-nitro-8-quinolyl) disulfide (Y = 90%) oxidized with concd. HNO_3 → 5-nitro-8-quinolinesulfonic acid. Y = 75%. H. Urist and G. L. Jenkins, *J. Am. Chem. Soc. 63*, 2943 (1941); *C.A. 1942*, 425.

Sodium polysulfide Na_2S_x

Thiophene Ring Closure   O

486.

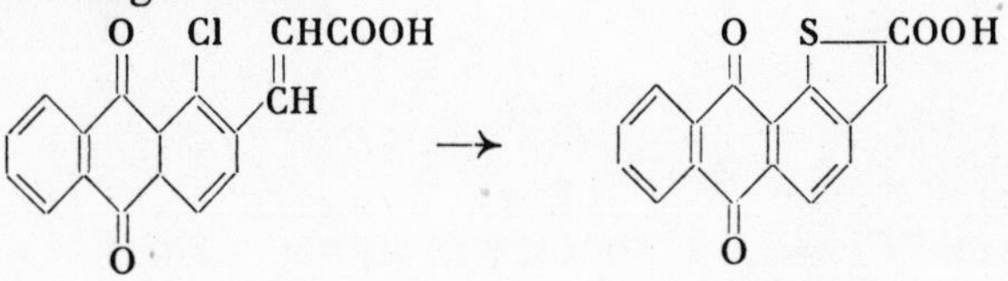

1-Chloro-2-anthraquinonacrylic acid is refluxed for 15 hrs. with Na_2S_x → 1,2-(thiopheno-2',3')-anthraquinone-5'-carboxylic acid. Y = 63%. E. B. Hershberg and L. F. Fieser, *J. Am. Chem. Soc. 63*, 2561 (1941); *C.A. 1942*, 458.

Sodium thiosulfate $Na_2S_2O_3$

Disulfides via Bunte Salts   R · S · S · R ·

487. The prepn. via the Bunte salts (alkylthiosulfates) is recommended for every radical whose Bunte salt can readily be obtained. The Bunte salt soln. [from the alkyl bromide and $Na_2S_2O_3$, according to Westlake and Dougherty, *J. Am. Chem. Soc. 63*, 658 (1941)] is treated according to Price and Twiss, *J. Chem. Soc. 95*, 1489 (1909), with I_2 in small portions until the color remains, or is cooled and allowed to stand with H_2O_2. The liq. products are extracted with EtOH and distilled *in vacuo* after evaptn. of the EtOH; the solid products are recrystallized from EtOH or glacial AcOH. Ex: BuBr → Bu_2S_2. Y = 56%. Heptyl Br → heptyl disulfide. Y = 65%. F.e.s. H. E. Westlake, Jr., and G. Dougherty, *J. Am. Chem. Soc. 64*, 149 (1942); *C.A. 1942*, 1293.

Sodium sulfite Na_2SO_3

Sulfonic Acids   · Hal → · SO₃H

488. β-Bromopropiophenone is refluxed for 2 hrs. in aq. Na_2SO_3 and purified via the benzylthiuronium salt → β-propiophenonesulfonic acid Na salt. Y = 80%. F.e.s. K. Kratzl, *Ber. 76*, 895 (1943); *C.A. 1944*, 2941.

489. $H_2NCH_2CH_2OH$ is treated with 48% HBr, using an efficient Raschig column to remove H_2O → $BrCH_2CH_2NH_2 \cdot HBr$ (Y = 91%) with an equiv. amt. of Na_2SO_3 in H_2O → taurine (Y = 80%). H. Desseigne, *Bull. soc. chim. Mém.* [5] 9, 786 (1943); *C.A. 1944*, 3250.

Potassium thiocyanate   KSCN

Thiazoline Ring Closure   O

490.
$$H_2C \cdot NH_2 \qquad \qquad \qquad H_2C - N$$
$$| \qquad \qquad + \quad C \equiv N \quad \to \quad | \quad ||$$
$$H_2CCl \qquad \qquad / \qquad \qquad H_2C \quad C \cdot NH_2$$
$$KS \qquad \qquad \qquad \backslash S /$$

$ClCH_2CH_2NH_2 \cdot HCl$ is refluxed with KCNS in H_2O for several hrs. → 2-aminothiazoline. Y = 70%. G. W. Raiziss and LeRoy W. Clemence, *J. Am. Chem. Soc. 63*, 3124 (1941); *C.A. 1942*, 424.

Pyridine

Organic Thiocarboxylic Acids $\cdot$ COHal $\rightarrow$ $\cdot$ CO(SH)
from Acid Chlorides

91. Carboxylic acid chlorides give organic thio acids with H_2S in anhyd. C_5H_5N in 60–65% yields. Ex: Acetyl chloride $\rightarrow$ thiolacetic acid, F.e.s. S. Sunner and T. Nilson, *Svensk. Kem. Tid. 54*, 163 (1942); *C.A. 1944*, 3249.

Copper   *Cu*

Sulfones $R \cdot SO_2 \cdot R$

$$H_3CO\langle\rangle I + NaS\langle\rangle OCH_3 \rightarrow H_3CO\langle\rangle S\langle\rangle OCH_3 \rightarrow$$

$$H_3CO\langle\rangle SO_2\langle\rangle OCH_3 \leftarrow$$

92.

p-IC_6H_4OMe and p-$MeOC_6H_4SNa$ is heated with Cu at 240° $\rightarrow$ 4,4'-dimethoxydiphenyl sulfide (Y = 65–80%) which is oxidized with $KMnO_4$ in hot glacial AcOH $\rightarrow$ 4,4'-dimethoxydiphenyl sulfone (Y = 85–90%). F.e.s. G. Machek and H. Haas, *J. prakt. Chem. 160*, 41 (1942); *C.A. 1943*, 5040.

Via intermediate products

Mercaptans via Isothiourea Compounds $\cdot$ Hal $\rightarrow$ $\cdot$ SH

93. $C_{12}H_{25}Br$ and $SC(NH_2)_2$ are boiled for several hrs. in EtOH $\rightarrow$ N-dodecylisothiourea hydrobromide which is boiled with NaOH $\rightarrow$ $C_{12}H_{25}SH$. Y = 79–83%. F.e.s. G. G. Urquhart, J. W. Gates, Jr., and R. Connor, *Organic Syntheses 21*, 36 (1941); *C.A. 1941*, 6235.

94.

$$CH_2Cl \qquad \rightarrow \qquad CH_2SC\langle^{NH}_{NH_2} \qquad \rightarrow \qquad CH_2SH$$

10-Chloromethyl-1,2-benzanthracene heated with $CS(NH_2)_2$ in EtOH and C_6H_6 $\rightarrow$ 1,2-benzanthryl-10-S-thiourea hydrochloride (Y = 86%). This heated with a mixture of 2 N soda, Na_2SO_3, and MeOH $\rightarrow$ 1,2-benzanthryl-10-methyl mercaptan. Y = 82%. J. L. Wood and L. F. Fieser, *J. Am. Chem. Soc. 62*, 2674 (1940); *C.A. 1940*, 7901.

95. 2-Bromopyridine and $CS(NH_2)_2$ are refluxed and the reaction mixt. is allowed to stand for 5 days with NH_4OH at room temp. $\rightarrow$ 2-pyridinethiol. Y = 47%. M. A. Phillips and H. Shapiro, *J. Chem. Soc. 1942*, 584; *C.A. 1943*, 124.

With Xanthogenate

496. α-Bromolauric acid is treated with Na ethylxanthogenate and the
reaction product is treated with NH$_3$. The amide formed is refluxed
with aq. alc.–HCl. A renewed alkaline saponification removes the last
traces of ester → 2-mercapto-1-dodecanoic acid. Y = 90%. P. Rumpf,
Bull. soc. chim. Mém. [5], *9*, 661 (1942); *C.A. 1944*, 2951.

Formation of Remaining Bonds by:

Elimination

Halogens ⋏   **OL ⇑ Hal**

Sodium sulfide   *Na$_2$S*

Ditellurides   2 RTeCl$_3$ → RTe · TeR

497.   2 CH$_3$O⟨ ⟩TeCl$_3$ →   CH$_3$O⟨ ⟩Te · Te⟨ ⟩OCH$_3$

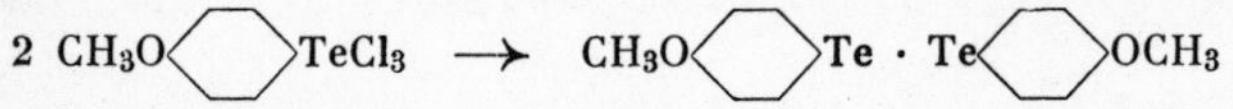

p-Anisyltellurium trichloride is refluxed for 10 min. at 100° with
Na$_2$S + H$_2$O → di-*p*-anisyl ditelluride. Y = quant. L. Reichel and
E. Kirschbaum, *Ber. 76*, 1105 (1943); *C.A. 1944*, 4918.

Formation of Bonds between Remaining Elements and C by:

Addition

Addition to Carbon $\qquad$ RC $\Downarrow$ CC

Without additional reagents

β-Hydroxy-α-Amino Acids from α,β-Unsaturated Carboxylic Acids via Organomercury Compounds

$$\cdot CH = CH \cdot \ \longrightarrow \ \cdot CH \cdot CH(OCH_3) \cdot$$
$$\overset{|}{HgOCOCH_3}$$

8.
$$CH_2 = CHCO_2CH_3 \ \longrightarrow \ CH_3OCH_2CH(HgOAc)CO_2CH_3 \ \longrightarrow$$
$$CH_3OCH_2CH(HgBr)CO_2CH_3 \ \longrightarrow \ CH_3OCH_2CHBrCO_2CH_3 \ \longrightarrow$$
$$CH_3OCH_2CHBrCO_2H \ \longrightarrow \ CH_3OCH_2CH(NH_2)CO_2H \ \longrightarrow \ CH_2(OH)CH(NH_2)CO_2H$$

Me acrylate is converted with MeOH and Hg(OAc)$_2$ by allowing it to stand for several days, into the β-methoxy-α-acetoxy Hg propionate, which is treated with KBr and brominated in direct sunlight in CHCl$_3$ at 50–55° → Me α-bromo-β-methoxypropionate (Y = 81–86%); it is carefully saponified with dil. aq. NaOH below 30° and heated with conc. NH$_4$OH at 90–100° for several hrs. in an autoclave. The methoxy group is split off by boiling with 48% HBr → dl-serine (Y = 30–40%). H. E. Carter and H. D. West, *Organic Syntheses 20*, 81 (1940); *C.A. 1940*, 5052.

$$CH_3CH = CHCO_2H \ \longrightarrow \ CH_3CH(OCH_3)CH(HgOAc)CO_2H \ \longrightarrow$$
$$CH_3CH(OCH_3)CH(HgBr)CO_2K \ \longrightarrow \ CH_3CH(OCH_3)CHBrCO_2H \ \longrightarrow$$
$$CH_3CH(OCH_3)CH(NHCHO)CO_2H \ \longrightarrow \ CH_3CH(OH)CH(NH_2)CO_2H$$

9. Crotonic acid is treated with Hg(OAc)$_2$ in MeOH; this is converted to the bromide and cleaved with Br in KBr (in its aq. soln.) in direct sunlight → α-bromo-β-methoxybutyric acid (crude Y = 88–93%); this compound is treated with conc. NH$_3$ soln. at 90–100° in an autoclave and the formed amino acids treated with HCO$_2$H and Ac$_2$O → formyl-dl-O-methylthreonine (Y = 25%). This is refluxed with HBr and the bromide formed treated with NH$_3$ → dl-threonine (Y = 85–90%). H. E. Carter and H. D. West, *Organic Syntheses 20*, 101 (1940); *C.A. 1940*, 5052.

Organomercury Compounds from Ethylene Derivatives

500.

Allylphthalimide is treated with $Hg(OAc)_2$ in MeOH → N-(2-acet-oxymercuri-3-methoxypropyl)phthalimide. Y = 60%. G. Carrara and E. Mori, *Gazz. chim. ital.* 73, 113 (1943); *C.A. 1944, 4928.*

Exchange

Nitrogen ⚓   RC ⚓ N

Cuprous chloride Cu_2Cl_2

Arylarsenic Acids $ArN_2 \cdot BF_4$ → $Ar \cdot AsO_3H_2$

501. Better yields and fewer side products are obtd. in most cases by pre-paring arylarsenic acids from diazonium borofluorides (prepn., see 258) and $NaAsO_2$. The reaction can be carried out at room temp. Prepn.: The amine is added dropwise to an aq. soln. of $NaAsO_2$ and CuCl in H_2O, stirred for an addnl. hr., allowed to stand overnight, warmed for 40 min. at 65°, and worked up. Ex: Phenylarsenic acid (Y = 58%). $p\text{-}O_2NC_6H_4$ deriv. (Y = 79%). $p\text{-}AcC_6H_4$ deriv. (Y = 70%). F.e.s. A. W. Ruddy, E. B. Starkey and W. H. Hartung, *J. Am. Chem. Soc.* 64, 828 (1942); *C.A. 1942, 3160.*

Halogen ⚓   RC ⚓ Hal

Without additional reagents

Organotellurium Compounds $R \cdot H$ → $R \cdot TeCl_3$ → $R \cdot Te\overset{O}{\underset{Cl}{\diagdown}}$

502.

Of many substances tried, only those containing sufficiently active hydrogen gave tellurium chloride compounds. Ex: 2-Phenyl-4-quino-linecarboxylic acid is refluxed with $TeCl_4$ in dry CCl_4 for 2 hrs. in the absence of moist air → p-(4-carboxy-2-quinolyl)phenyltellurium trichloride (Y = 47.6%); with H_2O → oxychloride deriv. L. Reichel and K. Ilberg, *Ber.* 76, 1108 (1943); *C.A. 1944, 4918.*

Lithium   *Li*

Phosphines

03. $2\ H_2N\langle\ \rangle Li + Cl_2P\langle\ \rangle \rightarrow$ (phenylbis(p-aminophenyl)phosphorus structure)

p-$H_2NC_6H_4Li$ (from $BrC_6H_4NH_2$ and BuLi in di-Et ether) is mixed with $PhPCl_2 \rightarrow$ phenylbis(p-aminophenyl)phosphorus. H. Gilman and C. G. Stuckwisch, *J. Am. Chem. Soc.* 63, 2844 (1941); *C.A. 1942, 423.*

Arsines

04. $2\ H_2N\langle\ \rangle Li + Cl_2As\langle\ \rangle \rightarrow$ (phenylbis(p-aminophenyl)arsenic structure)

p-$H_2NC_6H_4Li$ (from $BrC_6H_4NH_2$ and BuLi in di-Et ether) is mixed with $PhAsCl_2$ at -60 to $-45° \rightarrow$ phenylbis(p-aminophenyl)arsenic. Y = 91% (on basis of 70% yield of Li compound). H. Gilman and C. G. Stuckwisch, *J. Am. Chem. Soc.* 63, 2844 (1941); *C.A. 1942, 423.*

Magnesium   *Mg*

Organomercury Compounds $\cdot$ Br $\rightarrow$ $\cdot$ HgBr

05. $CH_3(CH_2)_{10}CH_2Br \rightarrow CH_3(CH_2)_{10}CH_2HgBr$

RMgBr is treated with a little more than the theor. amt. of $HgCl_2$ in di-Et ether. A mixt. of RHgCl and RHgBr is obtained in a 70% yield. Two methods are available for their separation. Ex: Dodecyl bromide $\rightarrow$ dodecyl HgBr. P. Rumpf, *Bull. soc. chim. Mém.* [5], 9, 535, 538 (1942); *C.A. 1943, 5016.*

Organosilicon Compounds $4\ R \cdot Mg \cdot Hal \rightarrow SiR_4$

06. When 5 times the theoretical amount of Na_2SiF_6 (compare, *C.Z. 1938 II*, 1947) is used in the preparation of organosilicon compounds from Grignard reagents, the yield is increased appreciably. A hydrogen atmosphere, temperature increase to 213–239°, and also heating for more than 1 hr. at 160–170°, have little or no effect on the yield. Ex: $PhCH_2Mg$ chloride $\rightarrow (PhCH_2)_4Si$. Y = 53%. J. M. Soshestvenskaya, *J. Gen. Chem. U.S.S.R. 10*, 1689 (1940); *C.A. 1941, 3240.*

Sodium polysulfide Na_2S_x

Selenophene Ring Closure

507.

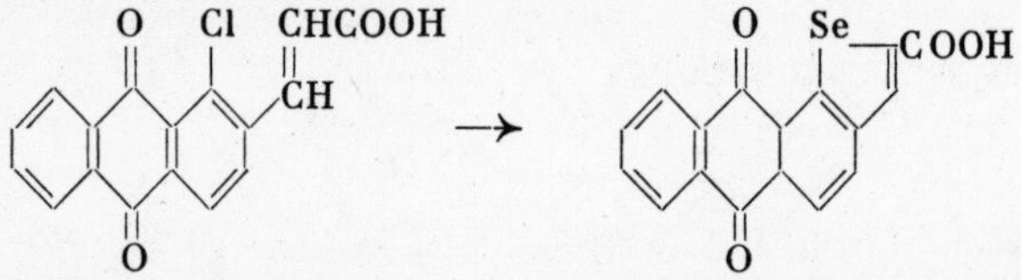

1-Chloro-2-anthraquinoneacrylic acid and Na_2Se_x are heated for 4 hrs. at 100–110° → 1,2-selenopheno-2′,3′-anthraquinone-5′-carboxylic acid (s.m. 113). Y = 77%. E. B. Hershberg and L. F. Fieser, *J. Am. Chem. Soc.* 63, 2561 (1941); *C.A. 1942*, 458.

Formation of C—C Bond by:

Addition

Addition to Oxygen and Carbon   CC ⇓ OC

Lithium   *Li*

Ethynyl Alcohols
  See 719.

Alcohols from Ketones

8. 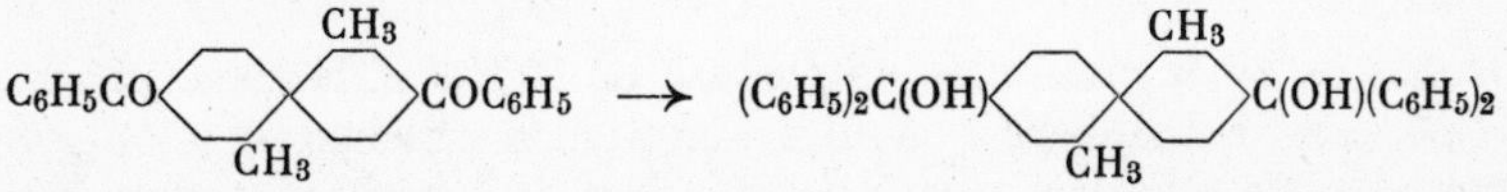 C_6H_5CO⟨CH_3 ... CH_3⟩COC_6H_5 → $(C_6H_5)_2C(OH)$⟨CH_3 ... CH_3⟩$C(OH)(C_6H_5)_2$

2,2'-Dimethyl-4,4'-dibenzoylbiphenyl is treated with PhLi in C_6H_6 → 4,4'-bis(diphenylhydroxymethyl)-2,2'-dimethylbiphenyl. Y = nearly quant. E. Müller and E. Hertel, *Ann. 555*, 157 (1944); *C.Z. 1944 II*, 1045.

Arylhydroxyanthracenes from Anthraquinones

9.

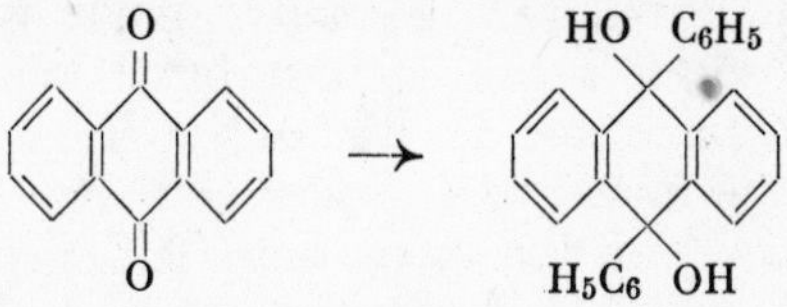

PhBr in anhydrous di-Et ether is added to Li in ether; after 2–3 hours anthraquinone is added in small portions, and the mixture is heated for 0.5 hour → 9,10-dihydro-9,10-diphenyl-9,10-dihydroxyanthracene (this is a mixture of both diastereo isomers). The yields are higher and the reaction goes smoother than with Mg. F.e.s. A. Willemart, *Bull. soc. chim. Mém.* [5] 9, 83 (1942); *C.A. 1943*, 5053.

Sodium hydroxide, soda, potash

Hydroxymethylation of Phenols
with Formaldehyde   ArH → ArCH₂OH

0. Method: The phenols are allowed to stand for several days with HCHO in the presence of NaOH, soda, or potash. Ex: *p*-Ethylphenol

→ 4-ethyl-2,6-bis(hydroxymethyl)-4-propylphenol; Y = 65%. *p*-Iso-propylphenol → 2,6-bis(hydroxyphenyl)-4-isopropylphenol; Y = 96%. 3,4,5-Trichlorophenol → 2,6-bis(hydroxymethyl)-3,4,5-trichlorophe-nol; Y = 78%. F.e.s. J. Strating and H. J. Backer, *Rec. trav. chim. 62,* 57 (1943); *C.A. 1945,* 2497.

Nitro Alcohols from Aldehydes

$$C\overset{O}{\underset{H}{\diagdown}} \rightarrow \overset{OH}{\underset{H}{C}} \cdot \overset{NO_2}{\underset{H}{C}} \cdot R$$

511. Three methods of condensing nitroparaffins with aldehydes gave reasonably good yields of nitro alcohols.

1. Addition of just enough alkali to give a reasonable reaction veloc-ity without resulting in a large amount of dehydration and polymeri-zation; a long reaction period is required and the yield decreases rapidly as the complexity of the starting products increases. Ex: $MeNO_2$ in MeOH and a trace of NaOH are stirred vigorously with octanol at 30–35° and the mixture is allowed to stand for 4 days at room temp. → 2-nitro-3-decanol. Y = 71.5%.

2. Addition of a molecular equivalent of 10 *N* NaOH gave yields of 85–90% only with $MeNO_2$ and straight-chain aldehydes; poor yields resulted with other primary nitroparaffins and with secondary nitro-paraffins the method failed. The side reactions below 10° were negligible. Ex: Molecular equivalents of $MeNO_2$, *n*-heptanol, and 10 *N* NaOH are mixed below 10°, and the mixture diluted with ice water → 1-nitro-2-octanol. Y = 88%.

3. A solution of the $NaHSO_3$ addition product of the aldehyde and the Na salt of the nitroparaffin are mixed while warm. Nitro com-pounds in 70–80% yields result without formation of undesired by products. Ex: 2-Nitrobutane in dilute NaOH and *n*-octanol in a $NaHSO_3$ solution are mixed while warm and after allowing to stand several hrs. are heated on the steam bath → 3-methyl-3-nitro-4-hen-decanol. Y = 40%. F.e.s. C. A. Sprang and E. F. Degering, *J. Am. Chem. Soc. 64,* 1063 (1942); *C.A. 1942,* 4092.

Sodamide

Ethynyl Alcohols

$$CO \xrightarrow{NaNH_2} C\overset{OH}{\underset{C \equiv CH}{\diagdown}}$$

512. $CH_3COCH_3 \rightarrow$ $\overset{H_3C}{\underset{H_3C}{\diagup}} C \overset{OH}{\underset{C \equiv CH}{\diagdown}}$

Me_2CO is transformed to the Na derivative with $NaNH_2$; this is reacted with C_2H_2 at −10° → dimethylethynylcarbinol; Y = 40–46%. Also: Methylethylethynylcarbinol; Y = 33%. 1-ethynyl-1-cyclohexanol; Y = 50%. D. D. Coffman, *Organic Syntheses 20,* 40 (1940); *C.A. 1940,* 5048.

Potassium cyanide   KCN

Benzoins

3.

Br(MeO)C$_6$H$_3$CHO (10 g.) is refluxed for 3 hours with KCN in 60%
EtOH → 5 g. 5,5′-dibromo-2,2′-dimethoxybenzoin (s.m. 156). R. Kuhn,
L. Birkofer and E. F. Möller, *Ber. 76*, 900 (1943); *C.A. 1944*, 2950.

2,3-Dihydroxyquinones   O

4.

Hydroxylated naphthoquinones are obtained by stirring a mixture of
o-phthalaldehyde and substituted phthalaldehydes with the bisulfite
compd. of glyoxal and a soda solution in the presence of KCN (which
prevents the autocondensation of glyoxal). Air is added at 20° while
the *p*H is held between 8 and 12. Ex: *o*-C$_6$H$_4$(CHO)$_2$ and [CH-
(OH)SO$_3$Na]$_2$ → isonaphthazarin. Y = over 50%. F. Weygand,
Ber. 75, 625 (1942); *C.A. 1943*, 3426.

5.

4,5-Pyrazoledicarboxaldehyde (prepn., see 532) in C$_5$H$_5$N-H$_2$O
(1:1) is treated with glyoxal, NaHSO$_3$, and KCN in 2 N Na$_2$CO$_3$
and air is passed through → 5,6-dihydroxyindazole-4,7-quinone. Y =
22%. Also: 1-Benzyltriazole-4,5-dicarboxaldehyde (prepn., see 290)
→ 1-benzyl-5,6-dihydroxybenzotriazole-4,7-quinone. Y = 44%.
F.e.s. F. Weygand and K. Henkel, *Ber. 76*, 818 (1943); *C.A. 1944*, 1743.

Piperidine

Substituted Glycolic Acids
from Ketones

6. The ketones are converted to the cyanohydrins by treatment with 1.2
moles of liquid HCN (prepared according to Gilman, *Organic Syntheses Coll. Vol. I*, 343) in the presence of some piperidine. After the
mixture has been allowed to stand for 1 hour at 0°, the cyanohydrin

formed is converted to the amide with strong H_2SO_4 (in the case of dialkyl derivs.) or with concd. HCl (in the case of Ph alkyl derivs.) without further purification. The glycolic acids are obtained in yields from 60–80% by saponification of the amide with 20% NaOH or HCl. Ex: Bu Me ketone → Bu Me glycolic acid. F.e.s. R. W. Stoughton, *J. Am. Chem. Soc.* 63, 2376 (1941); *C.A. 1941*, 7402.

Addition of Benzyl Cyanide to Glyoxalic Acids

517.

$$C_6H_5C(OH)COOH$$
$$|$$
$$C_6H_5CH(CN)$$

Phenylglyoxalic acid and benzyl cyanide in piperidine → diphenyl-hydroxysuccinic acid mononitrile. Y = 40%. If the condensation is carried out in aqueous solution with soda or potash, the yields are poor. P. Cordier and J. Moreau, *Compt. rend.* 214, 621 (1942); *C.A. 1944*, 5497.

Magnesium–magnesium iodide $Mg-MgI_2$

Bimolecular Reduction of Aldehydes to Glycols
See 689.

Calcium oxide CaO

Hydroxymethylation $H → CH_2OH$
See 575.

Calcium chloride $CaCl_2$

γ-Lactones from β-Hydroxyaldehydes

518.

$$CH_2(OH)C(CH_3)_2CHO \rightarrow \overset{\overline{\qquad O \qquad}}{CH_2C(CH_3)_2CH(OH)CO}$$

$HOCH_2CMe_2CHO$ is allowed to stand with $CaCl_2$ and KCN for 18 hrs. (occasional shaking) in the absence of air, then heated to 70–80° → α-hydroxy-β,β-dimethyl-γ-butyrolactone. Y = 77–81%. The intermediate cyanohydrin is hydrolyzed at ordinary temperatures by the $Ca(OH)_2$ formed in the reaction. The method shows a certain advantage over that of Reichstein and Grüssner (*C. 1940 II*, 1299). H. E. Carter and L. F. Ney, *J. Am. Chem. Soc.* 63, 312 (1941); *C.A. 1941*, 1382.

Aluminum chloride $AlCl_3$

Friedel-Crafts Synthesis with Acid Anhydrides

9.

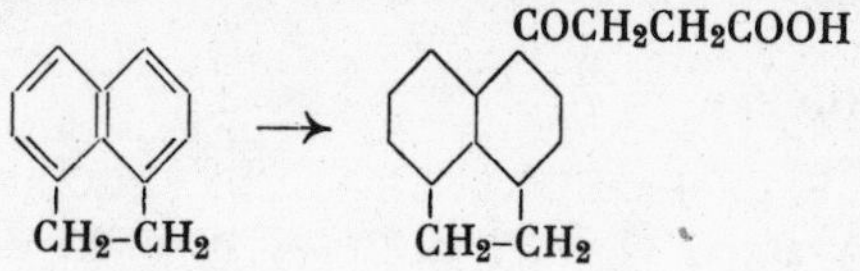

COCH₂CH₂COOH rendered as $COCH_2CH_2COOH$

CH₂–CH₂   →   CH₂–CH₂

Acenaphthene, succinic anhydride, and $AlCl_3$ in $PhNO_2$ at 0° →
β-(3-acenaphthoyl)-propionic acid. Y = 81%. L. F. Fieser, *Organic
Syntheses 20*, 1 (1940); *C.A. 1940*, 5075.

Potassium dihydrogen phosphate KH_2PO_4

Cyanohydrins $CO \rightarrow C\begin{smallmatrix} OH \\ CN \end{smallmatrix}$

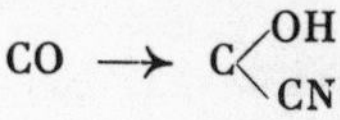

0.

$$(CH_3CH_2)_2CO \rightarrow (CH_3CH_2)_2C\begin{smallmatrix} OH \\ CN \end{smallmatrix}$$

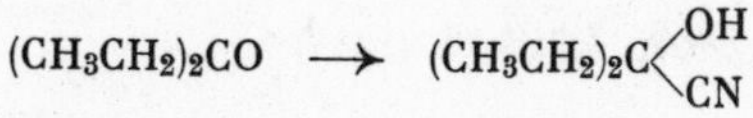

Et_2CO is treated with NaCN and KH_2PO_4 → α-ethyl-α-hydroxy-
butyronitrile. Y = 75%. J. Colonge and D. Joly, *Ann. Chim.* [11] *18*,
286 (1943); *C.A. 1944*, 5203.

Ammonium chloride NH_4Cl

1.

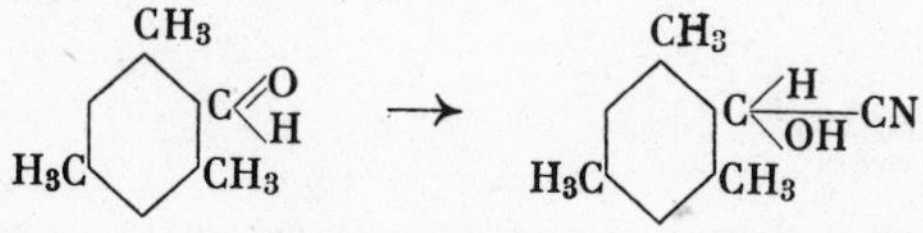

β-Isodurylaldehyde is shaken in petroleum ether with KCN and NH_4Cl
in H_2O → β-isodurylaldehyde cyanohydrin. Y = 91%. A. Weissberger
and D. B. Glass, *J. Am. Chem. Soc. 64*, 1724 (1942); *C.A. 1942*, 5807.

Addition to Nitrogen and Carbon   CC ⇓ NC

Lithium   *Li*

Ketones from Nitriles $\cdot CN \rightarrow \cdot \overset{.}{C}O R$

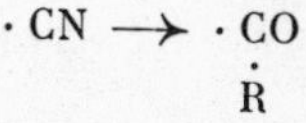

2.

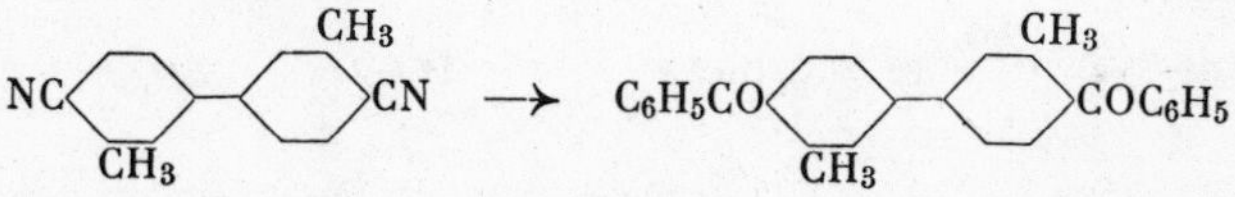

3,3'-Dimethyl-4,4'-dicyanobiphenyl is treated for 24 hours with excess
PhLi in C_6H_6 in an N_2 atmosphere and the diketimine formed is
saponified by boiling for 1 hr. with 60% H_2SO_4 → 3,3'-dimethyl-4,4'-
dibenzoylbiphenyl. Y = quant. F.e.s. E. Müller and E. Hertel, *Ann.
555*, 157 (1944); *C.Z. 1944 II*, 1045.

Triazine Ring   O
    See 285.

Magnesium   *Mg*

Ketones from Nitriles $\cdot CN \longrightarrow \cdot CO$

523. $CH_3OCH_2\,CN + C_6H_5MgBr \longrightarrow CH_3OCH_2COC_6H_5$ $\overset{\cdot}{R}$

MeOCH$_2$CN is reacted with PhMgBr → in di-Et ether ω-methoxy-acetophenone. Y = 71–78%. R. B. Moffett and R. L. Shriner, *Organic Syntheses 21*, 79 (1941); *C.A. 1940*, 6249.

524. Benzofurylnitrile and EtMgBr → 2-propylbenzofuran, $C_{11}H_{10}O_2$. Y = 80%. H. Normant, *Ann. Chim.* [11] *17*, 335 (1942); *C.A. 1944*, 3282.

Ammonia NH_3

Dithio-β-Isoindigo from Phthalonitrile

525. 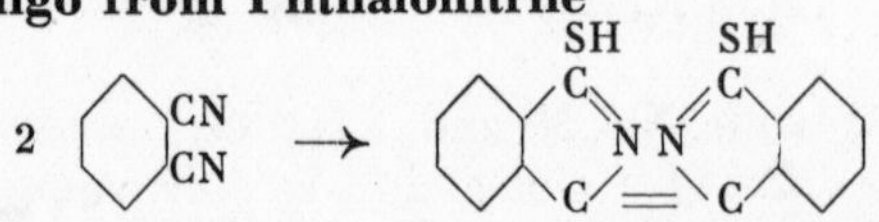   2 →

Phthalonitrile is treated with H_2S and NH_4OH in warm EtOH → dithio-β-isoindigo. Y = 96%. H. D. K. Drew and D. B. Kelly, *J. Chem. Soc. 1941*, 625–630; *C.A. 1942*, 768.

Addition to Carbon $CC \Downarrow CC$

Without additional reagents

Diene Synthesis O

526. C_2H_4 reacts with 1,3-dienes at 200° and 200–400 atm. pressure with 1,4 addition taking place. Ex: $(CMe : CH_2)_2$ and C_2H_4 → 1,2-dimethylcyclohexene. Y = 50%. L. M. Joshel and L. W. Butz, *J. Am. Chem. Soc. 63*, 3350 (1941); *C.A. 1942*, 1036.

527. Maleic anhydride and butadiene in C_6H_6 → Δ^4-tetrahydrophthalic anhydride (s.m. 697). Y = 90%. L. F. Fieser and F. C. Novello, *J. Am. Chem. Soc. 64*, 802 (1942); *C.A. 1942*, 3171.

528.

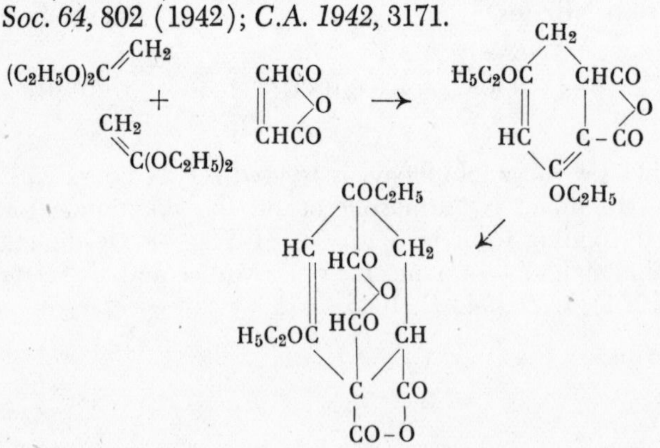

Maleic anhydride and $CH_2 : C(OEt)_2$ in di-Et ether are boiled and allowed to stand overnight. A yellow precipitate → 3,5-diethoxy-1,6-dihydrophthalic anhydride ($Y = 71\%$) results; this is heated with maleic anhydride in abs. C_6H_6 for 4 hrs. → bicyclo octene derivative, $C_{16}H_{16}O_8$ ($Y = 60\%$). S. M. McElvain and H. Cohen, *J. Am. Chem. Soc. 64*, 260 (1942); *C.A. 1942*, 1901.

29.

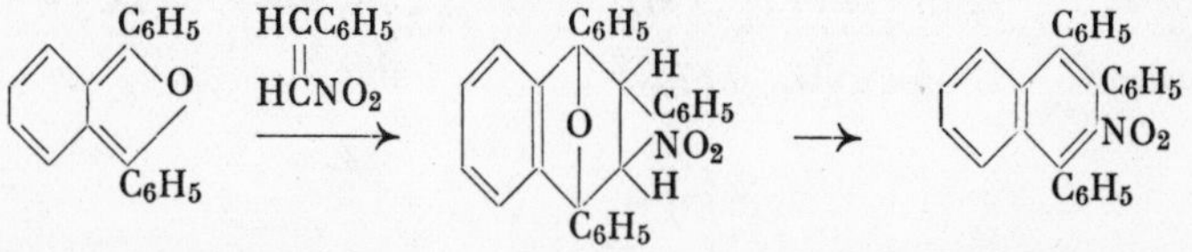

1,3-Diphenylisobenzofuran and β-nitrostyrene are refluxed for 3 hrs. in EtOH → 1,2,4-triphenyl-3-nitro-1,4-oxido-1,2,3,4-tetrahydronaphthalene ($Y = $ quant.). 10 g. of this with glacial AcOH–HBr → 7 g. 1,2,4-triphenyl-3-nitronaphthalene. F.e.s. C. F. H. Allen, A. Bell and J. W. Gates, Jr., *J. Org. Chem. 8*, 373 (1943); *C.A. 1943*, 5950.

Introduction of Carboxyl Group
into Pyrazole Ring   H → COOH

30.

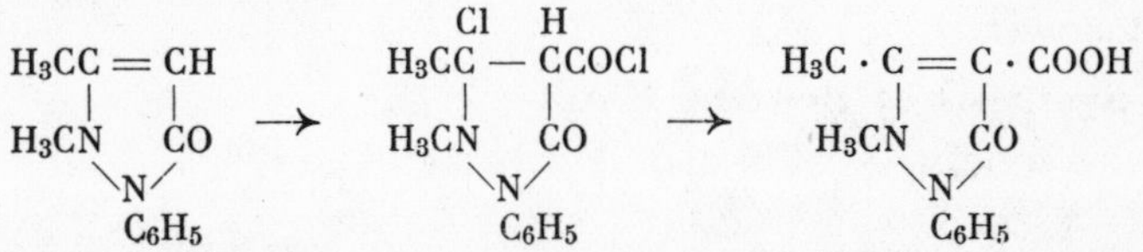

1-Phenyl-2,3-dimethyl-5-pyrazolone (antipyrine) is treated with $COCl_2$ in C_6H_6 and subsequently with aqueous NaOH → 1-phenyl-2,3-dimethyl-5-pyrazolone-4-carboxylic acid (antipyric acid). $Y = $ nearly quant. F.e.s. H. P. Kaufmann and Lan Sun Huang, *Ber. 75*, 1214 (1942); *C.A. 1943*, 4730.

Pyridine Ring   O

31.

$$2\ CH_2 : CHCHO + NH_3 \rightarrow$$

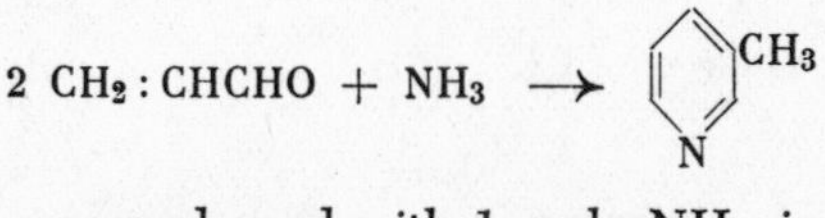

2 moles acrolein are condensed with 1 mole NH_3 in the gas phase at 350° (dilution with H_2O, C_6H_6, or MeOH vapors) → 3-methylpyridine (3-picoline). $Y = 57.3\%$. For extensive directions, see F. Stitz, *Vest. Chemiker-Ztg. 45*, 159 (1942); *C.A. 1944*, 2040.

Pyrazole o-Dialdehydes

32.

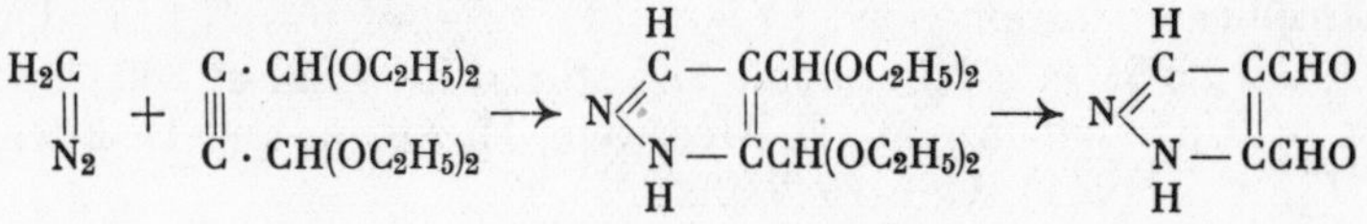

EtMgBr is treated with C_2H_2 and $HC(OEt)_3$ is added → [: CCH-$(OEt)_2]_2$ (Y = 70%) (s.m. 290); this is kept in the dark at 20° for 8 days with CH_2N_2 in di-Et ether → 4,5-pyrazole dicarboxaldehyde bis(di-Et acetal) (Y = 84%). This is heated 10 min. on a water bath with 0.5 N H_2SO_4 → 4,5-pyrazole dicarboxaldehyde (s. m. 515). Y = 98%. Also: 3-Carbethoxy-4,5-pyrazole dicarboxaldehyde. K. Henkel and F. Weygand, *Ber.* 76, 812 (1943); *C.A. 1944*, 1742.

Pyrazolenine Carboxylic Acids

533.

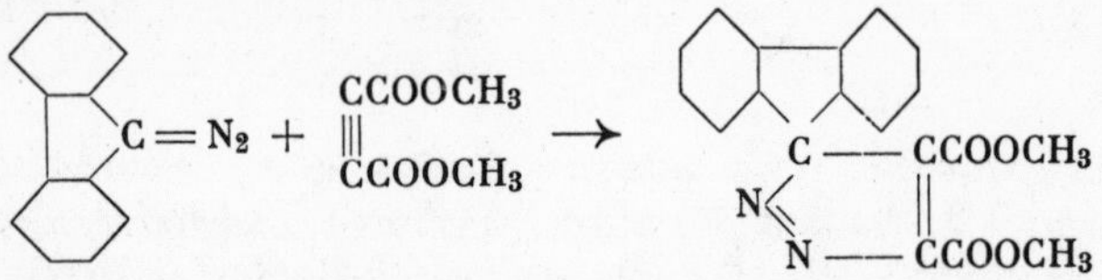

($CCO_2Me)_2$ and biphenylenediazomethane in absolute di-Et ether after one day → di-Me 3,3-biphenylenepyrazolenine-4,5-dicarboxylate. Y = nearly quant. J. von Alphen, *Rec. trav. chim.* 62, 491 (1943); *C.A. 1944*, 1744.

Sodium alcoholate   *NaOR*

Diene Synthesis of Benzene Rings

534.

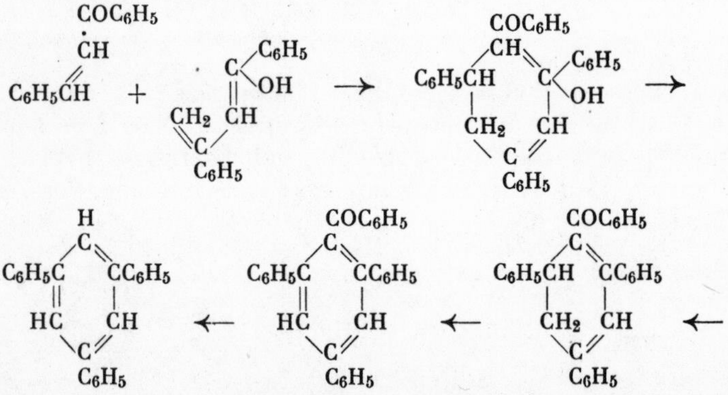

Dypnone and PhCH : CHCOPh are condensed with NaOEt in EtOH at −5° → 6-benzoyl-1,3,5-triphenyl-2-cyclohexen-1-ol (Y = 87%), which is warmed with HCl-saturated glacial AcOH for 2.5 hrs. at 70–80° → 2,3-dihydro-2,4,6-triphenylbenzophenone (Y = 87%). This is oxidized with $Pb(OAc)_4$ in glacial AcOH while CO_2 is passed through → 2,4,6-triphenylbenzophenone (Y = 81%). 2 g. of this is heated with KOH and PbO_2 in a Ni crucible and stirred for 1 hr. at 280–290° → 1.1 g. of triphenylbenzene. H. Meerwein, H. Adams and H. Buchloh, *Ber.* 77, 227 (1944); *C.A. 1945*, 3262.

Addition of Nitromethane

$$CH : CH \longrightarrow CH_2 \cdot CH$$
$$\overset{|}{C}H_2NO_2$$

5. 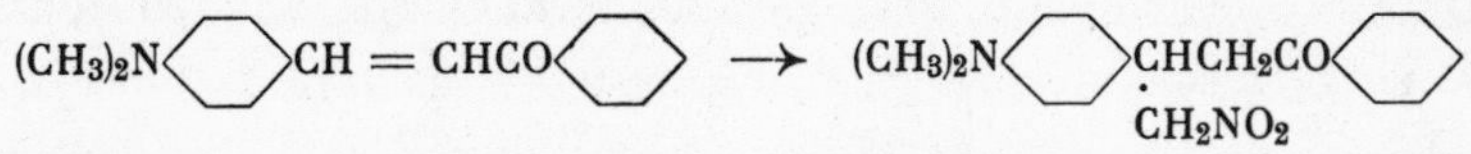 $(CH_3)_2N\langle\ \rangle CH = CHCO\langle\ \rangle \longrightarrow (CH_3)_2N\langle\ \rangle CHCH_2CO\langle\ \rangle$
$$\overset{|}{C}H_2NO_2$$

4-Dimethylaminochalcone (10 g.) is heated for 1 hr. on a steam bath with $MeNO_2$ in the presence of MeONa in MeOH $\rightarrow$ 8.5 g. γ-nitro-β-(p-dimethylaminophenyl)-butyrophenone. F.e.s. M. A. T. Rogers, *J. Chem. Soc. 1943*, 590; *C.A. 1944*, 1495.

Copper salts Cu^+

Methylation at the Carbon Atom $RH \rightarrow RCH_3$

6.

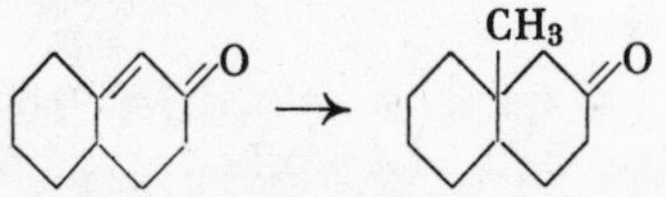

2-Keto-$\Delta^{1,9}$-octalin is treated with MeMgI in the presence of CuBr in di-Et ether $\rightarrow$ *cis*-2-keto-9-methyldecalin. Y = 60%. A. J. Birch and R. Robinson, *J. Chem. Soc. 1943*, 501; *C.A. 1944*, 337.

Rearrangement

Oxygen/Carbon Type   CC ↻ OC

Aluminum chloride $AlCl_3$

Phenyl Ketones from Phenyl Esters
Fries Rearrangement

7. In the Fries rearrangement, the reaction products depend upon the amount of $AlCl_3$ used (see 705). The rearrangement of Ph caprylate in the presence of various amounts of $AlCl_3$ was studied and the yields of reaction products determined. High temperature (140°) favors the formation of o-hydroxycaprylophenone; at 180°, the p-hydroxycaprylo-phenone already formed rearranges to the ortho isomer. A. W. Ralston, M. R. McCorkle and E. W. Segebrecht, *J. Org. Chem. 6*, 750 (1941); *C.A. 1941*, 7939.

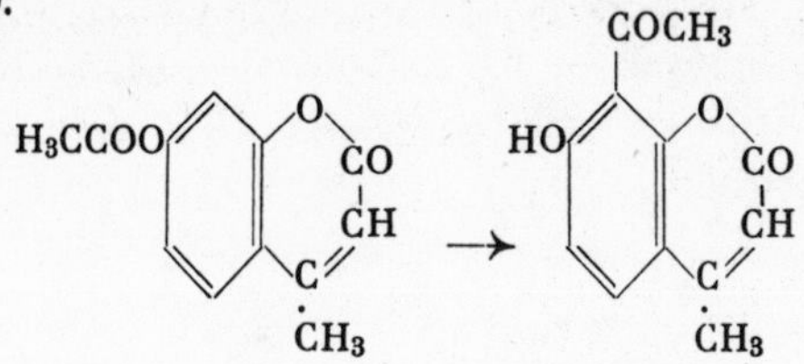

538. 4-Methyl-7-acetoxycoumarin (prepn., see 174) heated at 125–170° with AlCl₃ → 4-methyl-7-hydroxy-8-acetylcoumarin. Y = 73–77% (s.m. 104). A. Russell and J. R. Frye, *Organic Syntheses 21*, 22 (1941); *C.A. 1941*, 6249.

Carbon/Carbon Type   CC ∩ CC

Sodium nitrite   *NaNO₂*

Ring Expansion

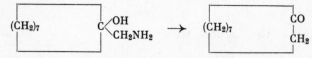

539.

1-Aminomethyl-1-cyclooctanol is heated for 0.5 hr. with NaNO₂ in AcOH–H₂O on a water bath and worked up after standing for 16 hrs. → cyclononanone. Y = 50–57%, isolated through the semicarbazone. L. Ruzicka, P. A. Plattner and H. Wild, *Helv. Chim. Acta 26*, 1631 (1943); *C.A. 1944*, 2935. See also M. W. Goldberg and H. Kirchensteiner, *Helv. Chim. Acta 26*, 288 (1943); *C.A. 1944*, 111.

540.

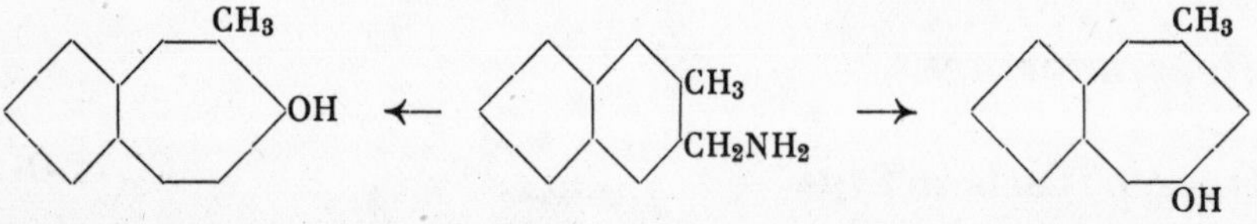

5-Methylhexahydro-6-indanmethylamine (35 g.) is warmed with NaNO₂ in AcOH until the reaction ceases → 19 g. 5-methylcyclopentanocyclopentanols -6 and -7 (a mixture). H. Arnold, *Ber. 76*, 777 (1943); *C.A. 1944*, 966.

541.

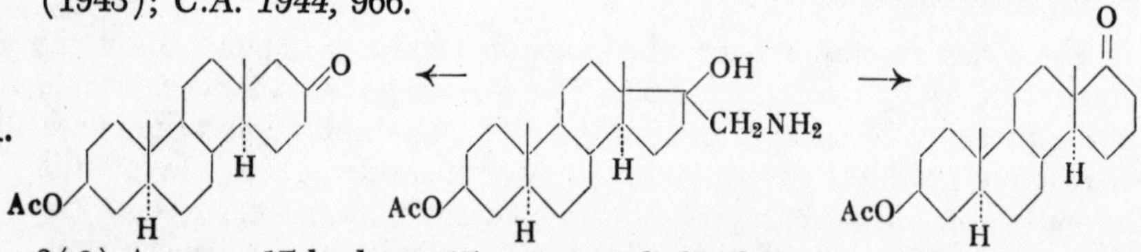

3(β)-Acetoxy-17-hydroxy-17-aminomethylandrostane (18 g.) is allowed to stand for 24 hrs. at 0° with an aqueous NaNO₂ solution in AcOH → 6.5 g. 3(β)-acetoxy-D-homo-17a-ketoandrostane and after chromatographic analysis → 0.8 g. 3-β-acetoxy-D-homo-17-ketoandrostane. M. W. Goldberg and E. Wydler, *Helv. Chim. Acta 26*, 1142 (1943); *C.A. 1944*, 367.

Platinum–carbon   *Pt*
    See 732.

Exchange

Hydrogen ⬆   CC ⇅ H

Sulfuric acid H_2SO_4

Benzanthrones   O
See 589.

Oxygen ⬆   CC ⇅ O

Without additional reagents

**α-Substituted Acrylic Acids
from Substituted Malonic Acids**
See 767.

Hantzsch's Pyridine Ring Synthesis   O

2.

3-Quinoline carboxaldehyde is heated for 7 hrs. at 100° in a sealed
tube with alcoholic NH_3 and $AcCH_2CO_2Et$ → di-Et 4,3'-quinolyl-2,6-
dimethyldihydro-3,5-pyridinedicarboxylate (Y = 79%). 2.7 g. of this
compound is boiled for a short time with 2 N HNO_3 → 2.3 g. di-Et
4,3'-quinolyl-2,6-dimethyl-3,5-pyridinedicarboxylate. This is saponified
with alcoholic KOH and the Ag salt of the acid formed is heated *in
vacuo* → 4-lutidylquinoline. Y = 50%. F.e.s. A. H. Cook, I. M. Heilbron and L. Steger, *J. Chem. Soc. 1943*, 413; *C.A. 1944*, 104.

Naphthyridines

3.

2,6-Diaminopyridine and $BzAcCHCO_2Et$ are heated at $180°$ → 7-amino-2(or 4)-hydroxy-4(or 2)-phenyl-1,8-naphthyridine. Y = 50–70%. F.e.s. A. Mangini and M. Colonna, *Gazz. chim. ital.* **72**, 183 (1942); *Boll. Sci. facoltà chim. ind. Bologna* **1941**, 85; *C.A.* **1943**, 3096.

Sodium   *Na*

1,2-Unsaturated Carboxylic Acid Esters $\cdot CHO \rightarrow \cdot CH : CH \cdot COOR$

544.

2-Furanacrolein (prepn., see 548) is treated with Et acetate and Na in the cold. Et γ-(2-furfurylidene)crotonate. Y = 73%. A. Hinz, G. Meyer and G. Schücking, *Ber.* **76**, 676 (1943); *C.A.* **1944**, 2334.

Acyloin Condensation

545. $2\ CH_2 = CH(CH_2)_8COOCH_3$

$\rightarrow CH_2 = CH(CH_2)_8COCHOH(CH_2)_8CH = CH_2$

$\rightarrow CH_2 = CH(CH_2)_8COCO(CH_2)_8CH = CH_2$

Me 10-hendecenoate is vigorously stirred with Na in xylene → 1,21-docosadiene-11-one-12-ol, Y = 50%, and 1,21-docosadiene-11,12-dione, Y = 2%. L. Ruzicka, P. A. Plattner and W. Widmer, *Helv. Chim. Acta* **25**, 604 (1942); *C.A.* **1942**, 6501.

Chromones

546.

o-HOC_6H_4Ac and $EtCo_2Et$ are added to powdered Na in ether. The product is poured on glacial AcOH and boiled with glacial AcOH and concd. HCl → 2-ethylchromone. Y = 70–75%. R. Mozingo, *Organic Syntheses* **21**, 42 (1941); *C.A.* **1941**, 6258.

Alkalis

Methylation $H \rightarrow CH_3$

547.

β-Naphthol (100 g.) is treated with a 40% formaldehyde solution and KOH → methylene-bis(2-naphthol) which is reduced with Zn and cuprammonium nitrate → 45–55 g. 1,2-Me $C_{10}H_6OH$. R. Robinson and F. Weygand, *J. Chem. Soc.* **1941**, 386; *C.A.* **1941**, 6965.

1,2-Unsaturated Aldehydes   · CHO → · CH : CH · CHO

48.

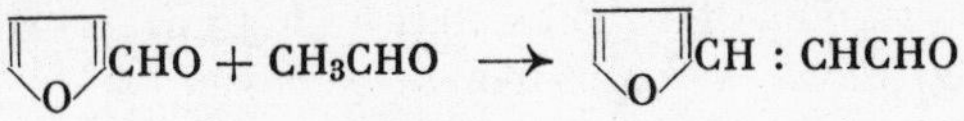

2-Furaldehyde in NaOH is added to AcH at 0° → 2-furanacrolein (s.m. 544, 549). Y = 88%. A. Hinz, G. Meyer and G. Schücking, *Ber.* 76, 676 (1943); *C.A. 1944*, 2334.

1,2-Unsaturated Ketones   · CHO → · CH : CH · CO ·

49.

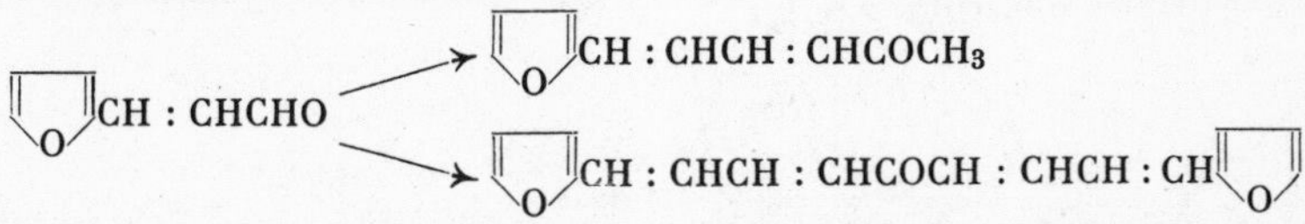

2-Furanacrolein (500 g.) (prepn., see 548) and 800 g. Me$_2$CO is added dropwise to 5 liters 0.5% NaOH → 1-(2-furyl)-5-oxo-1,3-hexediene. Y = 71.4%. 2-Furanacrolein (400 g.) and 110 g. acetone are stirred with 200 g. 10% NaOH in 3 liters EtOH at 8° → 1,9-bis(2-furyl)-5-oxo-1,3,6,8-nonatetraene. Y = 97%. H. Hinz, G. Meyer and G. Schücking, *Ber.* 76, 676 (1943); *C.A. 1944*, 2334.

Chalcones

50.

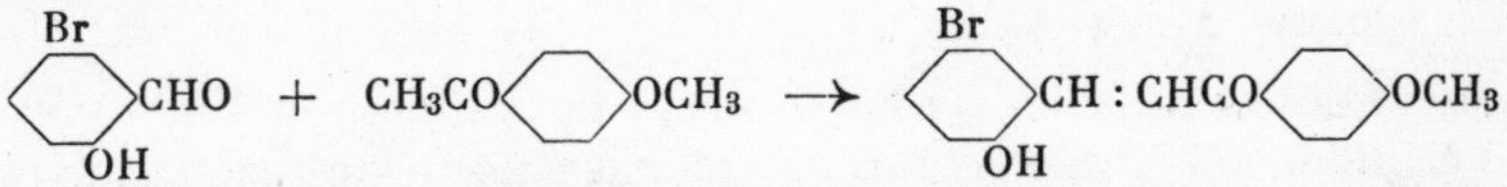

Prepn.: The mixture of ketone and aldehyde is treated in a warm alc. solution with saturated aq. NaOH and left for 1–2 days. After dilution with H$_2$O and addition of HCl, the reaction product separates. Ex: 5-Bromosalicylaldehyde and 4-methoxyacetophenone → 4-methoxyphenyl 2-hydroxy-5-bromostyryl ketone. Y = 60%. F.e.s. L. C. Raiford and L. K. Tanzer, *J. Org. Chem.* 6, 722 (1941); *C.A. 1942*, 434.

51. Protocatechualdehyde-4-β-D-glucoside (prepn., see 1) and o-HOC$_6$H$_4$-COMe in 4 N NaOH is allowed to stand at room temperature for 3 days → 2′4,5-trihydroxychalcone-4-β-D-glucoside, C$_{21}$H$_{22}$O$_9$ (s.m. 150, 245). Y = 54.5%. L. Reichel and J. Marchand, *Ber.* 76, 1132 (1943); *C.A. 1944*, 4944.

Flavanones Via Chalcones

52.

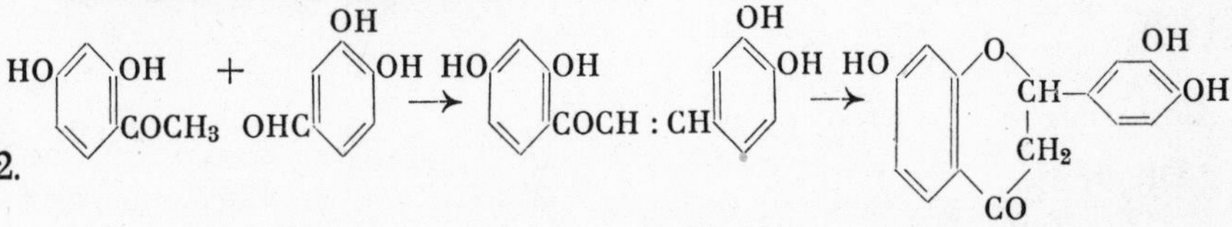

Resacetophenone and protocatechualdehyde is treated with 50% KOH in alc. at 60° and the reaction product is precipitated with 15% HCl at 20° → 3,4,2′,4′-tetrahydroxychalcone (butein) (crude Y = 30%). For apparatus, see original. This is treated with a citrate–HCl buffer (*p*H = 4.5) after 30 days → 7,3′,4′-trihydroxyflavanone (Y = 37%). For separation from chalcone, see *Ber.* 74, 1802 (1941). F.e.s. L. Reichel, W. Burkart and K. Müller, *Ann.* 550, 146 (1942); *C.A. 1943*, 2726.

553.

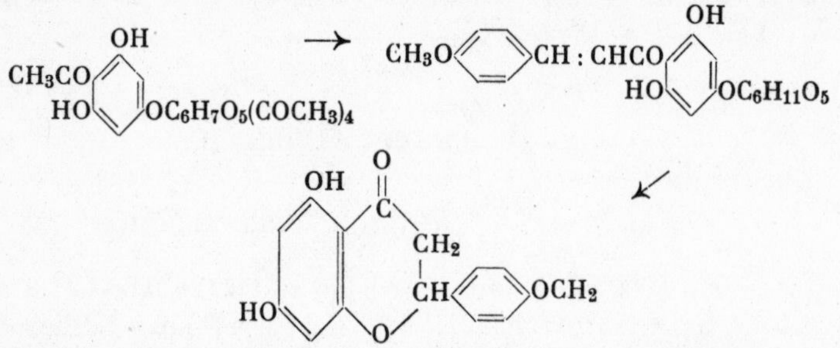

4-(Tetraacetylglucosido)phloracetophenone (5 g.) is shaken with *p*-MeOC$_6$H$_4$CHO in 60% KOH and 96% alcohol → 2.9 g. isosakuranefin-4′-glucoside (chalcone form). 0.305 g. of this is boiled with 2% HCl → 0.122 g. isosakuranetin (5,7-dihydroxy-4′-methoxyflavanone). G. Zemplén, R. Bognár and L. Mester, *Ber.* 75, 1432 (1942); *C.A. 1944*, 1237.

Ring Closure of γ-Diketones

554. Ring closure of Ac(CH$_2$)$_2$COCH$_2$R can be accomplished in an alkaline medium. Of 30 compounds tested, only acetonylacetone yielded no cyclopentenone, but resins. Ex: 2,5-Hendecanedione is refluxed 6 hrs. with 2% NaOH in aq. EtOH → 1-methyl-2-amylcyclopenten-3-one (dihydrojasmone). F.e.s. H. Hunsdiecker, *Ber.* 75, 455 (1942); *C.A. 1943*, 3404.

2-Substituted Quinolines

555.

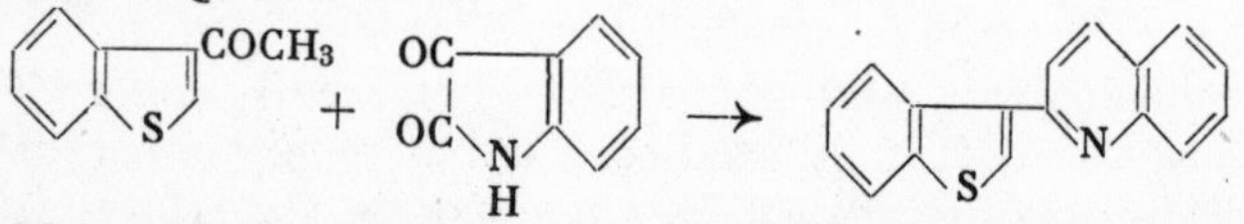

3-Acetylthianaphthene (3.5 g.) is heated with isatin in aq. alc. KOH → 5.5 g. 2-(3-thianaphthenyl)cinchoninic acid. F.e.s. N. P. Buu-Hoï and P. Cagniant, *Rec. trav. chim.* 62, 719 (1943); *C.A. 1944*, 5220. Methods, see Pfitzinger, *J. prakt. Chim.* [2] 38, 583 (1888); 56, 293, (1897).

Alcoholates   *MeOR*

β-Diketones

556.   C$_6$H$_5$COCH$_3$ + C$_6$H$_5$COOC$_2$H$_5$ → C$_6$H$_5$COCH$_2$COC$_6$H$_5$

PhAc and BzOEt are heated to 150–160° with EtONa → CH$_2$Bz$_2$

(dibenzoylmethane). Y = 62–71%. A. Magnani and S. M. McElvain, *Organic Syntheses* 20, 32 (1940); *C.A. 1940*, 5075.

α-Keto Acids

$$\cdot \text{COCOOH}$$

57. $CH_3(CH_2)_{10}COOC_2H_5 + C_2H_5OOC \cdot COOC_2H_5 \rightarrow CH_3(CH_2)_9C : \overset{\cdot}{C} \cdot OC_2H_5 \rightarrow$

$$\begin{array}{c} COOC_2H_5 \\[2pt] COOC_2H_5 \end{array}$$

$$CH_3(CH_2)_{10}COCOOH \quad \longleftarrow \qquad \overset{\cdot}{COOC_2H_5}$$

K, with the calc. amount of abs. EtOH in di-Et ether, is converted to alcohol-free ethylate; oxalo ester and lauric acid ethyl ester in pyridine are added, the mixture is heated at 70° for 100 hrs., poured into dil. H$_2$SO$_4$, saponified, and decarboxylated → α-ketotridecanoic acid. Crude Y = 15%. [For further examples, which give good yields even with simpler methods, see F. Adickes and G. Andresen, *Ann.* 555, 41 (1943); *C.A. 1944*, 1732.]

See also 562.

α-Ketocarboxylic Acid Esters
$\cdot$ COCOOR

See 784.

β-Ketocarboxylic Acid Esters
$\cdot$ CO $\cdot$ CH$_2$ $\cdot$ COOR

Synthesis of Thiophanes
O

$$C_2H_5OOC \cdot CH_2 \, COOC_2H_5 \quad \rightarrow \quad C_2H_5OOCCH-CO$$

58.

2-Carbethoxyethyl-1,5-dicarbethoxyamyl sulfide (prepn., see 480) is treated with NaOEt in toluene at 35° and finally at 45° → Et 2-(4-carbethoxybutyl)thiophan-3-one-4-carboxylate. Y = 82%. This is boiled with a mixture of H$_2$O, glacial AcOH, and H$_2$SO$_4$ → 2-(4-carboxybutyl)-3-thiophanone. Y = 100%. F.e.s. P. Karrer, R. Keller, E. Usteri, *Helv. Chim. Acta* 27, 237 (1944); *C.A. 1944*, 4941. P. Karrer and H. Schmid, *Helv. Chim. Acta* 27, 116, 124 (1944); *C.A. 1944*, 4588. P. Karrer and F. Kehrer, *Helv. Chim. Acta* 27, 142 (1944); *C.A. 1944*, 4591.

$$C_2H_5OOCCH_2 \, COOC_2H_5 \quad \rightarrow \quad C_2H_5OOCCH-CO$$

59.

EtO$_2$CCH$_2$CH$_2$SCH(CH$_2$CH$_2$CH$_2$OMe)CO$_2$Et   is   treated   with

NaOEt in toluene in an N_2 atmosphere → 2-(4-methoxybutyl)-4-carbethoxy-3-thiophanone (Y = 80%), which is boiled with H_2O, glacial AcOH, and H_2SO_4 → 2-(4-methoxybutyl)-3-thiophanone. Y = 77%. H. Schmid, *Helv. Chim. Acta* 27, 127 (1944); *C.A. 1944*, 4589.

α,γ-Diketocarboxylic Acid Esters

560.

$$
\begin{array}{ccccc}
H_2C - CH_2COOC_2H_5 & & H_2C - CH_2 & & H_2C - CH \cdot CO \cdot COOCH_3 \\
| & \rightarrow & |\quad\quad CO & \rightarrow & |\quad\quad CO \\
H_2C - CH_2COOC_2H_5 & & H_2C - CHCOOC_2H_5 & & H_2C - CH \cdot COOCH_3
\end{array}
$$

Di-Et adipate is converted with EtONa in abs. di-Et ether. The ether is distilled off and the product heated for 20 hrs. at 140° → cyclopentanone-α-carboxylate (Y = 75%) with $(CO_2Me)_2$ in the presence of Na methylate → di-Me diketohomonorcamphorcarboxylate. Y = 90%. G. Komppa and A. Talvitie, *Ann. Acad. Sci. Fennicae*, A57, No. 15, 3 (1941); *C.A. 1944*, 5496.

561.

Cyclohexanone in EtONa in di-Et ether is treated with $(CO_2Et)_2$ and CO is subsequently split off by heating at 140–150° → Et cyclohexan-1-one-2-carboxylate (s.m. 575). Y = 60%. Ki-Wei-Hiong, *Ann. chim.* [11] *17*, 269 (1942); *C.A. 1944*, 3269. Methods, see Kotz and Michael, *Ann. 350*, 210 (1906), somewhat changed.

Indole Synthesis

562.

2-Nitro-5-benzyloxytoluene (32.4 g.) (prepn., see 208) with $(CO_2$-Et$)_2$ and EtOK in di-Et ether is allowed to stand for 60 hrs. at room temp. and the ethereal soln. extd. with 4% NaOH → 23.4 g. crude (2-nitro-5-benzyloxyphenyl)pyruvic acid. This is dissolved in NH_4OH, reduced with aq. $FeSO_4$, and finally refluxed for 1 hr. → 5-benzyloxy-2-indolecarboxylic acid (s.m. 14). Y = 70%. F. Bergel and A. L. Morrison, *J. Chem. Soc. 1943*, 49; *C.A. 1943*, 3429 (3417).

α-Cyano Esters of Carboxylic Acid

$$\cdot CH_2CN \rightarrow \begin{array}{c} CH \cdot CN \\ | \\ COOR \end{array}$$

563. The nitrile is heated with an equimol. amt. of EtONa and 4–8 mol. equivs. of Et_2CO_3 → α-cyanocarboxylic acid ester. Higher nitrile

homologues give better yields than low ones. Phenylacetonitriles react easier than aliphatic nitriles. Unsatd. nitriles such as vinylacetonitriles form tars. Na and K alcoholate react equally well, but neither Mg nor Al alcoholate reacted. All the prim. alkyl carbonates react equally well, while sec. alkyl carbonates are not suitable for the reaction. Ex: Butyronitrile $\rightarrow$ NCCHEtCO$_2$Et; Y = 40%. Stearonitrile Et α-cyanostearate; Y = 75%. Phenylacetonitrile $\rightarrow$ PhCH(CN)CO$_2$Et; Y = 78%. p-MeC$_6$H$_4$CH$_2$CN $\rightarrow$ Et cyano(p-methylphenyl)acetate; Y = 87%. V. H. Wallingford, D. M. Jones and A. H. Homeyer, *J. Am. Chem. Soc.* 64, 576 (1942); *C.A.* 1942, 2526.

Alkylation of Monosubstituted Malonic Esters

$$\underset{R}{\overset{H}{>}}C\underset{COOR}{\overset{COOR}{<}} \rightarrow \underset{R}{\overset{R'}{>}}C\underset{COOR}{\overset{COOR}{<}}$$

64. The alkylation of monosubstituted malonic esters with alkyl carbonates is independent of the chain length of the substituents. When the substituent is a sec. aliphatic group, alkylation gives poor yields. Phenyl- and benzyl-substituted malonic esters are readily alkylated. The metal derivs. of the substd. malonic esters are prepd. by the action of metal alcoholates on the ester. In order to force the reaction to completion and avoid by-products, the alc. formed is distilled off under reduced pressure. The metal carbonate is then heated with 5–10 equivs. of alkyl carbonate for 4–5 hrs. at 125–175°. Ex: Diethylethylmalonate $\rightarrow$ diethyl diethylmalonate; Y = 54%. Dibutyl cetylmalonate $\rightarrow$ dibutyl butylcetylmalonate; Y = 83%. Diisoamyl ethylmalonate $\rightarrow$ diisoamyl ethylisoamylmalonate; Y = 60%. Dibutyl benzylmalonate $\rightarrow$ dibutyl benzylbutylmalonate; Y = 80%. F.e.s. V. H. Wallingford and D. M. Jones, *J. Am. Chem. Soc.* 64, 578 (1942); *C.A.* 1942, 2527.

3-Alkylindoles

65. Indoles (frequently also 2-indolecarboxylic acids) are converted to the 3-alkylindoles by heating for 12 hrs. with an alc. EtONa soln. under pressure at 210–220°. Ex: Indole and iso-PrOH in iso-PrONa $\rightarrow$ 3-isopropylindole (Y = 63%); also: 3-butylindole (Y = 62%); 3-benzylindole (Y = 66%). F.e.s. R. H. Cornforth and R. Robinson, *J. Chem. Soc.* 1942, 680; *C.A.* 1943, 884.

Alkali Salts of Organic Acids

α,β-Unsaturated Carboxylic Acids　　　CHO $\rightarrow$ CH : CH $\cdot$ COOH

66.　　　$\underset{O}{\bigcirc}$CHO $\rightarrow$ $\underset{O}{\bigcirc}$CH : CHCOOH

Furfural, Ac$_2$O, and freshly fused AcOK are heated to 150° $\rightarrow$ furylacrylic acid. Y = 65–70%. John R. Johnson, *Organic Syntheses* 20, 55 (1940); *C.A.* 1940, 5078.

Phthalides

567. Phthalic anhydride is treated with valeric anhydride and Na valerate → n-butilydene phthalide. Y = 77%. Y. R. Naves, *Helv. Chim. Acta* **26**, 1281 (1943); *C.A. 1944*, 1072.

α-Aminocarboxylic Acids from Ketones

568.

m-Methoxyphenoxyphenylacetone is heated with KCN and $(NH_4)_2$-CO_3 in an autoclave under 20 atm. CO_2 pressure at 100° → 5-(m-methoxyphenoxymethyl)-5-benzylhydantoin (Y = 85%), which is refluxed in a silver flask with 25% KOH → β-(m-methoxyphenoxy)-β-phenyl-α-aminoisobutyric acid. Y = 95%. P. Pfeiffer and H. Simons, *J. prakt. Chem.* **150**, 83 (1942); *C.A. 1943*, 4067.

Organic bases

1,2-Unsaturated Carboxylic Acids   CHO → CH : CH · COOH

569. $CH_2 : C(CH_3)CHO$ → $CH_2 : C(CH_3)CH : CHCOOH$

Careful Condensation to Compounds that Polymerize Easily

$CH_2(CO_2H)_2$ in pyridine and some piperidine in ice are added dropwise to $CH_2 : CMeCHO$ and, after 1.5 hrs., the mixt. is slowly heated to 50–55° and kept at this temp. for 24 hrs. The reaction product with a satd. $(CO_2H)_2$ soln. is poured into di-Et ether → 2-methyl-1,3-butadiene-4-carboxylic acid (isoprenecarboxylic acid). Y = 50%. T. Lennartz, *Ber.* **76**, 1006 (1943); *C.A. 1944*, 3611.

570.

$4\text{-}(4\text{-MeOC}_6H_4O)C_6H_4CHO$ is heated with $CH_2(CO_2H)_2$ and some piperidine in pyridine → 4-(4-methoxyphenoxy)cinnamic acid. Crude Y = 88%. James Walker, *J. Chem. Soc. 1942*, 347; *C.A. 1942*, 5153.

Alkylideneacetic Acid Ester from Aldehydes   CHO → CH : C(COCH₃)COOR

571. 0.5 mole of $AcCH_2CO_2Et$ and 0.55 mole of aldehyde are treated with

0.5 g. piperidine and 1 g. EtOH at 5–10° → alkylidene acetoacetate.
Ex: PrCHO and $AcCH_2CO_2Et$ → Et butylideneacetoacetate. Y = 81%.
2-Ethylbutanal and $AcCH_2CO_2Et$ → Et 2-ethylbutylideneacetoacetate.
Y = 71%. F.e.s. A. C. Cope and C. M. Hofmann, *J. Am. Chem. Soc. 63*, 3456 (1941); *C.A. 1942*, 1015.

Quinoline Ring   O

572.

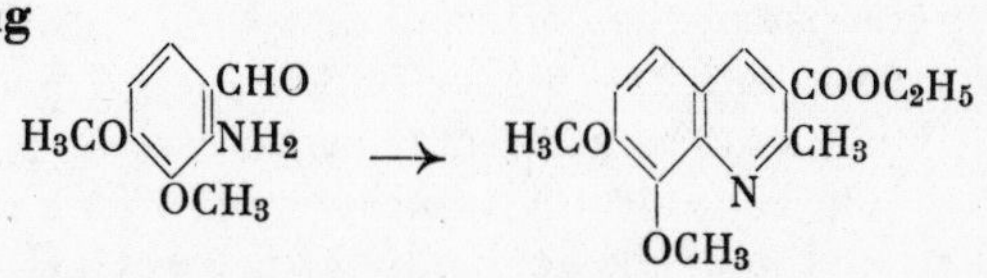

2-Aminoveratraldehyde is heated for 6 hrs. on a water bath with $AcCH_2CO_2Et$ and a few drops of piperidine → Et 2-methyl-7,8-dimethoxy-3-quinolinecarboxylate. Y = 90%. W. Borsche and W. Ried, *Ber. 76B*, 1011 (1943); *C.A. 1944*, 3653.

See also 400.

β,γ-Unsaturated α-Cyanocarboxylic Acid Esters

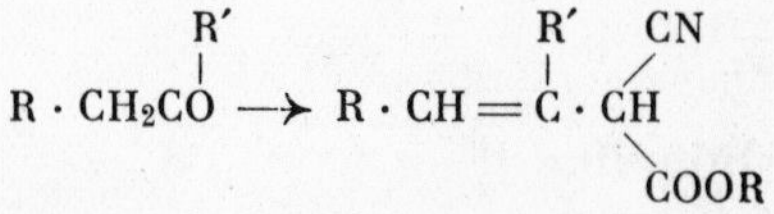

$$R \cdot CH_2CO \xrightarrow{R'} R \cdot CH = \overset{R'}{\underset{}{C}} \cdot \overset{CN}{\underset{COOR}{CH}}$$

573. Methyl *n*-hexyl ketone and Et cyanoacetate are refluxed with piperidine in boiling toluene → Et 2-cyano-3-methyl-Δ^2-nonenoate. Y = 80%. F.e.s. A. J. Birch and R. Robinson, *J. Chem. Soc. 1942*, 3488; *C.A. 1943*, 603.

Pyridones

574.

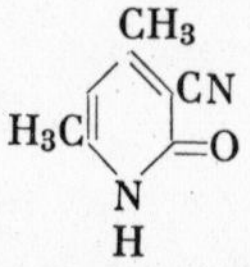

Cyanoacetamide and acetylacetone with C_5H_5N → 4,6-dimethyl-3-cyano-2-pyridone. Y = 87%. A. M. Van Wagtendonk and J. P. Wibaut, *Rec. trav. chim. 61*, 728 (1942).

Calcium oxide   *CaO*

Hydroxy Methylation   H → CH_2OH

575.

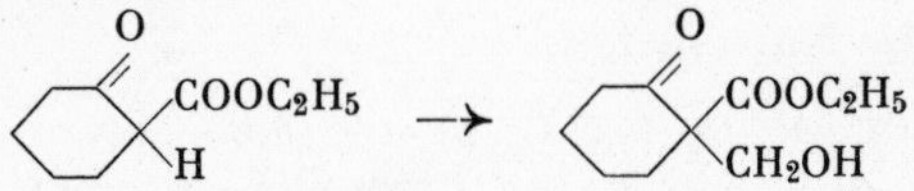

Et cyclohexan-1-one-2-carboxylate (prepn., see 561) is treated with CaO and 35% HCHO below 5° → Et 2-(hydroxymethyl) cyclohexan-1-one-2-carboxylate. Y = nearly 100%. Ki-Wei Hiong, *Ann Chim.* [11] 17, 269 (1942); *C.A. 1944*, 3269.

Zinc dust Zn

New Method for Introduction of Alkyl Groups into 4-Position of Pyridine Molecule

576. In the same manner by which 4-ethylpyridine is prepd. by the action of Zn dust on a mixt. of C_5H_5N, Ac_2O, and AcOH, other 4-alkyl derivs. are prepd. by the use of the corresponding acid anhydrides and acids; the yields decrease with the higher and branched homologues of the anhydrides. It is therefore advantageous to replace the anhydride by the corresponding chloride. The prepn. of 4-(β,β-dimethylpropyl) pyridine failed. Method: The acid anhydride and C_5H_5N are gradually mixed with Zn dust and, after addn. of the corresponding acid, the mixt. is heated to boiling. By addition of further amts. of Zn to the boiling soln. the reduction is completed. Ex: 4-Propylpyridine, $Y = 64\%$; 4-butylpyridine, $Y = 47\%$. F.e.s. J. F. Arens and J. P. Wibaut, *Rec. trav. chim. 61*, 59 (1942); *C.A. 1943*, 5063.

Zinc chloride $ZnCl_2$

Quinoline Ring
See 763.

Nitrostyrylacridines
See 585.

Phenones from Phenols

577.

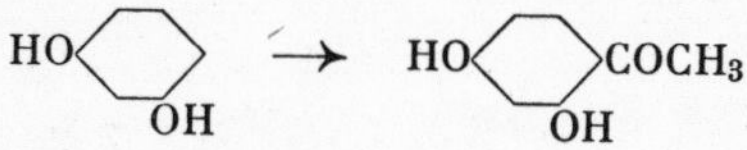

Resorcinol is heated with $ZnCl_2$ in glacial AcOH to 152-159° → 2,4-$(HO)_2C_6H_3Ac$ (resacetophenone). $Y = 61–65\%$. S. R. Cooper, *Organic Syntheses 21*, 103 (1941); *C.A. 1941*, 6249.

Skraup Quinoline Synthesis
See 590.

Boron fluoride BF_3

Alkylation of the Nucleus
$ArH \rightarrow ArR$

578. *p*-Dialkylbenzenes can be prepd. by the monoalkylation of toluene, (or Et benzene), as well as by the direct alkylation of C_6H_6, although this gives lower yields. The alkylation always occurs para to the alkyl group present, except in the ethylation of toluene where the ortho isomer is formed together with the para isomer. *n*-Primary alcohols generally give the highest yields. In the C_4–C_{12} series the yields are

over 80%. Prepn: (1) Alkylation of toluene: BF_3 is rapidly introduced into a cooled and agitated mixture of C_6H_6 and BuOH. P_2O_5 is added in the cold and, after heating at 75–80° for 3 hrs., the mixt. is worked up. Y = 90%. (2) Dialkylation of C_6H_6: BF_3 is introduced into a mixture of C_6H_6 and BuOH. P_2O_5 is added and, after heating at 75° for 2.5 hrs., another mole of BuOH is added in the cold. BF_3 is introduced once again and, after heating for 3.5 hrs., the mixture is worked up. Y = 68%. C. E. Welsh and G. F. Hennion, *J. Am. Chem. Soc. 63, 2603* (1941); *C.A. 1942, 417.*

β-Diketones from Ketones   · CO · CH₂CO ·

79. $CH_3COCH_3 + CH_3COOCOCH_3 \rightarrow CH_3COCH_2COCH_3$

Me_2CO and Ac_2O with $BF_3 \rightarrow CH_2Ac_2$. Y = 80–85%. C. E. Denoon, Jr., *Organic Syntheses 20, 6* (1940); *C.A. 1940, 5053.*

Aluminum chloride $AlCl_3$

Ketones   ArH → ArCOR

80. Toluene and butyric acid after standing with $AlCl_3$ are warmed on a water bath → p-methylbutyrophenone (Y = 72%). Phenetole and isovaleric acid with $AlCl_3$ → p-ethoxyisovalerophenone (Y = 82%) and 9% of p-hydroxyisovalerophenone as a by-product. I. Tsuckervanik and I. Terent'eva, *J. Gen. Chem. U.S.S.R. 11,* 168 (1941); *C.A. 1941,* 3621. F.e.s. M. S. Malinovski and A. A. Ljapina, *J. Gen. Chem. U.S.S.R. 11,* 168 (1941); *C.A. 1941,* 7384. Methods, see Groggius, Nagel and Stirton, *C.Z. 1935 II,* 1159–60.

Aluminum chloride–sodium chloride $AlCl_3$–$NaCl$

Hydroxynaphthoquinones   O

81.

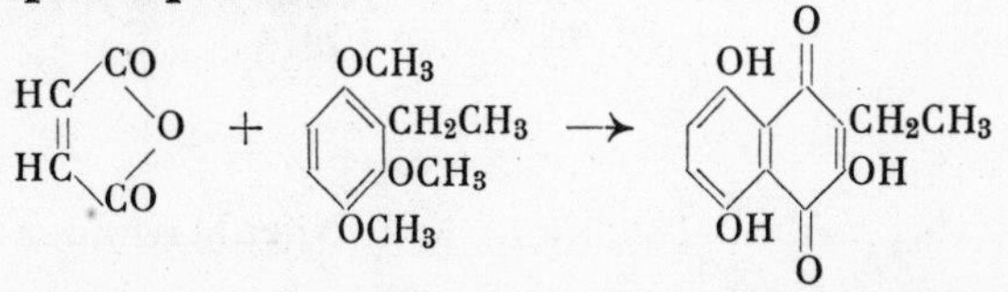

2,3,6-Trimethoxy-1-ethylbenzene (1 g.) is melted together with maleic anhydride and $AlCl_3$–NaCl at 210° → 0.33 g. 2-ethyl-3,5,8-trihydroxy-1,4-naphthoquinone. K. Wallenfels, *Ber. 75,* 785 (1942); *C.A. 1943,* 3425.

Acetic anhydride $(CH_3CO)_2O$
    See 585.

Acetic anhydride–pyridine

Thermolabile Cyanines

582.

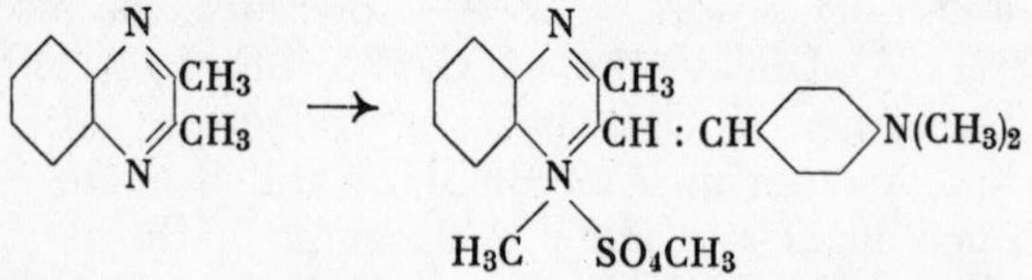

Anhyd. 2,3-dimethoxyquinoxaline is converted to the methosulfate with Me_2SO_4. This is treated with $p\text{-}Me_2NC_6H_4CHO$ in $Ac_2O\text{-}C_5H_5N \rightarrow$ 2-(1,3-dimethylquinoxaline)-1-(4-dimethylaminobenzene)dimethinecyanine methosulfate. Y = 60%. F.e.s. A. H. Cook, J. Garner and C. A. Perry, *J. Chem. Soc. 1942*, 710; *C.A. 1943*, 1433.

Acetic anhydride–acetyl chloride

Cyanines

583.

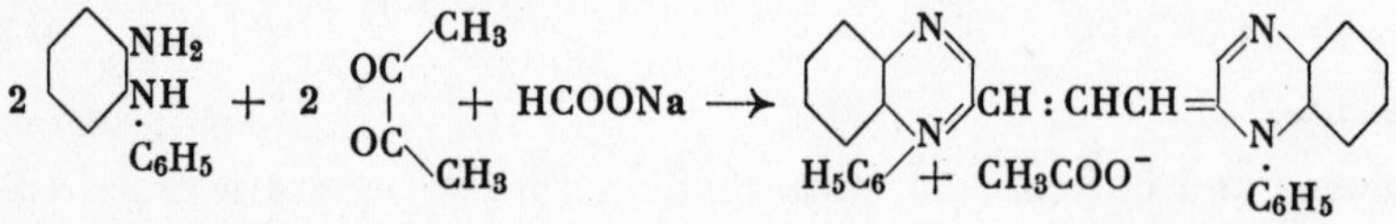

AcCl, Ac_2O, and HCO_2Na are added to the condensation product of $o\text{-}H_2NC_6H_4NHPh$ and $Ac_2 \rightarrow$ bis-2-(1-phenyl-3-methylquinoxaline)-trimethincyanine acetate. F.e.s. A. H. Cook, J. Garner and C. A. Perry, *J. Chem. Soc. 1942*, 710; *C.A. 1943*, 1433.

Stannic chloride $SnCl_4$

Chloromethylation $\cdot H \rightarrow \overset{*}{\cdot} CH_2Cl$

584. 2,4,6-Triisopropylbenzene is treated with $ClCH_2OMe$ and $SnCl_4$ in $CS_2 \rightarrow$ 2,4,6-triisopropylbenzyl chloride. Y = 85%. R. Fuson and co-workers, *J. Am. Chem. Soc. 64*, 30 (1942); *C.A. 1942*, 1307. Methods, see S. Sommelet, *Compt. rend. 157*, 1443 (1913).

Acetic anhydride $(CH_3CO)_2O$

Condensation of 9-Methylacridines with Nitrobenzaldehydes

585.

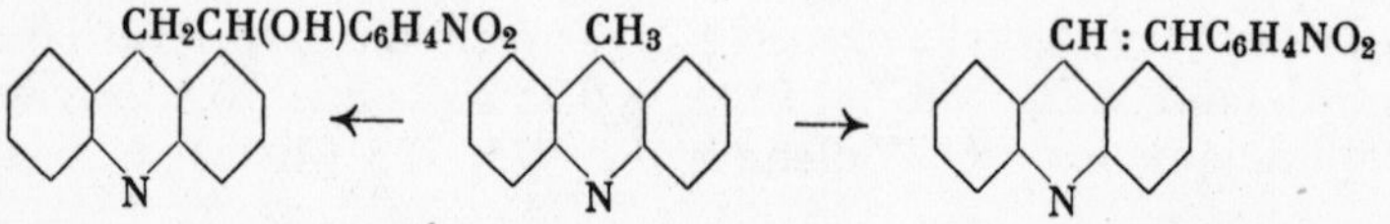

1. Without condensing reagents: 9-methylacridine (I) and $o\text{-}O_2NC_6H_4CHO$ are heated at 100° for 6 hrs. $\rightarrow$ 1-(o-nitrophenyl)-2-(9-acridyl)ethanol. Y = 81%. The reactions with m-nitrobenzaldehyde

(Y = 76%) and *p*-nitrobenzaldehyde (Y = 81%) proceed in the same manner.

2. With ZnCl$_2$: *m*-O$_2$NC$_6$H$_4$CHO and 9-methylacridine are heated at 130° for 3 hrs. with anhyd. ZnCl$_2$ → 9-*m*-nitrostyrylacridine; Y = 64%. Also (I) and *p*-nitrobenzaldehyde → 9-*p*-nitrostyrylacridine; Y = 90%. *o*-Nitrostyrylacridine could not be prepared.

3. With Ac$_2$O: 2.38 g. 3-NO$_2$-9-methylacridine (II) is heated with *p*-O$_2$NC$_6$H$_4$CHO in Ac$_2$O at 130° for 3 hrs. → 1.7 g. *β*-nitro-*p*-nitrostyrylacridine. No reaction or resins are obtained when (II) is heated with *p*-nitrobenzaldehyde alone or when ZnCl$_2$ is added. F.e.s. W. Sharp, M. M. J. Sutherland and F. J. Wilson, *J. Chem. Soc. 1943*, 5; *C.A. 1943*, 2009. *J. Chem. Soc. 1943*, 344; *C.A. 1943*, 6666.

Ammonium acetate, piperidine acetate

Alkalidene Cyanoacetic and Malonic Esters

86. Alkalidenecyanoacetic esters are prepd. from cyanoacetic esters with aliphatic and aromatic ketones in the presence of AcONH$_4$ and AcOH; alkalidenemalonic esters are prepd. from malonic esters and aliphatic aldehydes with piperidine acetate and AcOH. The condensation succeeded by 4 methods (see *C.A.* and original). Ex: Me Pr ketone and cyanoacetic isopropylate → 1-methylbutylidene deriv.; Y = 80–85%. Propiophenone and cyanoacetic ester → 1-phenylpropylidene deriv.; Y = 73%. Ph$_2$CO and cyanoacetic Et ester → 1-phenylbenzylidene deriv.; Y = 66%. Caproaldehyde and malonic ester → hexylidene deriv.; Y = 40–46%. A. C. Cope and co-workers, *J. Am. Chem. Soc. 63*, 3452 (1941); *C.A. 1942*, 1011.

Acetic acid　　　　　　　　　　　　　　　　　　　　　　　　　CH$_3$COOH

Pyrrole Ring　　　　　　　　　　　　　　　　　　　　　　　　　O

CH$_3$COCH$_2$COOC$_2$H$_5$ ⟶ CH$_3$COC(NOH)COOC$_2$H$_5$ ⟶

87.　H$_3$C⎡￣￣⎤COCH$_3$　CH$_3$COCH$_2$COCH$_3$

　C$_2$H$_5$OOC⎣N⎦CH$_3$　　　　　　←　CH$_3$COCH(NH$_2$)COOC$_2$H$_5$ ←
　　　　　　H

AcCH$_2$CO$_2$Et in glacial AcOH is treated with NaNO$_2$ at a low temp., and the isonitroso compound reduced directly with Zn dust in the presence of Ac$_2$CH$_2$ → 2,4-dimethyl-3-acetyl-5-carbethoxypyrrole. Y = 55–60%. H. Fischer, *Organic Syntheses 21*, 67 (1941); *C.A. 1941*, 6257.

Stannic chloride　　　　　　　　　　　　　　　　　　　　　　　SnCl$_4$
　See 584.

Sulfuric acid H_2SO_4

Bis-arylethanes

588. 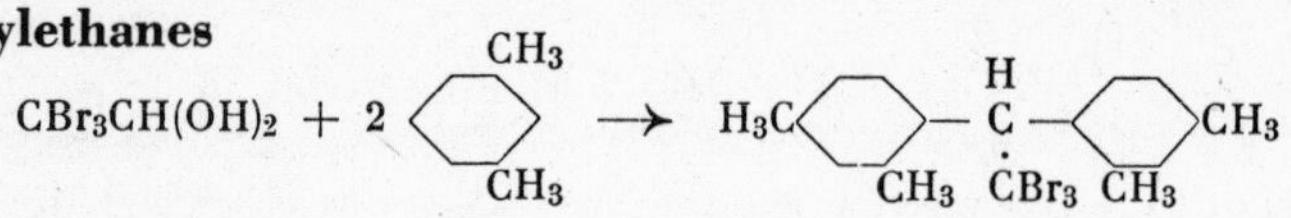 $CBr_3CH(OH)_2 + 2$

$Br_3CCH(OH)_2$ and 2 moles $m\text{-}C_6H_4Me_2$ are condensed with concd. $H_2SO_4 \rightarrow$ 1,1-bis(2,4-xylyl)-2,2,2-tribromoethane. Y = 70–80%. F.e.s. K. Brand and A. Busse Sundermann, *Ber.* 75B, 1819 (1943); *C.A. 1944*, 1491.

Benzanthrones   O

589.

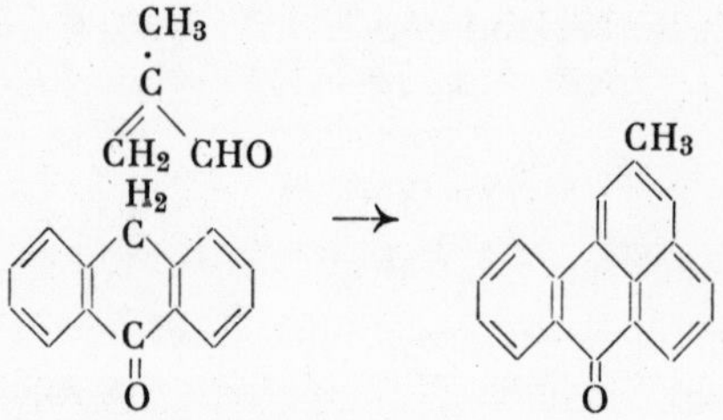

A soln. of $CH_2 : CMeCHO$ in dioxane is stirred into a soln. of anthrone in glacial AcOH and H_2SO_4 (d. 1.53) over a period of 20 min. at 80° → 2-methyl-*meso*-benzanthrone (s.m. 192, 414, 727). Y= 50–60%. D. H. Hey, A. J. Nicholls and C. W. Pritchett, *J. Chem. Soc. 1944*, 97; *C.A. 1944*, 3644.

Skraup Quinoline Synthesis

590.

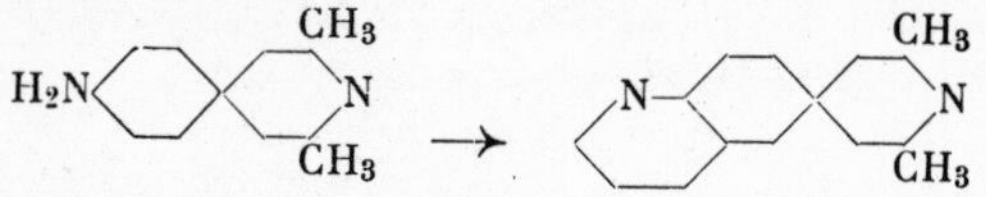

m-Aminobenzoic acid is boiled with nitrobenzene, glycerin, $B(OH)_3$ and concd. $H_2SO_4 \rightarrow$ quinoline-5-carboxylic acid. Y = 95%. 4-(*p*-Aminophenyl)-2,6-dimethylpyridine is boiled with 66% H_2SO_4, glycerin, and the sodium salt of *m*-nitrobenzenesulfonic acid → 6-lutidyl-quinoline. Y = 71%. F.e.s. A. H. Cook, I. M. Heilbron and L. Steger, *J. Chem. Soc. 1943*, 413; *C.A. 1944*, 104.

Coumarin Ring

591.

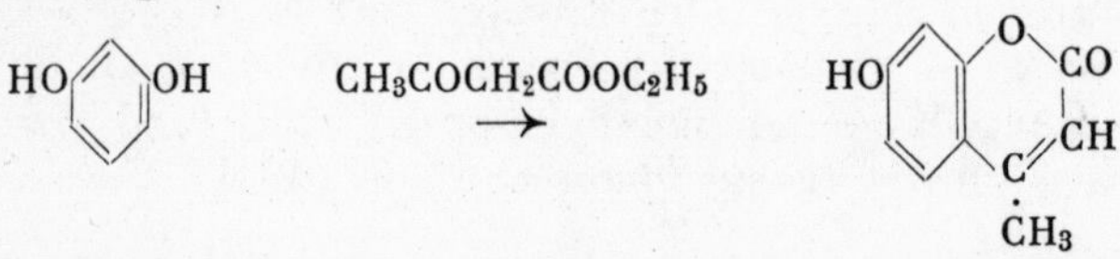

Resorcinol in $AcCH_2CO_2Et$ is added to a cooled soln. of concd. H_2SO_4 → 4-methyl-7-hydroxycoumarin (s.m. 174). Crude Y = 82–90%.

A. Russell and J. R. Frye, *Organic Syntheses 21*, 22 (1941); *C.A. 1941*, 6249.

Hydrochloric acid   *HCl*

Methylation   ArH → ArCH₃

92.

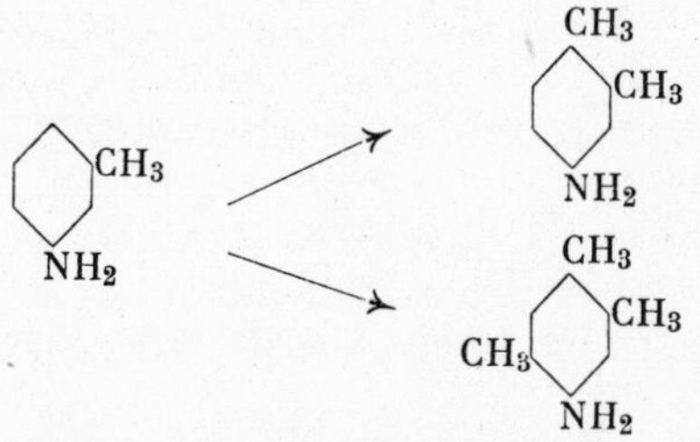

m-MeC₆H₄NH₂ · HCl is heated for several hrs. with 1 mole MeOH at 210–235° in an autoclave → 26–35% 3,4-Me₂C₆H₃NH₂; with 3 moles MeOH → 3,4,6-Me₂C₆H₃NH₂. Y = 54%. No phenolic by-products are formed by this method. R. W. Cripps and D. H. Hey, *J. Chem. Soc. 1943*, 14; *C.A. 1943*, 1997.

Chloromethylation   ArH → ArCH₂Cl

593.

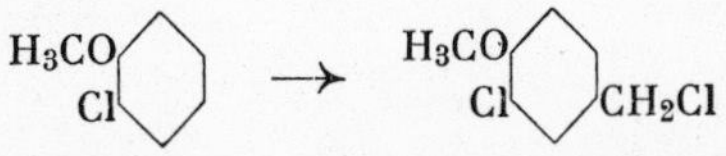

o-Chloroanisole is heated on a steam bath with 40% HCHO while HCl is passed through the soln. → 3-chloro-4-methoxybenzyl chloride. Y = 90%. O. Hromatka, *Ber. 75*, 123 (1942); *C.A. 1943*, 3419.

594.

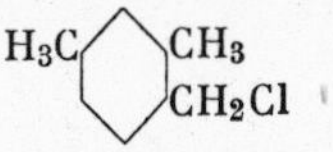

m-C₆H₄Me₂ is treated with HCHO and concd. gaseous HCl → 2,4-dimethylbenzyl chloride. Y = 66%. When ZnCl₂ was added, the yield dropped to 30%. F.e.s. D. V. Nightingale and O. G. Shanholtzer, *J. Org. Chem. 7*, 6 (1942); *C.A. 1942*, 1912. Methods, see Braun and Neller, *Ber. 67*, 1094; *C.A. 28*, 5415.

595.

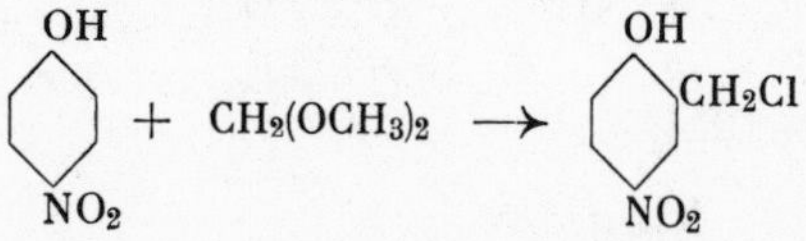

A mixture of p-O₂NC₆H₄OH, conc. HCl, some concd. H₂SO₄, and methylal is stirred at 70 ± 2°, while HCl is bubbled through → 2,5-HO(O₂N)C₆H₃CH₂Cl. Y = 69%. C. A. Buehler, F. K. Kirchner and G. F. Deebel, *Organic Syntheses 20*, 59 (1940); *C.A. 1940*, 5061. Methods, see German Pat. 132,475; *Friedländer 6*, 142 (1904).

Methylation

596.

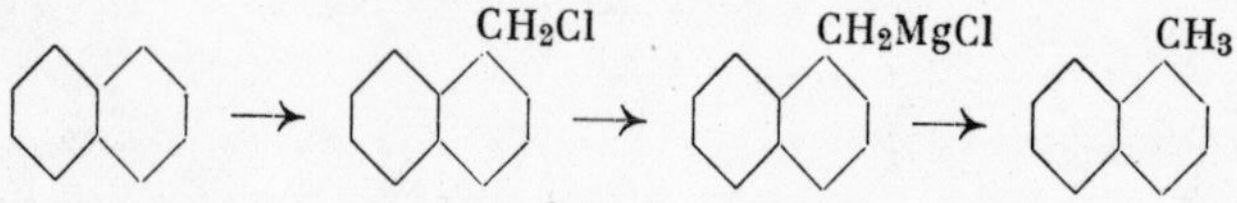

$C_{10}H_8$ is heated for 6 hrs. at 80–85° with paraformaldehyde, glacial AcOH, concd. HCl, and 85% H_3PO_4 (modified method of Cambron, *C.A. 1939*, 5387) → 1-$C_{10}H_7CH_2Cl$ (Y = 70–72%), which is dissolved in ether, added dropwise to a mixt. of Mg in ether while stirred and heated for 1 hr. → 1-$C_{10}H_7CH_2MgBr$ (88–92%) which is refluxed for 1 hr. with NH_4Cl soln. → 1-methylnaphthalene. Y = 80%. O. Grummitt and A. C. Buck, *J. Am. Chem. Soc. 65*, 295 (1943); *C.A. 1943*, 1712.

597.

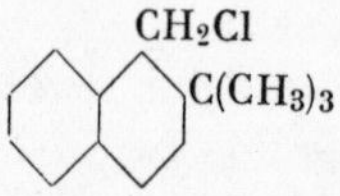

tert-β-Butylnaphthalene is chloromethylated for 15 hrs. at 50° followed by 8 hrs. at room temp. → 1-chloromethyl-2-*tert*-butylnaphthalene. Y = 91%. Buu-Hoi and P. Cagniant, *Rev. Sci. Instruments 30*, 271 (1942).

598.

Thiophene is treated with gaseous HCl and HCHO in concd. HCl soln. at 0–5° → thienylmethyl chloride (Y = 40%) and di-2-thienylmethane. Y = 38%. F. F. Blicke and J. H. Burckhalter, *J. Am. Chem. Soc. 64*, 477 (1942); *C.A. 1942*, 2551.

Amines

599.

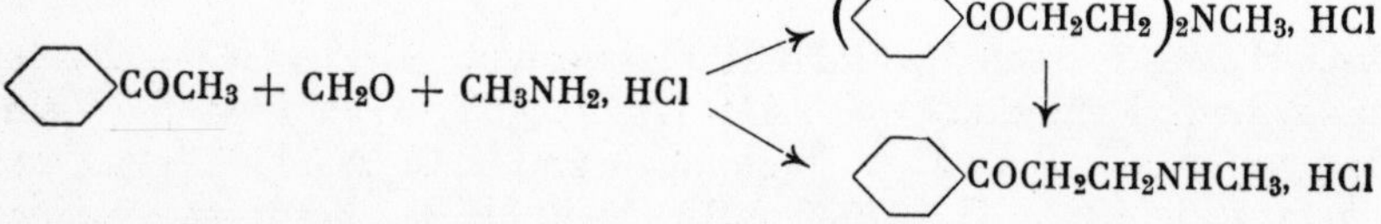

PhAc, HCHO, and $MeNH_2$ · HCl → 43% $(BzCH_2CH_2)_2NMe$ · HCl (I) and 29% $BzCH_2CH_2NHMe$ · HCl (II). (I) is steam distilled → 78% (II). F. F. Blicke and J. H. Burckhalter, *J. Am. Chem. Soc. 64*, 45 (1942); *C.A. 1942*, 1914.

Tetrahydropyridine Ring

600.

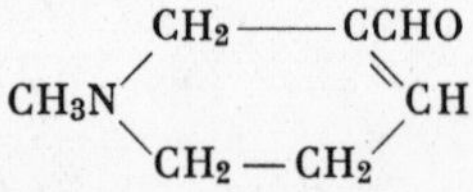

$MeNH_2$ · HCl (34 g.), HCHO, AcH, and H_2O are heated for 15 hrs.

in a champagne bottle at 70° → 15 g. crude arecaidic aldehyde.
C. Mannich, *Ber. 75, 1480* (1943); *C.A. 1944,* 1241.

601.

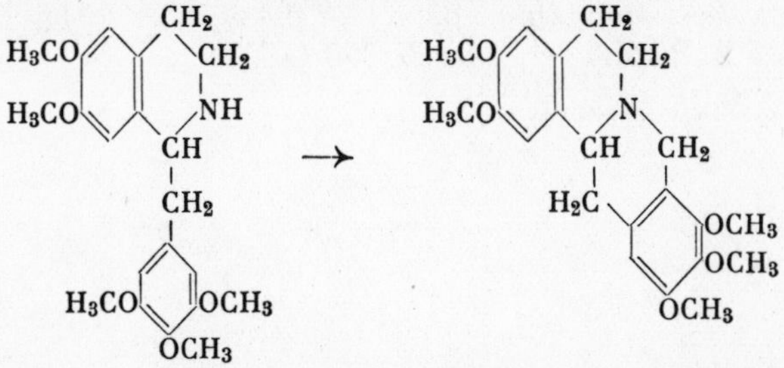

6,7-Dimethoxy-1-(3,4,5-trimethoxybenzyl)-1,2,3,4-tetrahydroisoquino-
line is allowed to stand for 3 days with a slight excess of HCHO in
MeOH at 18° and then warmed with HCl (1:1) on a steam bath →
2,3,11,12,13-pentamethoxyberbine hydrochloride. Y = 42%. E. Späth
and T. Meinhard, *Ber. 75B,* 400 (1942); *C.A. 1943,* 3099.

Styryl Benzothiazoles

602. 2-Methylbenzothiazole and *p*-Me$_2$NC$_6$H$_4$CHO in concd. HCl are
heated at 100° for 16 hrs. → 2-(*p*-dimethylaminostyrylbenzothiazole).
Y = 78%. L. G. S. Brooker and R. H. Sprague, *J. Am. Chem. Soc. 63,*
3203 (1941); *C.A. 1942,* 468.

Benzopyrylium Salts   O

603.

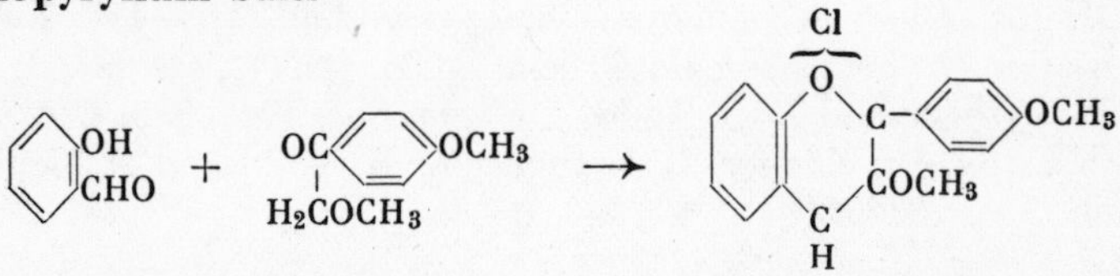

BzCH$_2$OMe and an equimolar amt. of *o*-HOC$_6$H$_4$CHO are dissolved
in glacial AcOH and dry HCl is passed through the soln. → 2-phenylyl-
3,4'-dimethoxybenzopyrylium chloride. Y = nearly quant. F.e.s.
P. Karrer, C. Trugenberger and G. Hamdi, *Helv. Chim. Acta 26,* 2116
(1943); *C.A. 1944,* 3980. See also *Helv. Chim. Acta 28,* 444 (1945).

Nitrogen ⋏   CC ⫻ N

Without additional reagents

Phenylation of the Nucleus   · H → · C$_6$H$_5$

604.

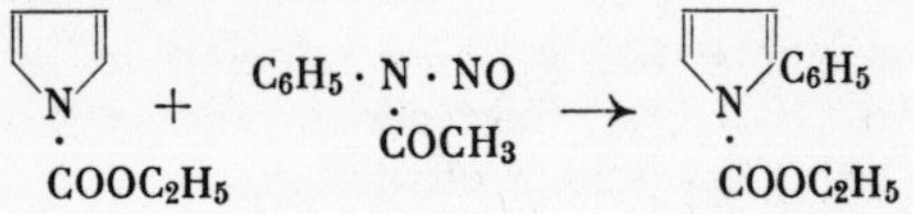

Et 1-pyrrolecarboxylate (32 g.) is mixed with PhNAcNO at 0° and kept at that temp. for 4 days → 6 g. Et 2-phenyl-1-pyrrolecarboxylate. I. J. Rinkes, *Rec. trav. chim. 62*, 116 (1943); *C.A. 1944*, 1741. For methods, see B. Bamberger, *Ber. 30*, 366 (1897).

Carbazoles from Triazoles
    See 614.

Sodium   *Na*
    See 606.

Sodium hydroxide   *NaOH*
    See 610.

Sodium ethylate   *NaOR*

Pyrimidine Ring   O

605.

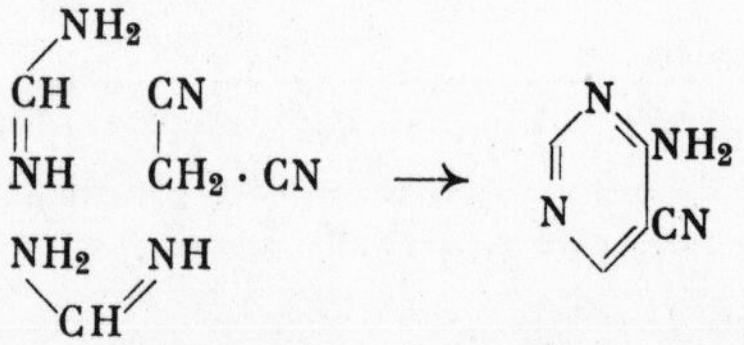

HN : CHNH$_2$–HCl and CH$_2$(CN)$_2$ are allowed to stand with EtONa in EtOH for 24 hrs. → 4-amino-5-cyanopyrimidine. Y = 45%. For the condensation of phenylazomalonitrile and CH$_2$(CN)$_2$, see 398. J. Baddiley, B. Lythgoe and A. R. Todd, *J. Chem. Soc. 1943*, 386; *C.A. 1943*, 6667. F.e.s. G. W. Kenner, B. Lythgoe, A. R. Todd and A. Topham, *J. Chem. Soc. 1943*, 388; *C.A. 1943*, 6668.

Sodamide   *NaNH$_2$*

Synthesis of Substances Related to the Sterols   •O

606.

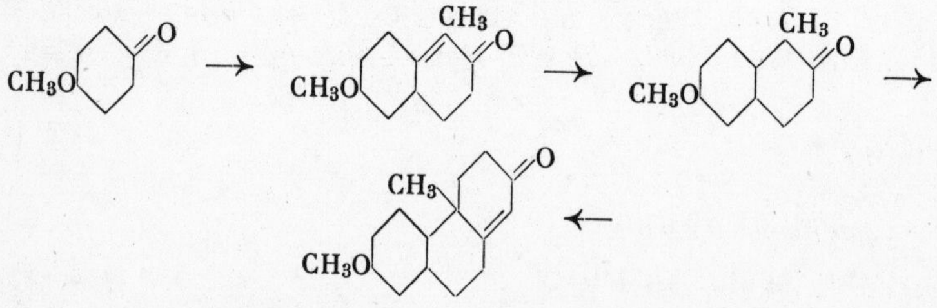

4-Methoxycyclohexanone (12 g.) is condensed in an aq. soln. with Et$_2$NH·HCl and (HCHO)$_x$; the reaction product is converted to the methyl iodide (100 g.) and 20 g. of the latter is boiled with Et sodioβ-ketovalerate, which is prepd. from Na and the ester → 4 g. 6-methoxy-1-methyl-$\Delta^{1,9}$-2-octalone; 2.3 g. of this is hydrogenated with 2% Pd–SrCO$_3$ for 24 hrs. at 3 atm. pressure → 2 g. 6-methoxy-1-methyl-2-decalone. Its Na deriv. (prepd. by refluxing with NaNH$_2$ in Et$_2$O) is refluxed with AcCH$_2$CH$_2$NEt$_2$ · MeI → 0.7 g. 2-keto-7-methoxy-12-methyl-$\Delta^{1,11}$-dodecahydrophenanthrene, together with 1 g. of unchanged ketone. F.e.s. J. G. Cook and R. Robinson, *J. Chem. Soc. 1941*, 391; *C.A. 1941*, 6966. R. Ghosh and R. Robinson, *J. Chem. Soc. 1944*, 506; *C.A. 1945*, 937.

Sodium nitrite   NaNO$_2$

Union of Aryl Nuclei
Via Triazenes

7.

Arom. amines are diazotized and converted with Me$_2$NH to the corresponding 1-aryl-3,3-dimethyltriazenes. From these, the diaryl derivs. are obtained in satisfactory yields by heating with arom. compounds such as C$_6$H$_6$, PhNO$_2$, C$_5$H$_5$N, 2-methoxynaphthalene in the presence of an acid. Method: After the diazonium soln. has been added dropwise to the NaOH–Me$_2$NH soln., the triazenes formed are dissolved in the second solvent and decomposed by introduction of HCl or gradual addition of glacial AcOH at 90–100°. Ex: Aniline → 1-phenyl-3,3-dimethyltriazene (Y = 93%) with AcOH and C$_6$H$_6$ → diphenyl (Y = 37%). Di-Me 4-aminophthalate → di-Me 1-phenyl-3,3-dimethyltriazene-3′,4′-dicarboxylate (Y = 84%), which with HCl → di-Me 4-phenylphthalate (Y = 66%). F.e.s. J. Elks and D. H. Hey, *J. Chem. Soc. 1943*, 441; *C.A. 1944*, 74.

Via Diazonium Salts

8.

8-Amino-6-methoxyquinoline (20 g.) is diazotized in HCl and the diazonium salt soln. is stirred into pyridine over a period of 1.5 hrs. at 40–50° → 10 g. 6-methoxy-8-α(β and γ)-pyridylquinoline. F.e.s. H. Coates, A. H. Cook, I. M. Heilbron, D. H. Hey, A. Lambert and F. B. Lewis, *J. Chem. Soc. 1943*, 404; *C.A. 1944*, 103.

Sodium acetate   Na(CH$_3$COO)
   See 619.

Piperidine

Quinoline Syntheses with Azomethines. Acridines

609.

In the Friedländer synthesis of quinoline, the 2-aminobenzaldehydes which are difficult to obtain can be replaced by their azomethines. This method can also be used to synthesize such polycyclic quinoline analogues as acridines. Ex: 2-NH$_2$C$_6$H$_4$CH : NC$_6$H$_4$-4'-Me and dihydrodimethylresorcinol are heated on a water bath for 8 hrs. with a little piperidine → 4-keto-2,2-dimethyl-1,2,3,4-tetrahydroacridine. Y = 80%. F.e.s. W. Borsche, M. Wagner-Roemmich and J. Barthenheier, *Ann. 550*, 160 (1942); *C.A. 1943*, 1435. Methods, see Borsche and Barthenheier; *C.A. 1943*, 5044.

610.

3,4,6-H$_2$N(MeO)$_2$C$_6$H$_2$CH : NC$_6$H$_4$Me is heated for 6 hrs. with AcCO$_2$H in aq. alc. NaOH on a water bath → 6,7-dimethoxyquinaldic acid (Y = 75%) of which 4.66 g. is heated with Cu-bronze at 225° until the gas evoln. ceases → 3 g. 6,7-dimethoxyquinoline which is heated at 180–190° with C$_5$H$_5$N · HCl [Prey, *Ber.* 74, 1219 (1941)] → 6,7-dihydroxyquinoline. Nonsubstituted quinaldic acid, nevertheless, can only be prepd. from 2-aminobenzaldehyde and not from 2-amino-benzal-4-toluidine. The authors investigated this limitation of the Borsche-Barthenheier modified Friedländer synthesis thoroughly.

3-Acylquinoline can easily be prepd. via the 3-acylquinaldic acid esters. They cannot be synthesized from 1,3-ketoaldehydes (hydroxymethylene ketones) with 2-aminobenzaldehyde. Ex: 6,3,4-H$_2$N-(MeO)$_2$C$_6$H$_2$CH : NC$_6$H$_4$Me is heated with AcCH$_2$COCO$_2$Et and a few drops of piperidine → Et 3-acetyl-6,7-dimethoxyquinaldate which is saponified with alc. aq. KOH to the free acid. This decomposes on melting at 190° → 3-acetyl-6,7-dimethoxyquinoline. Also: 2-Substd. 3-acylquinolines: Aminoveratraltoluidine and acetylacetone → 3-acetyl-6,7-dimethoxyquinaldine; Y = 90%. 2-Aryl-3-quinolinecarboxylate : aminobenzaltoluidine and BzCH$_2$CO$_2$Et → Et 2-phenyl-3-quinolinecarboxylate; Y = 90%. W. Borsche and W. Ried, *Ann. 554*, 269 (1943); *C.A. 1943*, 6265.

1. (2-Aminobenzal)-*p*-toluidine (21 g.) is heated with $AcCH_2CO_2Et$ and some piperidine for 24 hrs. on a steam bath → 19 g. 3-quinaldine-carboxylic acid Et ester. W. Borsche, W. Doeller and M. Wagner-Roemmich, *Ber. 76*, 1099 (1943); *C.A. 1944*, 4947.

Phosphorus oxychloride $POCl_3$

Introduction of Aldehyde Group in Aromatic Nuclei $\cdot H \to \cdot CHO$

2. $ArH + C_6H_5N(CH_3)CHO \longrightarrow ArCHO$

Anthracene and methylformanilide are heated with $POCl_3$ in o-$C_6H_4Cl_2$ for 1–2 hrs. at 90–95° → 9-anthraldehyde (Y = 74–84%). Also: β-$C_{10}H_7OEt$ → 1,2-$EtOC_{10}H_6CHO$ (Y = 74–84%). Only labile hydrogen atoms can be replaced by the aldehyde radical. L. F. Fieser and co-workers, *Organic Syntheses 20*, 11 (1940); *C.A. 1940*, 5075.

Copper Cu

Diazo Coupling

3.

p-Nitroaniline is diazotized and added to cynnamylideneacrylic acid in acetone in the presence of $CuCl_2$ and NaOAc → 1-(p-nitrophenyl)-4-phenyl-1,3-butadiene. Y = 25%. F.e.s. F. Bergmann and Z. Weinberg, *J. Org. Chem. 6*, 134 (1941); *C.A. 1941*, 2496. For methods, see Meerwein and co-workers, *C.A. 1940*, 2325.

Graebe-Ullman Synthesis of Carbazoles from Triazoles

4.

Contrary to previous experience, carbazoles can also be prepd. from triazoles with unsatd. substituents such as NO_2, $COCH_3$, and CN in the benzene ring. The reaction does not proceed as smoothly, how-ever, as with satd. substituents such as NH_2 or alkyl. Ex: 7-Nitro-1-phenylbenzotriazole is heated with Cu → 1-nitrocarbazole (Y = 18%). 5-Acetyl-1-phenyl-1,2,3-benzotriazole (prepn., see 263) is heated over a free flame → 3-acetylcarbazole (Y = 22%). R. W. G. Preston, S. H. Tucker and J. M. L. Cameron, *J. Chem. Soc. 1942*, 500; *C.A. 1943*, 642.

Mercuric oxide   *HgO*

Symmetrical Dialkyldiaryl Ethylene Compounds

615.

$$Br\langle\bigcirc\rangle COCH_2CH_3 \rightarrow \rangle C=N\cdot N=C\langle \rightarrow \rangle C=N\cdot NH_2$$

$$\rangle C=C\langle \leftarrow \rangle C-C\langle_{SO_2} \leftarrow \left[\rangle C\langle^N_N\right]$$

p-BrC$_6$H$_4$COEt is refluxed with N$_2$H$_4\cdot$H$_2$O in abs. EtOH → p-bromopropiophenone azine (Y = nearly quant.), which is heated with N$_2$H$_4$ at 120–130° for 30 hrs. → p-bromopropiophenone hydrazone (Y = 90%). The latter is shaken with HgO in petroleum ether, SO$_2$. is introduced into the red soln., and the crude sulfone is converted thermally → 1,1′-bis(p-bromophenyl)-1,1′-diethylethylene (Y = 70%). The hydrazone can also be prepd. directly from the ketone. F.e.s. L. Vargha and E. Kovács, *Ber. 75*, 794 (1942); *C.A. 1943*, 3424. For methods, see Staudinger and Pfeninger, *Ber. 49*, 1946 (1916).

Zinc Salts   *Zn^{++}*

Gatterman-Koch Syntheses
Aldehydes
                                     ArH → ArCHO

616. Further improvements of the modified method by Adams and Montgomery [*J. Am. Chem. Soc. 46*, 1518 (1924); *C.A. 1924*, 2144] include increasing the temp. to 70° and use of C$_2$H$_2$Cl$_4$ as solvent. Prepn: HCl is passed into the mixt. of 0.5 mole hydrocarbon and 1 mole Zn(CN)$_2$ in C$_2$H$_2$Cl$_4$ until the cyanide is decompd.; the mixt. is cooled to 0°, 1 mole AlCl$_3$ is added, and HCl is introduced for 8 hrs. at 70°; after pouring it onto ice and HCl and allowing it to stand overnight, the mixt. is refluxed for 3 hrs. and worked up as usual. Ex: Mesitylene → mesitaldehyde; Y = 82%. 2,4,6-Triethylbenzene → 2,4,6-triethylbenzaldehyde; Y = 70%. 2,4,6-Triisopropylbenzene → 2,4,6-triisopropylbenzaldehyde; Y = 65%. Guaiene → guaialdehyde; Y = 38%. R. C. Fuson and co-workers, *J. Am. Chem. Soc. 64*, 30 (1942); *Organic Syntheses 23*, 57 (1943); *C.A. 1942*, 1307. For methods, see Gattermann, *Ann. 357*, 313 (1907). Hinkel, Ayling and Beynon, *J. Chem. Soc. 1936*, 339; *C.A. 1936*, 2925.

617.

$$\underset{HO\langle\bigcirc\rangle OH}{\overset{CH_3}{}} \rightarrow \underset{HO\langle\bigcirc\rangle OH}{\overset{CH_3\ \ CHO}{}} \rightarrow \underset{HO\langle\bigcirc\rangle OH}{\overset{CH_3\ \ CH_3}{}}$$

Introduction of Methyl Group into Aromatic Nuclei

Orcine (3,5-dihydroxytoluene) is treated with Zn(CN)$_2$ and HCl →

2-formyl-3,5-dihydroxytoluene (Y = 60%), which is treated with Zn amalgam in HCl (Clemmensen reduction) → 1,2-dimethyl-3,5-dihydroxybenzene. Y = 72%. J. Strating and H. J. Backer, *Rec. trav. chim.* 62, 57 (1943); *C.A. 1945*, 2497.

Ketones   ArH → ArCOR

8.

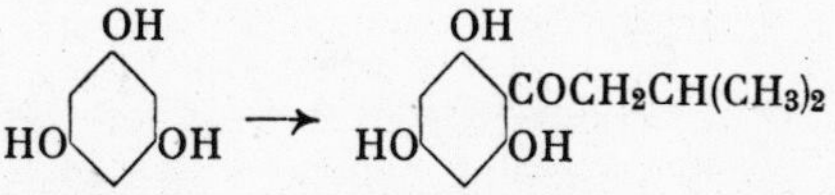

Anhyd. 1,3,5-C$_6$H$_3$(OH)$_3$ (15.7 g.), 10.4 g. iso-BuCN and anhyd. ZnCl$_2$ in abs. ether are satd. with HCl gas → 6 g. 2,4,6-trihydroxyisovalerophenone. E. Späth and K. Eiter, *Ber.* 74, 1851 (1941); *C.A. 1942*, 5817.

2,3-Substituted Quinolines and Acridines   O
See 620.

Acetic anhydride   (CH$_3$CO)$_2$O

Cyanine Dyes

9.

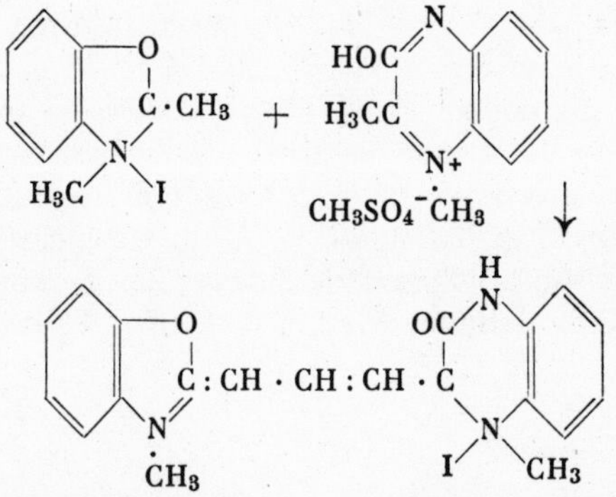

2-Methylbenzothiazole–MeI (2 g.) is boiled with Ac$_2$O and diphenylformamidine; NaAc and the Me$_2$SO$_4$ of 3-hydroxy-2-methylquinoxaline are added, and the soln. is boiled again → 1.7 g. [2-(3-hydroxy-1-methylquinoxaline)] [2-(1-methylbenzylthiazole)] trimethine cyanine iodide. A. H. Cook and C. A. Perry, *J. Chem. Soc. 1943*, 394; *C.A. 1944*, 362.

Hydrochlorides of bases

2,3-Substituted Quinolines and Acridines   O

20.

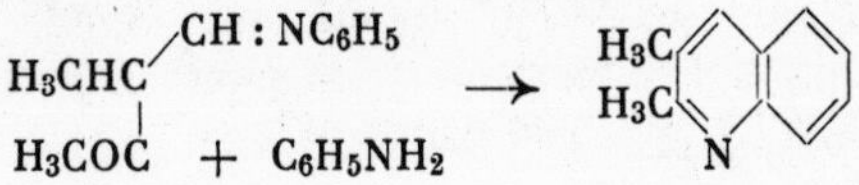

Anils are obtained in quant. yields from aliphatic β-keto aldehydes and primary arom. amines in alc. These anils when refluxed for 8–12 hrs. with 1–2 mols. of amine $\cdot$ HCl (and $ZnCl_2$ where needed) in abs. alc. give 2,3-substd. quinolines in yields up to 65%. Ex: 3-(Phenyl-iminomethyl)butan-2-one $\rightarrow$ 2,3-dimethylquinoline.

1-(m-Tolyliminomethyl)cyclohexan-2-one $\rightarrow$ 8-methyl-1,2,3,4-tetra-hydroacridine. F.e.s. V. A. Petrow, *J. Chem. Soc. 1942*, 693.

Boric acid H_3BO_3

Introduction of Aldehyde Group into Aromatic Nuclei $\cdot$ H $\rightarrow$ $\cdot$ CHO

621. **New General Method for Preparation of o-Hydroxyaldehydes from Phenols and Hexamethylene Tetramine.** o-Hydroxyaldehydes can be obtained by heating phenols with $(CH_2)_6N_4$ in the presence of H_3BO_3 and anhydrous glycerin. The yields are better than those obtained by using other anhyd. acid media, such as Ac_2O. Prepn: 150 g. $C_3H_5(OH)_3$ and 35 g. H_3BO_3 are heated for 30 min. at 170°, 25 g. $(CH_2)_6N_4$ is added, and (at 150–160°) 25 g. PhOH is added. After 15 min. 30 ml. concd. H_2SO_4 in 100 ml. H_2O are added at 110° and the aldehyde is steam distilled. 16 o-hydroxyaldehydes were prepd. Ex: 25 g. cresol $\rightarrow$ 4.5 g. 3,2-Me(HO)C_6H_3CHO and 1.5 g. diformyl-o-cresol. 25 g. carvacrol $\rightarrow$ 7.5 g. carvacrolaldehyde (2-hydroxy-3-methyl-6-isopropylbenzaldehyde). 25 g. naphthol $\rightarrow$ 8 g. 2-hydroxy-1-naphthaldehyde. F.e.s. J. C. Duff, *J. Chem. Soc. 1941*, 547; *C.A. 1942*, 1597.

Phosphorus oxychloride $POCl_3$
   See 612.

Sulfuric acid H_2SO_4

Ring Opening of o-Nitrophenols $\cdot$C

622.

4-Bromo-2-nitrophenol is slowly stirred into concd. H_2SO_4 at 110° $\rightarrow$ β-bromomuconic acid γ-lactone. Y = good. I. J. Rinkes, *Rec. trav. chim. 62*, 12 (1943); *C.A. 1945*, 2495.

Halogen ↑   CC Ɏ Hal

Without additional reagents (syntheses with diazomethane;
addition of 1 C atom)

α-Halogen Ketones $COCl \rightarrow COCH_2Hal$

3. $ICH_2CH_2COCl \longrightarrow ICH_2CH_2COCHN_2 \longrightarrow ICH_2CH_2COCH_2Cl$

β-Iodopropionyl chloride is treated with CH_2N_2 in abs. ether at 0° in
the dark. The diazo ketone is then treated with HCl gas at 0° → α-
chloromethyl β-iodoethyl ketone. Y = 60–80%. P. Karrer and
H. Schmid, *Helv. Chim. Acta* 27, 116 (1944); *C.A. 1944*, 4588.

4.

o-Nitrobenzoyl chloride → ω-bromo-o-nitroacetophenone. A. Butenandt, W. Weidel, R. Weichert and W. V. Derjugin, Z. *physiol. Chem.*
279, 27 (1943); *C.A. 1944*, 2044. Details: Arndt, Eistert and Partale,
Ber. 60B, 1364–1370; *C.A. 1927*, 2897.

5.

2-Aminonicotinyl chloride · HCl is treated with CH_2N_2 in CH_2Cl_2
→ 2-amino-3-diazoacetylpyridine (Y = 77%), which with HBr (d.
1.5) → 2-amino-3-bromoacetylpyridine (Y = 83%). For further deriv.
of the 2-amino-3-hydroxyacetylpyridines see K. Miescher and H. Kägi,
Helv. Chim. Acta 24, 1471 (1941); *C.A. 1942*, 4820.

α-Hydroxy Ketones $COCl \rightarrow COCH_2OH$

6.

Decahydro-1-naphthoic acid is converted to the chloride by treatment
with $SOCl_2$ in C_6H_6 in the presence of some pyridine. This is treated
with CH_2N_2 and the diazo ketone formed is decompd. at 40° with
2 N H_2SO_4 → 1-(1'-keto-2'-hydroxyethyl)decahydronaphthalene. Y =
40%. L. Long, Jr., and A. Burger, *J. Org. Chem.* 6, 852 (1941); *C.A.
1942*, 763.

Carboxylic Acids
Arndt-Eistert Synthesis of Acids $COOH \rightarrow CH_2COOH$

7. $RCOOH \longrightarrow RCOCl \longrightarrow RCOCHN_2 \longrightarrow RCH_2COOH$
Linoleic acid (25 g.) → 18 g. linoleic acid chloride which is treated

with diazomethane to give the ketone. This is treated with Ag_2O in EtOH → 9 g. 10,13-nonadecadienoic acid. P. Karrer and H. König, *Helv. Chim. Acta* 26, 619 (1943); *C.A. 1944*, 1469. For methods, see Arndt, Eistert, *Ber.* 69, 1805 (1936). B. Eistert, *Angew. Chem.* 54, 127 (1941); *C.A. 1941*, 4731.

628. H_3C⟨ ⟩$CH(CH_3)CH(CH_3)CH_2COOH$

α-Methyl-β-(p-methylphenyl)butyric acid is converted to the diazo ketone with CH_2N_2 and decomposed with Ag_2O, aq. $Na_2S_2O_3$, and 5% NaOH → β-methyl-γ-(p-methylphenyl)valeric acid. Y = 87%. F.e.s. W. P. Campbell and M. D. Soffer, *J. Am. Chem. Soc.* 64, 417 (1942); *C.A. 1942*, 1922.

629.   ⟨⟨⟨ ⟩⟩⟩$CH(CH_3)CH_2CH_2COOH$

β-(3-Phenanthryl)butyric acid with SO_2Cl_2 in ether → the acid chloride, which on treatment with CH_2N_2 in di-Et ether → the diazo ketone, which when treated with Ag_2O in alc. and boiled → the Me ester; when this is saponified with 10% NaOH → γ-(3-phenanthryl)-valeric acid. Y = 80%. (s.m. 780.) W. E. Bachmann and J. M. Chemerda, *J. Org. Chem.* 6, 36 (1941); *C.A. 1941*, 2504.

630. Also: 4-Fluorenecarboxylic acid → 4-fluoreneacetic acid. Y = 86%. F.e.s. W. E. Bachmann and J. C. Sheehan, *J. Am. Chem. Soc.* 62, 2687 (1940); *C.A. 1940*, 7897.

Acid Amides $COCl → CH_2CONHR$

631.

H_3CO ⟨ ⟩ $COCl$ + CH_2N_2 + $H_2NCH_2CH_2$⟨ ⟩OCH_3 (with H_3CO, H_3CO on left ring; OCH_3, OCH_3 on right ring)

↓

H_3CO ⟨ ⟩ $CH_2CONHCH_2CH_2$⟨ ⟩OCH_3 (with H_3CO, H_3CO on left ring; OCH_3, OCH_3 on right ring)

3,4,5-Trimethoxybenzoyl chloride (10 g.) is treated with CH_2N_2 in abs. ether at 0–18° → 3,4,5-$(MeO)_3C_6H_2CON_2$, to which 3,4-$(MeO)_2C_6H_3CH_2CH_2NH_2$ and Ag_2O in alc. are added at 55–60° → 7.45 g. 3,4,5-trimethoxyphenacet-(3,4-dimethoxyphenethyl)amide. E. Späth and T. Meinhard, *Ber.* 75, 400 (1942); *C.A. 1943*, 3099. For methods, see Eistert, *Angew. Chem.* 54, 124 (1941); *C.A. 1941*, 4731.

Lithium (see also *Magnesium*)   *Li*

Replacement of Bromine by a Methyl Group $\cdot Br → \cdot CH_3$

2. 1-Bromo-2-methylnaphthalene is treated with Li in abs. di-Et ether; (Me)$_2$SO$_4$ in abs. ether is added dropwise and the mixt. is boiled for 1 hr. on a water bath → 1,2-dimethylnaphthalene (s.m. 708). Y = 76%. P. A. Plattner and A. Ronco, *Helv. Chim. Acta* 27, 400 (1944); *C.A. 1944*, 4585.

Ethynyl Alcohols
  See 719.

Sodium and sodium alcoholate   *Na*

Wurtz-Fittig Synthesis

3.

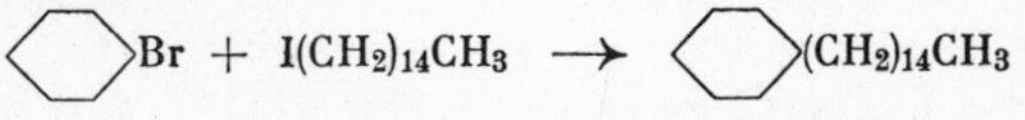

Na wire is introduced into a mixt. of cetyl iodide and bromobenzene. This is boiled for 6 hrs. and distilled → hexadecylbenzene. Y = 40%. F.e.s. J. P. Wibaut, J. Overhoff and E. W. Jonker, *Rec. trav. chim.* 62, 31 (1943); *C.A. 1945*, 1630.

β-Arylisopropylamines from Aromatic Aldehydes
Via Glycidic Acid Esters

4.

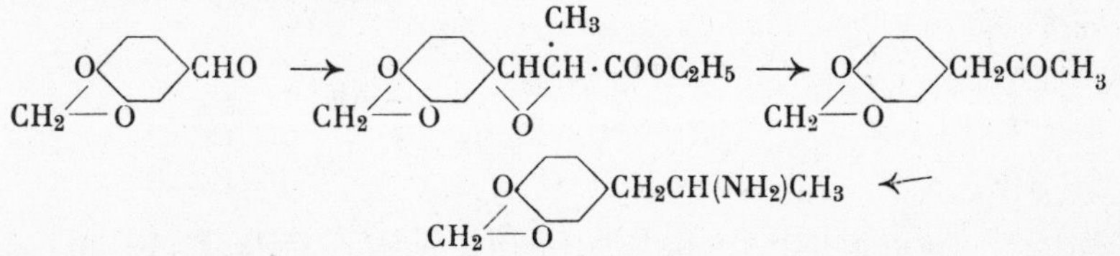

Piperonal and MeCHBrCO$_2$Et are treated with EtONa → β-3,4-methylenedioxyphenyl-α-methylglycidic Et ester (Y = 48%). This is boiled with NaOH in 90% EtOH and heated with Cu powder at 180° for 18 hrs. → 3,4-CH$_2$O$_2$C$_6$H$_4$CH$_2$Ac (Y = 44.5%), which is heated with HCO$_2$NH$_4$ at 160–165° and hydrolyzed with HCl (d. 1.16) → 2-(3,4-methylenedioxyphenyl)isopropylamine. Y = 20%. J. Elks and D. H. Hey, *J. Chem. Soc. 1943*, 15; *C.A. 1943*, 1995.

Replacement of Active Hydrogen
by Alkyl and Acyl Groups   : CH → : C · R

5. **Alkyl Carbonates as Solvents for Metalation and Alkylation Reactions.** Alkyl carbonates are successfully used as solvents in the metalation and alkylation of a series of β-keto-, malonic-, and α-cyano-esters. It is particularly advantageous, in distinction to the alcohol usually used, that cleavage of a carboxyl group by alcoholysis is avoided and the formation of the metal deriv. by removal of the alc. from the reaction mixture may be forced substantially to completion.

This synthesis can be used in a series of cases in which alkylation reactions formerly resulted in poor yields (introduction of the ethyl or allyl group into *sec*-Bu malonates) or in which they failed entirely (malonates with *sec*-alkyl groups as substituents). General method: Prepn. of Na or K alcoholate from the metal and alc., which is distilled at reduced pressure. An equimolar amt. of ester and 4–6 mole equivs. of alkyl carbonate are added. After stirring until dissolved, the alc. formed is removed by fractionation under reduced pressure. The alkyl halide is added in 10–15% excess and the well-stirred reaction mixture is heated carefully at 95–105° until no longer alkaline to phenolphthalein. The cooled mixture is then poured into H_2O, neutralized with AcOH, extracted with isopropyl ether, and the ether extract is dried and fractionated. F.e.s. V. H. Wallingford, M. A. Thorpe and A. H. Homeyer, *J. Am. Chem. Soc. 64*, 580 (1942); *C.A. 1942*, 2527.

636. Alkylation of β-Keto Esters $\cdot CO\cdot CH_2\cdot COOR \rightarrow COCHCOOR$
$$\underset{Alc}{}$$

Prepn., see 635. Ex: $AcCH_2CO_2Et$ and BuBr → *n*-Bu acetoacetate; Y = 58%. $AcCH_2CO_2Et$ and *n*-hexyl bromide → *n*-hexyl acetoacetate; Y = 62%. $AcCHBuCO_2Et$ and BuBr → $AcCHBu_2CO_2Et$; Y = 49%. F.e.s. V. H. Wallingford, M. A. Thorpe and A. H. Homeyer, *J. Am. Chem. Soc. 64*, 580 (1942); *C.A. 1942*, 2527.

637. 2-Ethyl-2-isopropylethyl iodide is treated with $AcCH_2CO_2Et$ and Na in abs. EtOH → Et α-(2-ethyl-2-isopropylethyl)acetoacetate. (Y = 57.7%), which is hydrolyzed with 10% NaOH and heated → 6-methyl-5-ethyl-2-heptanone. Y = 82%. W. Dirscherl and H. Nahm, *Ber. 76*, 635 (1943); *C.A. 1944*, 1747.

638.

Et 2-oxocyclohexanecarboxylate is treated with Na and allyl bromide in xylene → Et 1-allyl-2-oxocyclohexanecarboxylate. Y = 85%. R. Grewe, *Ber. 76*, 1072 (1943); *C.A. 1944*, 4935.

Alkylation of Malonic Esters

639. $C_6H_5CH_2SCH_2CHBrCH_3 \rightarrow C_6H_5CH_2SCH_2CH(CH_3)CH(COOC_2H_5)_2$

1-Benzylthio-2-bromopropane (prepn., see 404) and di-Et malonate

are treated with Na in abs. EtOH → Et γ-benzylthio-β-methyl-α-carbethoxybutyrate (s.m. 643). Y = 82%. F. Kögl, J. H. Verbeek, H. Erxleben and W. A. J. Borg, Z. physiol. Chem. 279, 121 (1943); C.A.
1944, 3978.

Malonic Ester Synthesis   · Hal → · CH₂COOH

0.

$$\text{H} \quad \text{CH}_2\text{COOH}$$

9-Bromofluorene is treated with Na malonic ester (from Na and
diethyl malonate in abs. EtOH in N_2 atmosphere), saponified with 40%
NaOH, and heated to 200° → 9-fluoreneacetic acid. Y = 89%. W. E.
Bachmann and J. C. Sheehan, J. Am. Chem. Soc. 62, 2687 (1940);
C.A. 1940, 7897.

41.

$$OC_2H_5 \quad OC_2H_5 \qquad OC_2H_5 \quad OC_2H_5 \qquad OC_2H_5 \quad OC_2H_5$$

$$N = C - NH \qquad N = C - NH \qquad N = C - NH$$
$$\overset{\cdot}{C}H_2Cl \qquad \overset{\cdot}{C}H_2CH(COOC_2H_5)_2 \qquad \overset{\cdot}{C}H_2CH_2COOH$$

[N,N'-bis(4-ethoxyphenyl)guanyl]chloromethane (prepn., see 351)
is heated with CHNa(CO₂Et)₂ in EtOH → di-Et [bis-N,N'-(4-ethoxy-
phenyl)guanyl]methylmalonate (Y = 70%), which is boiled for 5 hrs.
with EtOH–KOH → β-[bis-N,N'-(4-ethoxyphenyl)guanyl]propionic
acid (Y = 80%). H. P. Kaufmann, J. Budwig and K. Mohnke, Ber. 75,
1585 (1943); C.A. 1944, 1215.

Alkylation of Mono-   ROOC\   ROOC\
substituted Malonic Esters   >CHR →   >CRAlc ·
                                        ROOC/   ROOC/

42. According to 635, with Et₂CO₃ as solvent, diethyl sec-butylmalonate
and EtBr → diethyl sec-butylethylmalonate. Y = 95%. Diethyl sec-
butylmalonate and allyl bromide → di-Et sec-butylallylmalonate. Y =
86%. F.e.s. V. H. Wallingford, M. A. Thorpe and A. H. Homeyer, J. Am.
Chem. Soc. 64, 580 (1942); C.A. 1942, 2527.

Replacement of Hydrogen by a Methyl Group   · H → · CH₃

43.

$$C_6H_5CH_2SCH_2CH \cdot CH(COOC_2H_5)_2 \longrightarrow C_6H_5CH_2SCH_2CH \cdot C(COOC_2H_5)_2$$
$$\overset{\cdot}{C}H_3 \qquad\qquad\qquad \overset{\cdot}{C}H_3 \; \overset{\cdot}{C}H_3$$

Et γ-benzylthio-β-methyl-α-carbethoxybutyrate (prepn., see 639) is
treated with CH₃I and EtONa → Et γ-benzylthio-α,β-dimethyl-α-carb-
ethoxybutyrate. Y = 74%. F. Kögl, J. H. Verbeek, H. Erxleben and
W. A. J. Borg, Z. physiol. Chem. 279, 121 (1943); C.A. 1944, 3978.

α-Aminocarboxylic Acids

644.

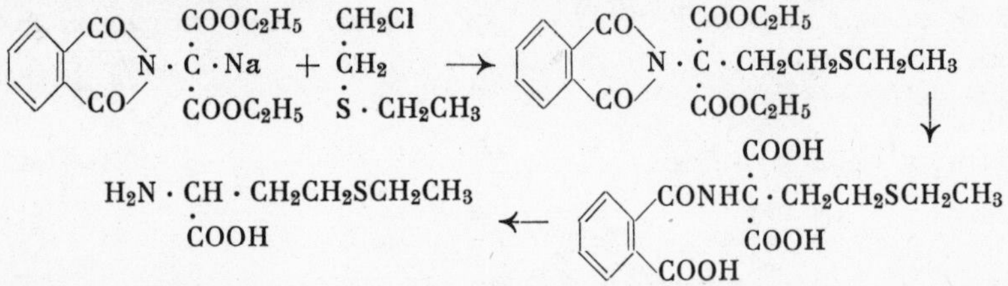

2-Chloro-di-Et sulfide and $C_6H_4(CO)_2NCNa(CO_2Et)_2 \rightarrow$ di-Et (2-ethylmercaptoethyl)phthalimidomalonate (Y = 73%), which is heated with 5 N NaOH $\rightarrow$ $HO_2CC_6H_4CONHC(CH_2CH_2SEt)(CO_2H)_2$ (Y = 97%), which on treatment with concd. HCl $\rightarrow$ ethionine (Y = 68%). R. Kuhn and G. Quadbeck, *Ber. 76*, 529 (1943); *C.A. 1943*, 6645. For methods, see G. Barger and T. E. Weichselbaum, *Organic Syntheses 14*, 58 (1934). See also E. Booth, U. C. E. Burnop and W. E. Jones, *J. Chem. Soc. 1944*, 666; *C.A. 1945*, 1624.

4-Hydroxy-2-Naphthoic Acids

645.

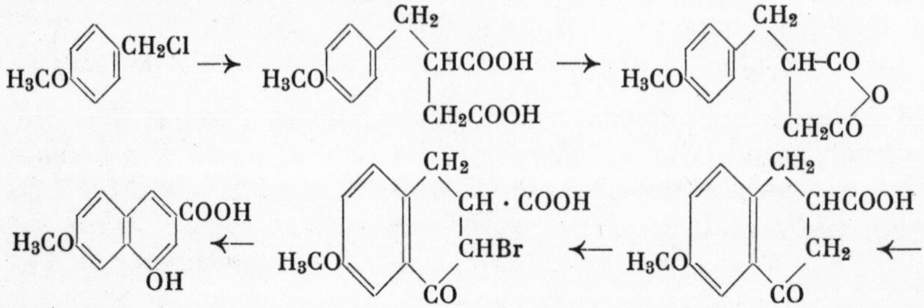

4-Methoxybenzyl chloride is refluxed with ethyl Na-α-acetosuccinate in toluene for 18 hrs. and the reaction product is hydrolyzed $\rightarrow$ 4-methoxybenzylsuccinic acid (Y = 20%) which is treated with cold AcCl $\rightarrow$ 4-methoxybenzylsuccinic acid anhydride Y = 92%). With AlCl$_3$ in nitrobenzene at room temp. $\rightarrow$ 6-methoxy-1,2,3,4-tetrahydro-2-carboxylic acid (Y = 60%). This is shaken with Br in CHCl$_3$ at room temp. $\rightarrow$ 3-bromo-6-methoxy-1,2,3,4-tetrahydro-2-carboxylic acid (Y = 70%) and heated with di-Et aniline for 6 hrs. at 100° $\rightarrow$ 4-hydroxy-6-methoxy-2-naphthoic acid (Y = 20%). F.e.s. R. D. Haworth, B. Jones and J. M. Way, *J. Chem. Soc. 1943*, 10; *C.A. 1943*, 2003.

646. Alkylation of
α-Cyanocarboxylic Acid Esters

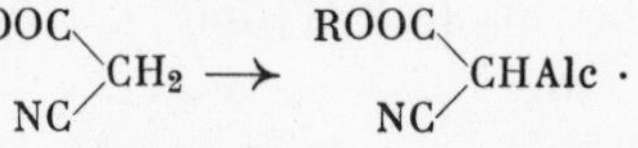

Prepn., according to 635 with alkyl carbonate as solvent. α-Cyanoisocaproate, Pr$_2$CO$_3$, and EtBr $\rightarrow$ Pr α-ethyl α-cyanoisocaproate; Y = 78%. Et cyano (p-methylphenyl)acetate, Et$_2$CO$_3$, and EtBr $\rightarrow$ Et ethyl-cyano(p-methylphenyl)acetate; Y = 60%. F.e.s. V. H. Wallingford, M. A. Thorpe and A. H. Homeyer, *J. Am. Chem. Soc. 64*, 580 (1942); *C.A. 1942, 2527.*

Phenylcyano-Substituted Carboxylic Acids

$C_6H_5CH(CN)COOC_2H_5 \succ C_6H_5C(CN) \cdot CH_2COOC_2H_5 \succ C_6H_5CH(CN)CH_2COOC_2H_5$
$\quad\quad\quad\quad\quad\quad\quad\quad\quad\quad | $
$\quad\quad\quad\quad\quad\quad\quad\quad\quad\quad COOC_2H_5$

Ph(NC)CHCO$_2$Et, prepd. from PhCH$_2$CN and Et$_2$CO$_3$ with Na [Hessler, *Am. Chem. J. 32*, 127 (1904)], is condensed as the Na salt with haloaliphatic acids in EtOH. The yields of acid vary from 53% to 89%. Ex: The Na salt of Ph(NC)CHCO$_2$Et (from the ester and Na alcoholate) is refluxed with ClCH$_2$CO$_2$Et on a water bath → di-Et α-phenyl-α-cyanosuccinate (Y = 81%), which is hydrolyzed with alc. KOH on a water bath → β-phenyl-β-cyanopropionic acid (Y = 89%). F.e.s. S. Wideqvist, *Svensk. kem. Tid. 54*, 34 (1942); *C.A. 1943, 5046.*

Me α-Acyllevulinate

$CH_3COCH_2COOR \succ CH_3(CH_2)_4COCH_2COOR \succ CH_3(CH_2)_4COCH(COOR)CH_2COCH_3$

The Na deriv. of the acetoacetic ester is treated with the acid chloride in MeOH → Me acetates (Y = 65–70%). The Na derivs. of these esters are condensed with bromoacetone → α-acyl levulinate (Y = 40–60%). Ex: Acetoacetic ester → caproyl acetoacetate → α-caproyl levulinate. F.e.s. H. Hunsdiecker, *Ber. 75*, 447 (1942); *C.A. 1943, 3403.*

ω-Halogen-β-Ketocarboxylic Acid Esters (s.m. 771). 13-Bromotridecanoic acid chloride is treated with AcCH$_2$COMe and Na in ether and the resulting product with MeONa in MeOH → Me 15-bromo-3-oxopentadecanoate. Y = 67%. Me 7-bromo-3-oxohexanoate cannot be prepd. in this manner. F.e.s. H. Hunsdiecker, *Ber. 75B*, 1190 (1942); *C.A. 1943, 4697.*

See also 770.

Enol Lactones

Apocamphoric anhydride is treated with the Na salt of di-Et malonate in C$_6$H$_6$ → di-Et apocamphorylmalonate (Y = 74.4%), which is treated with Na–Hg while CO_2 is passed through [Winzer, *Ann.* 257, 298 (1890)] → hydroapocamphorylacetic acid. Y = 60–65%. G. Komppa and Å. Bergström, *Ber.* 75, 1607 (1943); *C.A. 1944*, 1223.

β,β'-Diketonic Carboxylic Acid Esters Which Are Also 1,4-Diketones

651.

$$\begin{array}{c} CH_2-CO \\ | \quad\quad >O \\ CH_2-CO \end{array} \rightarrow \begin{array}{c} CH_2-C=C<^{COOC_2H_5}_{COOC_2H_5} \\ | \quad\quad >O \\ CH_2-CO \end{array} \rightarrow \begin{array}{c} CH_2COCH<^{COOC_2H_5}_{COOC_2H_5} \\ \quad\quad\quad /CN \\ CH_2COCH \\ \quad\quad\quad \backslash COOC_2H_5 \end{array}$$

Enol lactones of the type of butanolidenemalonic esters are cleaved by Na salts of $CH_2(CO_2R)_2$, $AcCH_2CO_2R$, and similar β-keto esters, β-diketones, and analogous compounds with reactive CH_2 groups. For preparative purposes this is a useful method. Ex: Malonic ester is stirred dropwise into Na powder in abs. ether in the cold and, after stirring overnight, finely powd. succinic anhydride is added and the mixture is refluxed for 4 hrs. → butanolidenemalonic ester. Y = 63%. 5 g. of this is added to warm abs. ether with $NCCHNaCO_2Et$ (from $NCCH_2CO_2Et$ in di-Et ether and finely powd. Na), stirred, and refluxed for 1 hr. on a water bath. After standing overnight → 5 g. tri-Et 1-cyanohexane-2,5-dione-1,6,6-tricarboxylate. P. Ruggli and A. Maeder, *Helv. Chim. Acta* 27, 436 (1944); *C.A. 1945*, 62.

Potassium hydroxide   KOH

Polyaryl Condensation

652.

3-Chloro-2-methyl-*meso*-benzanthrone (prepn., see 414) is added to a mixt. of KOH in alc. at 140° and warmed for 0.5 hr. at 150–155°, → 6,15-dimethylisodibenzanthrone. Y = nearly quant. D. H. Hey, R. J. Nicholls and C. W. Pritchett, *J. Chem. Soc. 1944*, 97; *C.A. 1944*, 3644.

Sodamide   NaNH₂

Preparation of NaNH₂ and KNH₂

653. To prepare $NaNH_2$, NH_3 is passed through molten Na at 350–360° (for apparatus, see original). Y = 90–95%. Also KNH_2; Y = 95%. F. W. Bergstrom, *Organic Syntheses* 20, 86 (1940); *C.A. 1940*, 6539.

Synthesis of α-Acetylenecarboxylic Acids · C ≡ C · COOH

4.
$$C_4H_9Br \longrightarrow C_4H_9C \equiv C \cdot COOH$$

BuBr and NaC⦂CH prepd. in liq. NH_3 and treated with $NaNH_2$ in liq. NH_3 at $-35°$ to $-45°$; after removal of the NH_3, solid CO_2 is added → $BuC⦂CCO_2H$. Y = 48%. F.e.s. A. O. Zoss and G. F. Hennion, *J. Am. Chem. Soc.* 63, 1151 (1941); *C.A. 1941*, 3601.

Alkylation of Ketones

5.

$$C_6H_5COCH \atop \overset{|}{C}H_3 \quad + \quad \underset{(CH_3)_3C}{\bigwedge}\overset{CH_3}{\underset{CH_3}{\bigvee}}CH_2Cl \quad \longrightarrow \quad \underset{(CH_3)_3C}{\bigwedge}\overset{CH_3}{\underset{CH_3}{\bigvee}}CH_2 \cdot \overset{CH_3}{\underset{\overset{|}{C}H_3}{C}} \cdot COC_6H_5$$

2-Chloromethyl-1,3-dimethyl-5-*tert*-butylbenzene is added to iso-PrCOPh which has been treated with $NaNH_2$ in C_6H_6 → β-(2,6-dimethyl-4-*tert*-butylphenyl)-α,α-dimethylpropionylbenzene. Y = good. N. P. Buu-Hoi and P. Cagniant, *Bull. soc. chim. Mém.* [5] 9, 889 (1942); *C.A. 1944*, 2937.

Alkylation of Nitriles

6.

$$\underset{H}{\overset{CH_3CH_2}{CH_3(CH_2)_{11}}}C \cdot CN \quad \longrightarrow \quad \underset{CH_3(CH_2)_9}{\overset{CH_3CH_2}{CH_3(CH_2)_{11}}}C \cdot CN$$

α-Ethylmyristic acid nitrile (14 g.) and 14 g. $C_{10}H_{21}Br$ is treated with $NaNH_2$ in abs. toluene → 6 g. decyldodecylethylacetonitrile. N. P. Buu-Hoi and P. Cagniant, *Ber.* 76, 689 (1943); *C.A. 1944*, 2314. For methods, see K. Ziegler and H. Ohlinger, *Ann.* 495, 689 (1932).

Sodium cyanide   *NaCN*

Nitriles from Halides · Hal → · CN

7. 2-(3-Bromopropyl)coumaran is heated with NaCN in EtOH for 7 hrs. → 2-(3-cyanopropyl)coumaran($C_{12}H_{13}NO$). Y = 90%. H. Normant, *Ann. chim.* [11] 17, 335 (1942); *C.A. 1944*, 3282.

Carboxylic Acid from Halides Hal → · COOH

8.

$$\overset{OC_2H_5 \qquad OC_2H_5}{\underset{N = C - \underset{\overset{|}{C}H_2COOH}{NH}}{\bigcirc \qquad \bigcirc}}$$

[Bis-*N,N'*-(4-ethoxyphenyl)guanyl]chloromethane (prepn., see 351) is boiled with NaCN in EtOH and the nitrile produced is hydrolyzed with dil. H_2SO_4 → [bis-*N,N'*-(4-ethoxyphenyl)guanyl]acetic acid.

Y = 80%. H. P. Kaufmann, J. Budwig and K. Mohnke, *Ber. 75,* 1585 (1943); *C.A. 1944,* 1215.

Pyridine C_5H_5N

Furan Ring Synthesis   O

659.

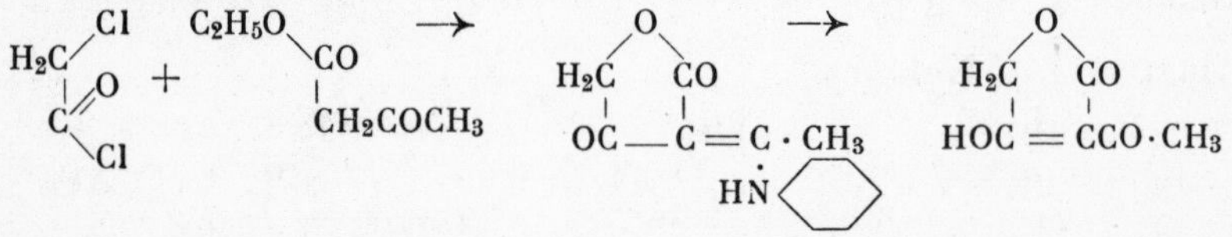

Me acetoacetate (168 g.) and PhNH₂ are allowed to stand overnight with 1 drop concd. HCl. The reaction product is mixed with ClCH₂-COCl in anhyd. C_5H_5N–ether and heated for 4 hrs. at 120–130° → 121 g. α-acetyltetronic acid anilide, which is hydrolyzed by shaking with aq. NaOH for 24 hrs. → 63 g. α-acetyltetronic acid. W. Baker, K. D. Grice and A. B. A. Jansen, *J. Chem. Soc.* 1943, 241; *C.A. 1943,* 5024.

Copper   *Cu*

Diaryl Compounds from Aryl Halides   2 ArHal → Ar · Ar

660.

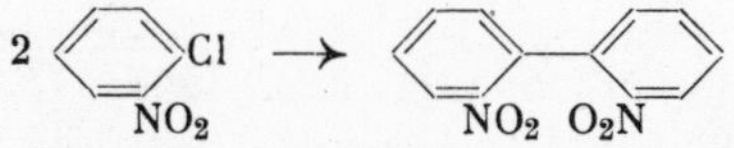

o-ClC₆H₄NO₂ mixed with 1.5 times its weight of dry sand and heated with Cu bronze at 215–225° → 2,2'-dinitrobiphenyl. Y = 52–61%. R. C. Fuson and E. A. Cleveland, *Organic Syntheses 20,* 45 (1940); *C.A. 1940,* 5074.

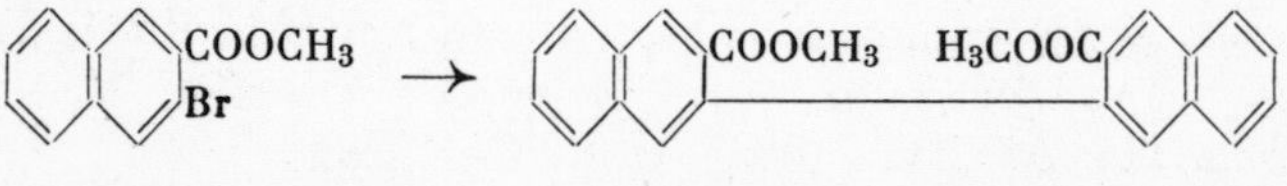

661. 2,3-Br-C₁₀H₆CO₂Me (25 g.) is heated with Cu-bronze at 190–200° → 15.8 g. 2,2'-binaphthyl-3,3'-dicarboxylic acid di-Me ester. R. H. Martin, *J. Chem. Soc.* 1941, 679; *C.A. 1942,* 446.

662.

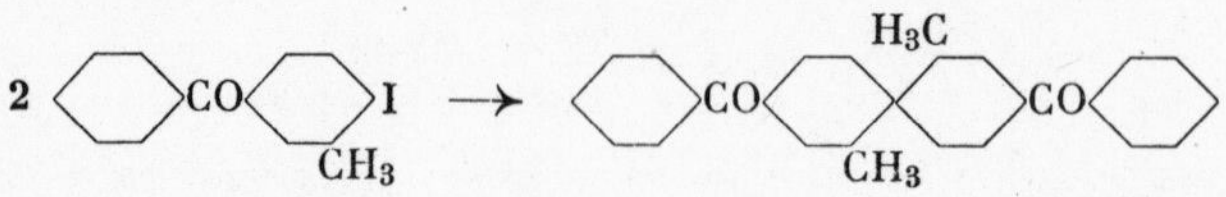

3-Methyl-4-iodobenzophenone (prep., see 438) is heated for 4 hrs. at

230° with native Cu-C → 2,2'-dimethyl-4,4'-dibenzoylbiphenyl. Y = 77%. E. Müller and E. Hertel, *Ann. 555*, 157 (1944).

Copper cyanide   CuCN

Rosenmund-von Braun Nitrile Synthesis   · Hal → · CN

The nitrile synthesis from aromatic halogen derivatives and CuCN was quantitatively investigated and the optimum conditions for carrying out the reaction were ascertained. The following compounds show an increasing reactivity: p-$Ph_2CHC_6H_4Br$ < m-MeC_6H_4Br < p-$PhCOC_6H_4Br$ < o-MeC_6H_4Br < $PhBr$ < $1,3,5$-$Me_3C_6H_2Br$ < 1-$C_{10}H_7Br$ < p-$BrC_6H_4CO_2H$. The reaction is practically finished in 2 hrs. in all cases. At 250°, the addn. of a few drops of tolunitrile and a trace of $CuSO_4$ has a marked promoting effect. Prepn: The aromatic bromide and an eq. amt. of CuCN are heated in biphenyl vapor in a sealed tube. C. F. Koelsch and A. G. Whitney, *J. Org. Chem. 6*, 795 (1941); *C.A. 1942*, 756.

1-Iodo-6-methoxynaphthalene is heated with CuCN at 220–230° → 6-methoxy-1-naphthonitrile (s.m. 189). Y = 82%. L. Long, Jr., and A. Burger, *J. Org. Chem. 6*, 852 (1941); *C.A. 1942*, 763.

3,5-Diethylbromobenzene is refluxed with CuCN and C_5H_5N at 235–240° → 3,5-diethylbenzonitrile (s.m. 188). Y = 67%. H. R. Snyder, R. R. Adams and A. V. McIntosh, Jr., *J. Am. Chem. Soc. 63*, 3280 (1941); *C.A. 1942*, 1025.

Also: α-Bromonaphthalene → α-naphthonitrile. Y = 82–90%. M. S. Newmann, *Organic Syntheses 21*, 89 (1942); *C.A. 1941*, 6253.

See also 772.

Copper–magnesium alloy   Cu–Mg
    See 681.

Magnesium (see also *Lithium*)   Mg

Organo-(1)-2-Chloroacetylenes from Dichloroacetylenes

Dodecyl-MgBr and C_2Cl_2 → 1-dodecyl-2-chloroacetylene. Y = 40%. PhMgBr and C_2Cl_2 → Ph-chloroacetylene. Y = 70%. F.e.s. E. Ott and W. Bossaller, *Ber. 76*, 88 (1943); *C.A. 1943*, 5014.

Synthesis of Phenanthrene Ring

668.

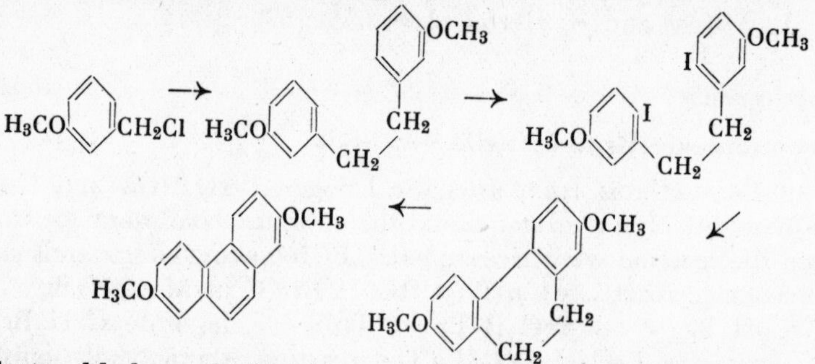

FeCl$_3$ is added to a boiling mixt. of m-MeOC$_6$H$_4$CH$_2$Cl (prepn., see 430), Mg, and ether → 3,3'-dimethoxybibenzyl (Y = 80%), which is treated with Hg(OAc)$_2$ and powd. iodine in AcOH → 6,6'-diiodo-3,3'-dimethoxybibenzyl (I). Y = 93%. Cu-bronze is heated with (I) at 230–290° → 2,7-dimethoxy-9,10-dihydrophenanthrene (Y = 70%), which is heated with S at 220–230° until H$_2$S evoln. ceases → 2,7-dimethoxyphenanthrene (Y =60%). J. W. Cornforth and R. Robinson, J. Chem. Soc. 1942, 684; C.A. 1943, 881.

Hydrocarbons from Ketones

669.

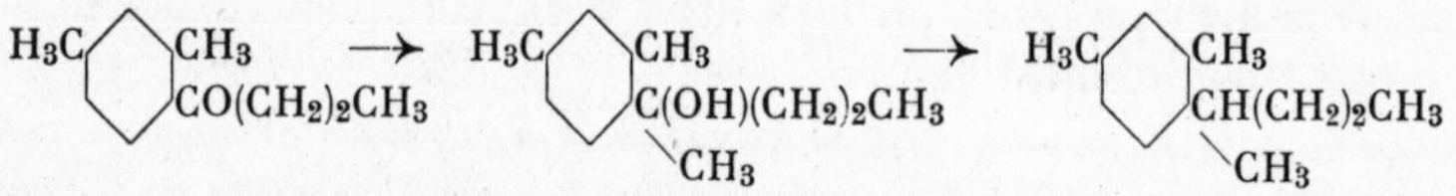

The reaction product of 1,3-dimethyl-4-butyrylbenzene and MeMgI is added to Ac$_2$O and 4 drops of H$_2$SO$_4$, and the mixt. is distd. The olefin obtained is hydrogenated with Raney Ni in MeOH at a pressure of 150–225 atm. and a temp. of 25–210° → 2-(2,4-dimethylphenyl)-pentane. Y = 78%. F.e.s. D. V. Nightingale and O. G. Shanholtzer, J. Org. Chem. 7, 6 (1942); C.A. 1942, 1912.

670. **p-Substituted Aromatic Ethylenes.** Improved method based on boiling the reaction product in C$_6$H$_6$ for several hrs. Ex: After preparing CH$_3$MgBr from MeBr and Mg in ether, the latter is replaced by C$_6$H$_6$; Michler ketone is added and boiling is continued for 3 more hrs. → (p-Me$_2$NC$_6$H$_4$)$_2$C : CH$_2$. Y = theoretical. Roleff, Chem.-Ztg. 67, 81 (1943); C.A. 1944, 5207.

See also 753.

671.

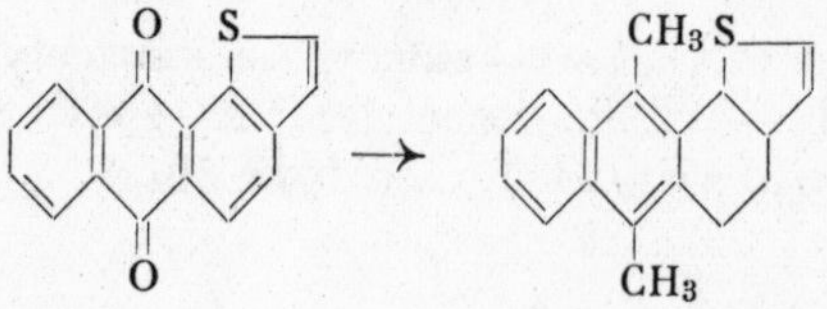

Anthracene Homologues from Anthraquinones

1,2-(2′,3′-Thiopheno)anthraquinone is treated with excess MeMgCl in ether; the reaction product is converted into the iodide with HI in AcOH; the iodide is reduced with $SnCl_2$ and HCl in dioxane → 9,10-dimethyl-1,2-(2′,3′-thiopheno)anthracene. Y = 37%. F.e.s. E. B. Hershberg and L. F. Fieser, *J. Am. Chem. Soc. 63,* 2561 (1941); *C.A. 1942,* 458.

Primary Alcohols
Tiffeneau Rearrangement

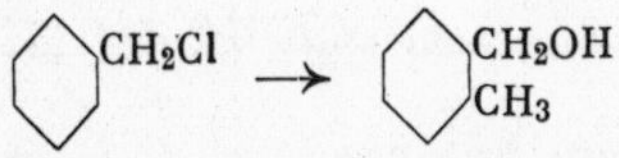

$PhCH_2Cl$ is converted into Grignard compd. and is treated with paraformaldehyde → *o*-$MeC_6H_4CH_2OH$. Y = 70%. L. I. Smith and L. J. Spillane, *J. Am. Chem. Soc. 62,* 2639 (1940); *C.A. 1940,* 7892.

Syntheses with Ethylene Oxide

· Hal → CH_2CH_2OH

$[CH_3(CH_2)_3]_2Mg$ + 2 $CH_2 \cdot CH_2$ (O) → 2 $CH_3(CH_2)_4CH_2OH$ Y : 82%

$CH_3(CH_2)_3MgBr$ + 2 $CH_2 \cdot CH_2$ (O) —Room Temp.→ $CH_3(CH_2)_4CH_2OH$ Y : 71%

$CH_3(CH_2)_3MgBr$ + $CH_2 \cdot CH_2$ (O) —50°→ $CH_3(CH_2)_4CH_2OH$ Y : 70%

Di-alkyl magnesium compounds or alkyl magnesium halides are treated with 2 moles $(CH_2)_2O$ at room temp., or heated with 1 mole $(CH_2)_2O$. (*Tert*-alkyl Grignard compounds do not give the desired alcohol.) Ex: 1-Bromopropane via the Grignard reagent → *n*-amyl alcohol. Y = 76–90%. F.e.s. R. C. Huston and A. H. Agett, *J. Org. Chem. 6,* 123 (1941); *C.A. 1941,* 2478.

4.

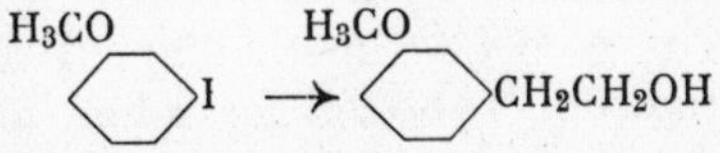

m-Iodoanisyl and EtBr dissolved in ether are gradually added to Mg shavings in ether. After addn. of C_6H_6 the mixture is boiled and the boiling is repeated each time after $(CH_2)_2O$ has been introduced twice → 2-*m*-anisylethyl alc. Y = 85%. Without the EtBr or the second $(CH_2)_2O$ treatment, the yields decrease. W. E. Bachmann and D. G. Thomas, *J. Am. Chem. Soc. 64,* 94 (1942); *C.A. 1942,* 1327.

675. 5-Bromoacenaphthene and EtBr in Et_2O are added to a suspension of Mg in Et_2O over a period of 4 hrs. After heating for 6 hrs. the mixt. is cooled to $-10°$ and ethylene oxide is added. After standing for 6 hrs. and being worked up → 5-acenaphthylethyl alcohol. Y = 56%. N. P. Buu-Hoi and P. Cagniant, *Compt. rend. 214*, 493 (1942); *C.A. 1943*, 2370.

676. 2-Thienyl bromide via the Grignard compd. is treated with $(CH_2)_2O$ → 1-(2-thienyl)-2-hydroxyethane. Y = 53%. F.e.s. F. F. Blicke and J. H. Burckalter, *J. Am. Chem. Soc. 64*, 477 (1942); *C.A. 1942*, 2551.

Tertiary Alcohols from Ketones

β-Hydroxy Esters

$$CO \rightarrow C{\overset{OH}{\underset{R}{\big<}}}$$

677. $(CH_3CH_2CH_2)_2CO + BrCH(CH_3)CO_2C_2H_5 \rightarrow (CH_3CH_2CH_2)_2C(OH)CH(CH_3)COOC_2H_5$

Ketones are condensed to β-hydroxy esters with α-halogen esters in the presence of amalgamated Mg in ether. Ex: Butyrone and Et α-bromo-propionate → Et 2-methyl-3-propyl-3-hexanoate (s.m. 757). Y = 70%. F.e.s. J. Colonge and D. Joly, *Ann. Chim.* [11] *18*, 306 (1943); *C.A. 1944*, 5203.

678. Tocopherol Synthesis

Hexahydrofarnesyl halide (I) is treated with Mg and a few drops of MeI to start the reaction in ether → (I) Mg deriv., which is added to a Et_2O–C_6H_6 soln. of 3,4,6-trimethyl-2-methoxy-5-hydroxybenzyl-acetone (2.78 g.); the soln. is boiled for 3 hrs., after which the sub-stance is hydrolyzed with 5% MeOH–KOH by boiling for 45 min. (all operations under N_2). The resulting monoether is oxidized with $FeCl_3$ in EtOH → nor-α-tocophenylquinone. This is reduced with Zn in glacial AcOH. Ring formation is completed by refluxing with HBr (d. 1.49) in glacial AcOH → nor-α-tocopherol. Y = 1.5–2 g. as the allophanate. F.e.s. W. John and H. Herrmann, *Z. physiol. Chem. 273*, 191 (1942); *C.A. 1943*, 3092.

Separate Preparation of Grignard Reagent

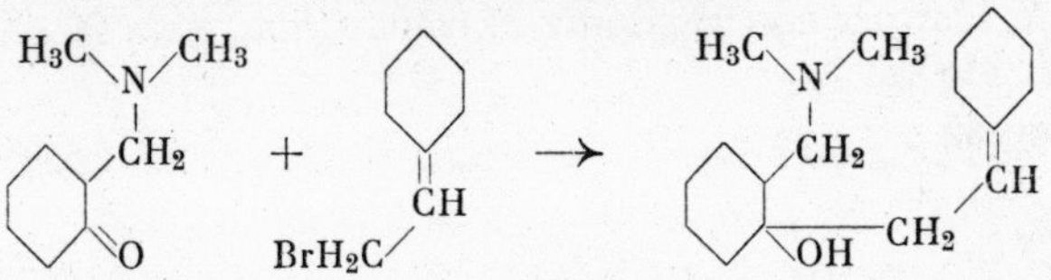

The Grignard reagent is prepd. separately according to Gilman and Glumphy, *Bull. soc. chim.* **43**, 1325 (1928), in order to prevent the organo-Mg halide from reacting further after a Wurtz synthesis. Ether is poured over pulverized and finely screened Mg and 25.8 g. cyclohexylidene-EtBr is added dropwise over a period of 2 hrs. under N_2 without heating. The soln. is poured rapidly from the excess Mg and 21.2 g. 2-(dimethylaminomethyl)cyclohexanone is added over a period 2 hrs. under $N_2 \rightarrow$ 10.6 g. 1-(cyclohexylidene)-2-[1-hydroxy-2-(dimethylaminomethyl)cyclohexyl]ethane. K. Dimroth, E. Dietzel and E. Stockstrom, *Ann.* **549**, 256 (1941); *C.A. 1943*, 3753.

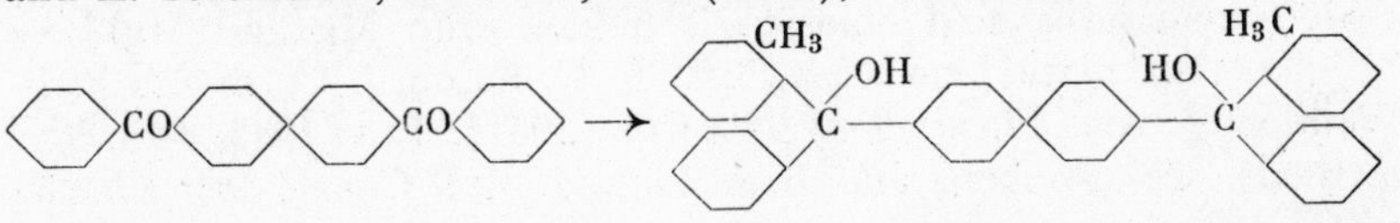

p-p'-Dibenzoyldiphenyl is boiled for 12 hrs. with excess *o*-tolyl-MgBr in $C_6H_6 \rightarrow$ *p-p'*-bis(phenyl-*o*-tolylhydroxymethyl)biphenyl. Y = nearly quant. E. Müller and E. Hertel, *Ann.* **555**, 157 (1944).

Syntheses of N-Disubstituted 3-Chloropropylamines

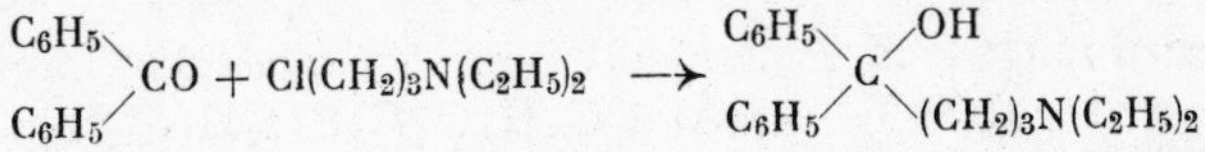

Because the formation of Grignard compounds from 2-chloroethyl-N-di-Et-amine failed, a series of N-disubstituted 3-chloropropylamines could be converted to organomagnesium compounds. Ex: 3-Chloro-N,N-diethylpropylamine is treated with Mg and Gilman Mg–Cu-alloy in ether. EtBr is added to start the reaction and the reaction mixt. is treated portionwise with Ph_2CO at 45–50° $\rightarrow$ diphenyl-(3-diethyl-aminopropyl)carbinol. Y = 66%. F.e.s. A. Marxer, *Helv. Chim. Acta* **24E**, 209 (1941); *C.A. 1942*, 5134.

Thioalcohols   See 44.

Tertiary Alcohols from Esters

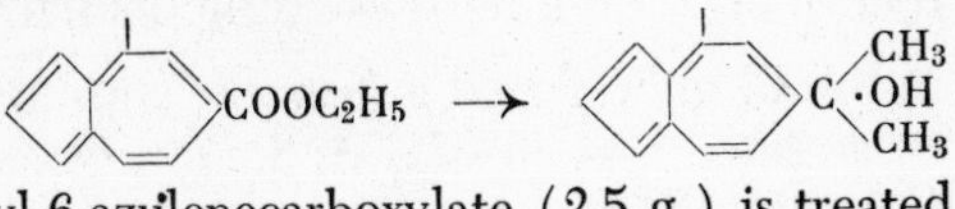

Et 4,8-dimethyl-6-azulenecarboxylate (2.5 g.) is treated with Mg and

MeI in ether → 1.7 g. 4,8-dimethyl-6-(hydroxisopropyl)azulene (s.m. 751). P. A. Plattner and H. Roniger, *Helv. Chim. Acta 26*, 905 (1943); *C.A. 1944*, 1487.

See also 752.

Ethers
                                                            $R \cdot O \cdot R$
See 775.

Aldehydes
                                                     $\cdot Hal \rightarrow \cdot CHO$

683. α-Bromonaphthalene is treated with orthoformate (via the Grignard deriv.) → 1-naphthaldehyde. Y = 57%. N. P. Buu-Hoi and P. Cagniant, *Rev. Sci. Instruments 80*, 384 (1942); *C.A. 1945*, 3276.

Benzils from Acid Chlorides

684.

$$2\ H_3C\underset{CH_3}{\overset{CH_3O\ \ CH_3}{\diagup\!\!\diagdown}}COCl \longrightarrow H_3C\underset{CH_3}{\overset{CH_3O\ \ CH_3}{\diagup\!\!\diagdown}}COCO\underset{H_3C}{\overset{H_3C\ \ OCH_3}{\diagdown\!\!\diagup}}CH_3$$

3-Methoxymesitoic acid chloride is treated with Mg and MgI_2 → 3,3'-dimethoxymesitylene. Y = 62%. R. C. Fuson, J. Corse and P. B. Welldon, *J. Am. Chem. Soc. 63*, 2645 (1941); *C.A. 1942*, 449. For methods, see Gomberg and Bachmann, *J. Am. Chem. Soc. 49*, 236 (1937).

Compare 689.

Carboxylic Acids
                                                     $\cdot Hal \rightarrow \cdot COOH$

685. $CH_3O\langle\ \rangle CH_2CH(CH_3)CH_2Br \longrightarrow CH_3O\langle\ \rangle CH_2CH(CH_3)CH_2COOH$

The Grignard reagent of 2-methyl-3-(p-methoxyphenyl)-1-propyl bromide is treated with CO_2 → p-$MeOC_6H_4C_4H_8CO_2H(C_4H_8 = CH_2$-$CHMeCH_2$). Y = 40–73%. J. M. van der Zanden, M. G. de Vries and P. Westerhof, *Rec. trav. chim. 62*, 383 (1943); *C.A. 1944*, 3274.

686.

$$H_3C\overset{CH_3}{\underset{CH_3}{\diagup\!\!\!\diagdown}}Br \longrightarrow H_3C\overset{CH_3}{\underset{CH_3}{\diagup\!\!\!\diagdown}}COOH$$

Bromomesitylenes via the Grignard reagent are treated with solid CO_2 → mesitoic acid (β-isodurylic acid). Y = 55–61%. R. P. Barnes, *Organic Syntheses 21*, 77 (1941); *C.A. 1941*, 6249.

Keto Carboxylates

688. $CH_3COCH_2COOC_2H_5 + CH_3COCl \longrightarrow (CH_3CO)_2CHCOOC_2H_5$

$AcCH_2CO_2Et$ and AcCl are refluxed in benzene with Mg shavings → ethyl diacetylacetoacetate. Y = 46–52%. A. Spasov, *Organic Syntheses 21*, 46 (1941); *C.A. 1941*, 6240.

Magnesium-magnesium iodide   Mg–MgI$_2$

Bimolecular Reduction of Aldehydes to Glycols

$$2 \ H_3C\!\!\!\diagdown\!\!\!\bigcirc\!\!\!\diagup^{CH_3}_{CH_3}\!\!\!CHO \ \rightarrow \ H_3C\!\!\!\diagdown\!\!\!\bigcirc\!\!\!\diagup^{CH_3}\!\!\!\overset{OH}{\underset{H}{C}}\!\!-\!\!\overset{H}{\underset{OH}{C}}\!\!\diagdown\!\!\!\bigcirc\!\!\!\diagup^{CH_3}_{CH_3}$$

Mesitaldehyde (67 g.) is reduced in abs. C_6H_6 with Mg–MgI$_2$ mixture → 2 diastereomers (13 g. and 36 g.) hydromesitoin. R. C. Fuson and co-workers, *J. Am. Chem. Soc.* 64, 30 (1942); *C.A. 1942*, 1307. For methods, see Gomberg and Bachmann, *J. Am. Chem. Soc.* 49, 236 (1927).

Compare 684.

Magnesium amalgam   Mg–Hg
    See 677.

Zinc   Zn

Reformatskii Synthesis
β-Hydroxy Acids

$$CO \ \rightarrow \ C\!\!\diagup^{OH}_{CH_2COOR}$$

β-Hydroxy acids could not be prepd. from the corresponding amino acids through diazotization; preparation by the reaction of O$_3$ on allylalkyl carbinols [P. A. Levene and H. L. Haller, *J. Biol. Chem. 76*, 421 (1928)] gave yields of only 4–7%. The acids were therefore prepared from aldehydes with 2 less C atoms and BrCH$_2$CO$_2$Et by the Reformatskii reaction with yields of 10–12% (for literature, see original). Ex: Butyraldehydes and BrCH$_2$CO$_2$Et → β-hydroxyvalerate → β-hydroxyvaleric acid. F.e.s. F. Adickes and O. Andresen, *Ann.* 555, 41 (1943); *C.A. 1944*, 1732.

$$\bigcirc\!\!\!\diagup CHO \ \rightarrow \ \bigcirc\!\!\!\diagup CH(OH)CH_2COOC_2H_5$$

BrCH$_2$CO$_2$Et and benzaldehyde in the presence of Zn → ethyl β-phenyl-β-hydroxypropionate. Y = 61–64%. Also: Et α,α-dimethyl-β-phenyl-β-hydroxypropionate. Y = 73%. C. R. Hauser and D. S. Breslow, *Organic Syntheses 21*, 51 (1941); *C.A. 1941*, 6250.

$$\overset{\bigcirc}{\underset{CH_2-CH=CH_2}{\bigcirc}}\!\!\diagup^{COOC_2H_5}_{OH}$$

2-Allylcyclohexanone and PhCH$_2$CHBrCO$_2$Et with Zn → 2-allyl-1-(αcarbethoxyphenethyl)cyclohexanol. Y = 75%. R. Grewe, *Ber. 76*, 1076 (1943); *C.A. 1944*, 4936.

693.

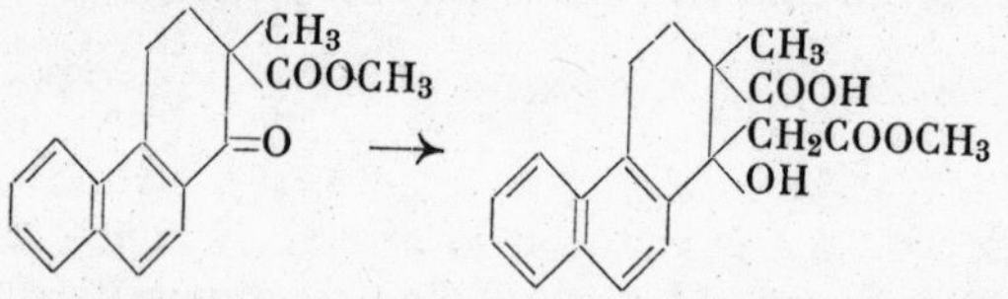

7-Methoxy-2-methyl-2-carbomethoxy-1-keto-1,2,3,4-tetrahydrophenan-threne and $BrCH_2CO_2Me$ with Zn and a little I_2 in thiophene-free C_6H_6 → di-Me 7-methoxy-2-methyl-2-carboxylate-1-hydroxy-1,2,3,4-tetrahydrophenanthrene-1-acetate. Y = 85–90%. W. E. Bachmann, Wayne Cole and A. L. Wilds, *J. Am. Chem. Soc. 62*, 824 (1940); *C.A. 1940*, 3757.

γ-Lactones from α-Keto Aldehydes

694.

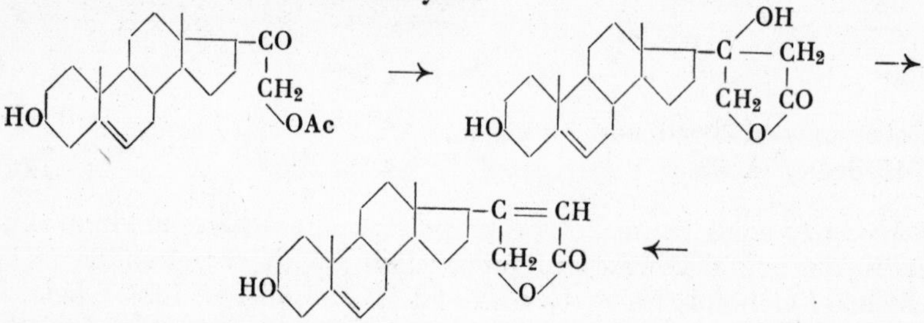

Pregnenonediol diacetate (4.0 g.) and Zn shavings in abs. benzene are partly distd.; $BrCH_2CO_2Et$ is added and the mixture is further distd. until start of the reaction when 2 cc. abs. alc. are added over a period of 30 min. while refluxing to accelerate the reaction. The mixt. is filtered and the Zn washed with hot alc.; the filtrate is warmed for 1.5 hrs. with 2 N HCl on a steam bath; the reaction product is filtered off and extd. with $CHCl_3$; the 2.57 g. $\Delta^{5,6,20,22}$-3(β),21-dihydroxynorcholadienic acid lactone (and its acetate) which is formed, is heated for 18 hrs. with Ac_2O → appr. 3.5 g. $\Delta^{5,6,20,22}$-3(β),21-dihydroxynorcholadienic acid lactone (and its acetate). L. Ruzicka, P. A. Plattner and A. Fürst, *Helv. Chim. Acta 25*, 79 (1942); *C.A. 1942*, 4514. For methods, see L. Ruzicka, T. Reichstein and A. Fürst, *Helv. Chim. Acta 24*, 76 (1941); *C.A. 1941*, 4773. See also, P. A. Plattner, L. Ruzicka and A. Fürst, *Helv. Chim. Acta 27*, 2274 (1943); *C.A. 1944*, 3986.

Zinc alkyls

Ketones from Carboxylic Acids　　　　　　　　　· COOH → · COR

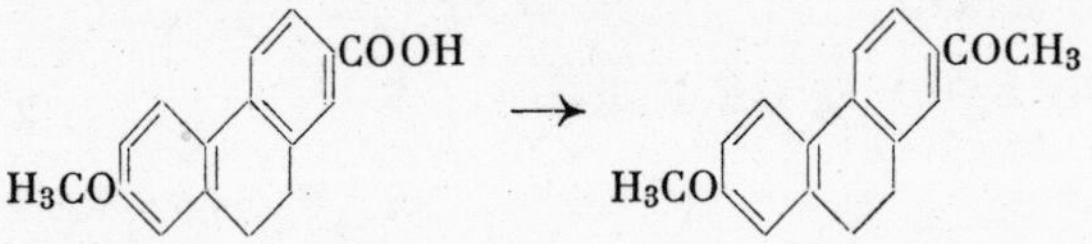

The chloride from 6 g. 7-methoxy-9,10-dihydro-2-phenanthrenecarboxylic acid is converted into the acid chloride, and this in a CO_2 atm. is treated with $ZnMe_2$ → 4.5 g. 2-acetyl-7-methoxy-9,10-dihydrophenanthrene. E. Dane and O. Höss, *Ann.* **552**, 113 (1942); *C.A. 1943*, 5055.

Zinc alkyl halides

$CH_3CH_2CH = C(C_3H_7)CH(CH_3)COCl$ ≻ $CH_3CH_2CH = C(C_3H_7)CH(CH_3)COCH_2CH_3$

2-Methyl-3-propyl-3-hexenoic acid (prepn., see 757) is heated at 70° with 1.25 moles $SOCl_2$ → 2-methyl-3-propyl-3-hexenoyl chloride (Y = 85%), which is treated with C_2H_5ZnI → 4-methyl-5-propyl-5-octen-3-one (Y = 78%). F.e.s. J. Colonge and D. Joly, *Ann. chim.* [11] *18*, 306 (1943); *C.A. 1944*, 5203.

Ketones from Acid Anhydrides

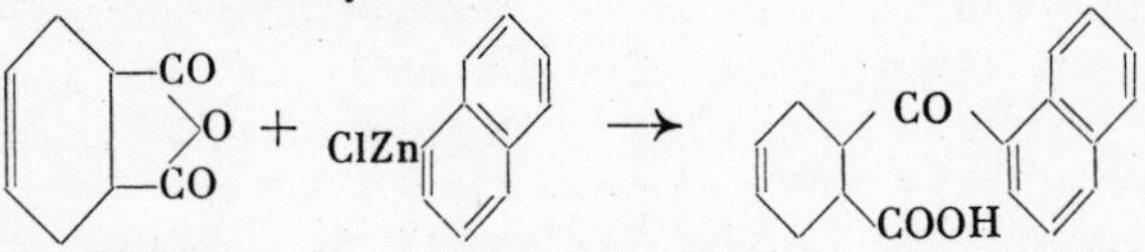

Δ^4-Tetrahydrophthalic anhydride (prepn., see 527) is reacted with 1-$C_{10}H_7ZnCl$ (prepd. from α-naphthyl-MgBr and $ZnCl_2$ in EtOH) → 2-(1-naphthoyl)-4-cyclohexene-1-carboxylic acid (s.m. 61). Y = 57%. L. F. Fieser and F. C. Novello, *J. Am. Chem. Soc.* **64**, 802 (1942); *C.A. 1942*, 3171.

Zinc chloride $ZnCl_2$

Coumaran or Chroman Derivatives   O
from Disubstituted Phenols

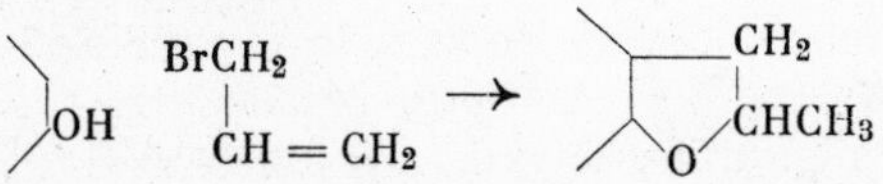

The Me substitution products of the hydroquinones are the most suitable phenol derivs. with respect to their reactivity with allyl halides. Corresponding catechol and resorcinol derivs. are either not at all, or only to a small extent, converted to coumaran or chroman derivs. by allyl halides in the presence of $ZnCl_2$. P. Karrer and E. Schick, *Helv. Chim. Acta 26*, 800 (1943); *C.A. 1944*, 1503.

Mercury and silver   **Hg, Ag**

Synthesis by Splitting Off Halogen $2 RCl \rightarrow R \cdot R$

699.   2 [structure: $C\langle^{Cl}_{COOC_2H_5}$ with two cyclohexyl rings] $\rightarrow$ $H_5C_2OOC \cdot C - C \cdot COOC_2H_5$ [with four cyclohexyl rings]

Ph_2CClCO_2Et is refluxed with "molecular" Ag [Prepn., see Houben, Vol. II, 736 (1925)] in ether and C_6H_6 for 3 hrs. in an N_2 atm. (Y = 84%), or shaken with Hg in ether–C_6H_6 for 48 hrs. (Y = 61%) $\rightarrow$ di-Et tetraphenylsuccinate. B. Witten and F. Y. Wiselogle, *J. Org. Chem.* 6, 584 (1941); *C.A. 1941*, 7389.

Aluminum amalgam   **Al-Hg**

Alkylation of Isocyclic Compounds $ArH \rightarrow ArR$

700. $AlCl_3$ can be replaced by aluminum amalgam (activated just before use by some alkyl chloride) in the Friedel-Crafts synthesis of alkyl-benzenes and naphthalenes. The formation of tars and side re-actions are hereby avoided. Prepn: The mixture of alkyl chloride and hydrocarbon is added to the aluminum and is left overnight. Ex: EtCl and $C_6H_6 \rightarrow$ PhEt (Y = 76%). PrCl and $C_6H_6 \rightarrow$ PhPr (Y = 15.2%) and iso-PrPh (Y = 52.2%). Iso-PrCl and $C_6H_6 \rightarrow$ iso-PrPh (Y = 83.8%). *sec*-BuCl and $C_{10}H_8 \rightarrow$ 1-*sec*-butylnaphthalene (Y = 48%). F.e.s. L. J. Diuguid, *J. Am. Chem. Soc.* 63, 3527 (1941); *C.A. 1942*, 1019.

Aluminum chloride   **AlCl₃**

Hydrocarbons
ω-Chloroallyl Compounds

701.   The action of 1,3-dichloropropene on aromatic hydrocarbons leads to the corresponding ω-chloroallyl aromatic hydrocarbons in 50–80% yields. In the monosubstituted benzene hydrocarbons, the ω-chloroallyl group enters in the para position; in polysubstituted derivatives, the group enters in the same position as the Br atom on bromination in the cold. As starting materials, benzene, ethylbenzene, and *p*-cymene were used. F.e.s. P. Bert, *Compt. rend.* 213, 619 (1941); *C.A. 1943*, 4373.

702. CH_3O—[benzene ring]— $+ ClCH = CHCH_2Cl \rightarrow CH_3O$—[benzene ring]—$CH = CHCH_2Cl$

PhOMe and $CHCl : CHCH_2Cl$ are treated with $AlCl_3 \rightarrow p\text{-}MeOC_6\text{-}$

$H_4CH_2CH : CHCl$. Y = 70%. These compounds give good yields of alkooxycinnamyl ethers ($ROC_6H_4CH = CHCH_2OR'$) from which the corresponding alcohols, aldehydes, alkoxy-, and hydroxycinnamic acids can easily be prepared. From the alkoxycinnamyl ethers, the aldehydes ($RO - C_6H_4 - CHO$) can easily be obtained by oxidation. L. Bert, *Compt. rend.* **213**, 797 (1941); *C.A.* **1943**, 4710. See also, *Compt. rend.* **214**, 230 (1942); *C.A.* **1943**, 2728; *Compt. rend.* **213**, 873 (1941); *C.A.* **1943**, 4060.

Ketones   ArH → ArCOR
Nucleus Acylations by Friedel-Crafts Reaction

3. 1. The acylation of the nucleus containing unsaturated groups, such as NO_2, COR, and CN, which hinder acylation, is made possible by introduction of alkoxy groups. Ex: $2\text{-}O_2NC_6H_4OMe$ in ice-cold nitrobenzene → 3-nitro-4-methoxyacetophenone. Y = 50%.
2. No acylation of the nucleus takes place with *m*- and *p*-nitroanisoles, a methyl group being replaced by an acetyl group instead. Ex: 3-$O_2NC_6H_4OMe$ → 3-$O_2NC_6H_4OAc$; Y = 80%. 4-$O_2NC_6H_4OMe$ → 4-$O_2NC_6H_4OAc$; Y = 70%. F.e.s. W. Borsche and J. Barthenheier, *Ann.* **553**, 250 (1942); *C.A.* **1943**, 5044.

4. 3. Unsaturated groups do not hinder the Friedel-Crafts reaction when there is at least one methylene bridge between the unsaturated group and the nucleus.

4. The reactivity of acid halides in the Friedel-Crafts reaction decreases as follows: haloacetic acids—aliphatic acids—aromatic-aliphatic acids—aromatic acids. Method: 1 to 2 moles of acid chloride and an excess of $AlCl_3$ in CS_2 are used. The mixture is allowed to stand for 14–16 hrs. at room temp., is heated on a steam bath, and is worked up in the usual manner. W. Borsche and F. Sinn, *Ann.* **553**, 260 (1942); *C.A.* **1943**, 5044.

5. **Orientation in the Acylation of Phenol and the Rearrangement of Phenolic Esters.** Mixtures of *o*- and *p*-hydroxy ketones result in Friedel-Crafts acylation of phenol, as well as in the Fries rearrangement (see 537) of phenolic esters. The results of the study of the influence of experimental conditions upon the orientation were: (*1*) High $AlCl_3$ content favored the formation of *p*-hydroxy ketones in both reactions. (*2*) Certain solvents influence the orientation strongly as the list, increasing in ortho-directing influence, shows: $PhNO_2$, Skellysolve "B," $C_2H_2Cl_4$, CS_2. A. W. Ralston, M. R. McCorkle and S. T. Bauer, *J. Org. Chem.* **5**, 645 (1940); *C.A.* **1941**, 1045. Compare A. W. Ralston, M. R. McCorkle and E. W. Segebrecht, *J. Org. Chem.* **6**, 750 (1941); *C.A.* **1941**, 7939.

706. **Investigation of Ease of Acylation of Benzene Nucleus of Indoles and Quinolines** by the Friedel-Crafts reaction. W. Borsche and H. Groth, *Ann. 549,* 238 (1941); *C.A. 1943,* 3754.

707. Naphthalene is treated with behenoyl acid chloride in CS_2 in the presence of $AlCl_3 \rightarrow$ heneicosyl naphthyl ketone, $C_{32}H_{50}O$. Y = 80%. F.e.s. L. A. Mickesda and C. A. Cohen, *J. Org. Chem. 6,* 787 (1941); *C.A. 1942,* 741.

708. 1,2-Dimethylnaphthalene (prepn., see 632) is treated with AcCl and $AlCl_3$ in $PhNO_2 \rightarrow$ 1,2-dimethyl-4-acetylnaphthalene. Y = 75%. When CS_2 is used as the solvent, Y = 65%. P. A. Plattner and A. Ronco, *Helv. Chim. Acta 27,* 400 (1944); *C.A. 1944,* 4585.

709.

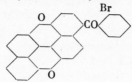

Dinaphthalene dioxide and $AlCl_3$ in PhCl are treated with an equimolar amount of $o\text{-}BrC_6H_4COCl$ at 70° → *o*-bromobenzoyldinaphthalene dioxide (s.m. 768). Crude yield = 87%. R. Pummerer and coworkers, *Ann. 553,* 103 (1942); *C.A. 1943,* 5059.

Acylhydroquinone Ethers

710.

$$\underset{OCH_3}{\overset{OCH_3}{\bigcirc}} \rightarrow \underset{OCH_3}{\overset{OCH_3}{\bigcirc}} CO(CH_2)_x\,CH_3$$

Hydroquinone ether is stirred for 12 hrs. with palmitic acid chloride and $AlCl_3$ in $C_2H_2Cl_4 \rightarrow$ 2,5-dimethoxypalmitophenone. Y = 69%. Also: Hydroquinone diEt ether and myristic acid chloride → 2,5-diethoxymyristophenone. Y = 62%. F.e.s. A. H. Cook, I. M. Heilbron and F. B. Lewis, *J. Chem. Soc. 1942,* 659; *C.A. 1943,* 876.

711. γ-Phenyl-γ-benzylpyrotartaric acid chloride [$PhCH_2CHPhCH(CO_2H)\text{-}CH_2CO_2Cl$] is dissolved in $PhNO_2$, treated gradually with $AlCl_3$ at room temp., and heated at 50° for a few hours → 3-phenyl-1-oxotetralin-2-acetic acid. Y = 65–70%. For other less advantageous cyclization methods, by which the acid is treated with H_2SO_4 in ether (resulting in lower yields) at 0°, or from the anhydride with $AlCl_3$, see W. Borsche and F. Sinn, *Ann. 555,* 70 (1943); *C.A. 1944,* 1740.

Introduction of COCOOH, CHOHCOOH, and CH₂COOH Groups into Aromatic Nuclei

712. Phenylglyoxylates can be obtd. from alkylbenzenes and phenol ethers

with $ClCOCO_2Et$ and $AlCl_3$ in $BzNO_2$. Red. with Mohr's Pd in glac. AcOH yields mandelates and addn. of $H_2SO_4 + HBr$, $HClO_4$ or $ZnCl_2 + HCl$ as accelerators yields the aryl acetates. Ex: Toluene and $ClCOCO_2Et \rightarrow$ Et p-methylphenylglyoxylate $(Y = 79\%) \rightarrow p$-methyl-mandelic acid $\rightarrow$ Et p-Me-phenylacetate $(Y = $ at least 70%). Et 3,4-pyrocatechinacetate $\rightarrow$ 3,4-di-EtO deriv. $(Y = 81\%) \rightarrow$ 3,4-diEtO-phenyl acetate $(Y = $ at least 70%). F.e.s. K. Kindler, W. Metzendorf and Dschi-yin-Kwok, *Ber.* 76, 308 (1943); *C.A. 1943*, 5709.

Iodine I_2
See 693.

Ferric chloride $FeCl_3$
See 668.

Sulfur ⚞   CC ⚟ S

Without additional reagents

Substituted Butadienes as Diene Components

2-Chlorobutadienes are converted to sulfones (with a reactive Cl atom, despite its attachment to a C double bond) with SO_2. They react, for example, with mercaptides to form thio ethers, or with acetoacetic esters, malonic esters, or pyrroles. On heating, these sulfones are converted back to butadienes. As these are unstable, they are only liberated in the diene synthesis in the presence of dienophile compounds. Ex: 2-Chloro-3-methyl-1,3-butadiene (prepn., see 406) with $SO_2 \rightarrow$ 3-chloro-4-methyl-1-thia-3-cyclopentene-1-dioxide $(Y = 30\%)$, with MeSNa in boiling EtOH $\rightarrow$ 4-methyl-1-thia-3-cyclopentene-1-dioxide 3-Me-thio ether $(Y = 71\%)$. This is heated with maleic anhydride and boiled with NaOH $\rightarrow$ 5-methyl-4-cyclohexene-1,2-dicarboxylic acid 4-Me-thio ether $(Y = 54\%)$. H. I. Backer and T. A. H. Blass, *Rec. trav. Chim.* 61, 785 (1942); *C.A. 1944*, 3646. See also, H. I. Backer and J. Strating, *ibid.* 62, 815 (1943); *C.A. 1944*, 6283.

Ethylene Derivatives from Sulfones $\cdot CH - CH \cdot \rightarrow \cdot CH : CH \cdot$
See 615. $\diagdown SO_2 \diagup$

Pyridine C_5H_5N

Cyanine Synthesis

714.

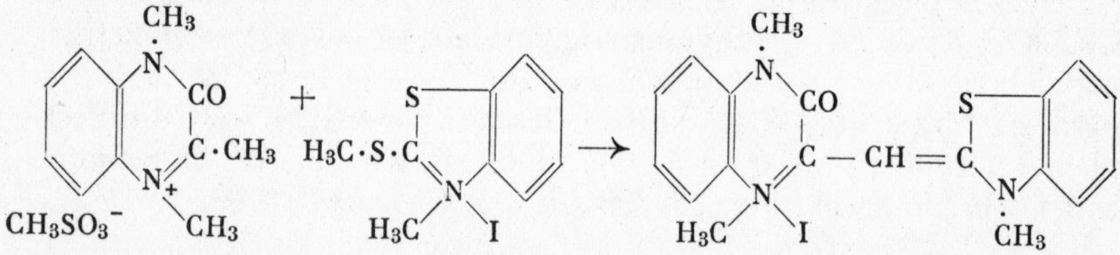

2-Keto-1,3-dimethyl-1,2-dihydroquinoxaline is heated with Me_2SO_4 for 30 min. at 180°. 1 g. of the reaction product is boiled with 2-methylbenzothiazolyl sulfide and MeI in C_5H_5N → 2-(1-methylbenzothiazole)-2-(3-keto-1,4-dimethyl-3,4-dihydroquinoxaline)monomethinecyanide iodide (1.65 g.). F.e.s. A. H. Cook and R. F. Naylor, *J. Chem. Soc. 1943*, 397; *C.A. 1944*, 363.

Carbon ⋏   CC ⋎⋏ C

Electrolysis   ⅄

Ketones from Carboxylic Acids According to Kolbe

$$\cdot CH_2 \cdot COOH \atop + \atop \cdot CH_2 \cdot COOH \quad \rightarrow \quad {\cdot CH_2 \atop | \atop \cdot CH_2}$$

$$CH_3COCH_2CH_2COCH_2CH_2COOH + HOOC(CH_2)_4CH_3 \succ CH_3COCH_2CH_2CO(CH_2)_6CH_3$$

715. 4,7-Diketooctanoic acid and caproic acid are electrolyzed with 1 g. Na in MeOH → 2,5-dodecanedione. Y = 30–45%. F.e.s. H. Hunsdiecker, *Ber. 75*, 447 (1942); *C.A. 1943*, 3403.

716. $$2\ C_2H_5OOC(CH_2)_8COOK \rightarrow C_2H_5OOC(CH_2)_{16}COOC_2H_5$$

The K salt of monoethyl sebacate is electrolyzed with Pt electrodes → ethyl 1,16-hexadecanedicarboxylate. S. Swann, Jr., R. Oehler and P. S. Pinkney, *Organic Syntheses 21*, 48 (1941); *C.A. 1941*, 6240.

Sodium hydroxide

Thioindoxyl Synthesis   O

717.

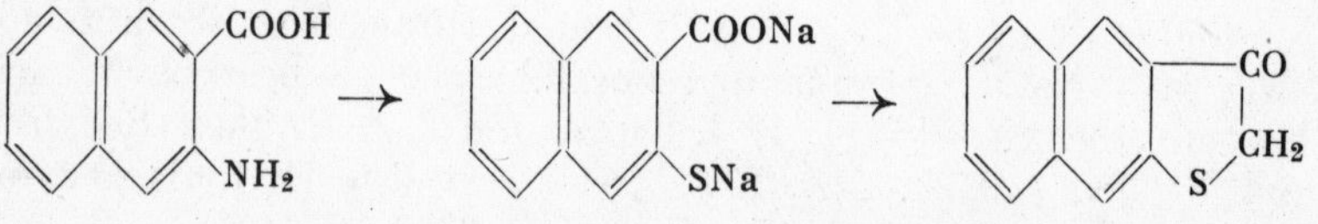

2,3-$H_2NC_{10}H_6CO_2H$ (93 g.) is diazotized in a HCl soln.; the diazonium salt is converted to the disulfide with Na_2S_2 and this is reduced with $Na_2S_2O_4$ in an alkaline soln. → 2,3-$HSC_{10}H_6CO_2Na$, which reacts with $ClCH_2CO_2Na$ and aq. NaOH → 87 g. 5,6-benzothioindoxyl. J. H. Mason and F. G. Mann, *J. Chem. Soc. 1942*, 404; *C.A. 1942*, 5650.

Chromic acid CrO_3

Ketones from Two Molecules of Alcohol or Aldehyde or from Aldols

8. The method for the prepn. of ketones through the simultaneous dehydrogenation and condensation of primary alcohols with Cr catalysts also lends itself to the preparation of mixed ketones, especially methyl ketones. Aldehydes and aldols give the same reaction and better yields than the alcohol. Reduced pressure increases the yield. Ex: *n*-Octyl alcohol at 125–135 mm. pressure → di-*n*-heptyl ketone; Y = 74%. 75% (by vol.) *n*-octyl alcohol and 25% (by vol.) EtOH → methyl *n*-heptyl ketone; Y = 41.7%. Equivalent amounts of *n*-amyl and *n*-decyl alcohols → *n*-butyl *n*-nonyl ketone; Y = 27.2%. V. I. Komarewsky and J. R. Coley, *J. Am. Chem. Soc. 63*, 3269 (1941); *C.A. 1941*, 2851. Compare, *J. Am. Chem. Soc. 63*, 700 (1941).

Elimination

Hydrogen ↟   CC ⇑ H

Lithium   *Li*

Ethinyl Alcohols

9.
$$C_6H_5CH = CHBr \xrightarrow{C_6H_5Li} C_6H_5C \equiv CLi \xrightarrow{+ (C_6H_5)_2CO} C_6H_5C \equiv C \cdot COH(C_6H_5)_2$$

CHPh : CHBr is treated with LiPh in abs. Et_2O in an atm. of N_2; this is followed by treatment with $COPh_2$ in Et_2O → 1,1,3-triphenyl-2-propyn-1-ol. Y = 95%. G. Wittig and D. Waldi, *J. prakt. Chem. 160*, 242 (1942); *C.A. 1943*, 5399.

Aluminum chloride $AlCl_3$

Chrysenes   O

0. 1-(2-Methylphenyl)-2-(1,2-dimethyl-5-naphthyl)ethane (4.5 g.) is shaken with an equal amount of $AlCl_3$ in CS_2 for 3 days → 0.4 g. crude

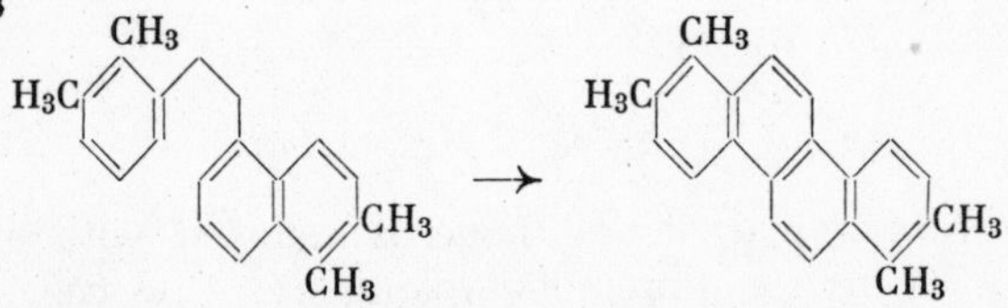

1,7,8-trimethylchrysene. L. Ruzicka, A. Grob and G. Anner, *Helv. Chim. Acta 26*, 254 (1943); *C.A. 1944*, 345.

Lead tetraacetate $Pb(CH_3COO)_4$

Dehydrogenation $\cdot CH_2 \cdot CH_2 \cdot \rightarrow \cdot CH : CH \cdot$
See 534.

Sulfur   S

721. **S Substituted for Se in Dehydrogenations.** Dehydrogenations which were usually carried out with Se at 300° are now accomplished (partly with the same compounds) by heating with S in a round vessel with a vertically raised tube. L. Ruzicka, H. Schinz and P. H. Müller, *Helv. Chim. Acta 27*, 195 (1944); *C.A. 1944*, 4582.

722. 6,7-Dimethoxy-3,4-dihydronaphthalene-1,2-dicarboxylic anhydride (2 g.) is heated for 15 min. at 250° with S → 6,7-dimethoxynaphthalene-1,2-dicarboxylic anhydride (1.8 g.). G. Bruckner, *Ber. 75*, 2034 (1943); *C.A. 1944*, 1228.

See also 668.

Selenium   Se
See 721.

723.

1,2-Diphenyl-3,4-dihydronaphthalene is heated with Se at 280–290° → 1,2-diphenylnaphthalene. Y = 80%. F. Bergmann, H. E. Eschinazi and D. Schapiro, *J. Am. Chem. Soc. 64*, 557 (1942); *C.A. 1942*, 2547.

See also 397.

Chloranil

724.

4-Bromo-5,6,7,8-tetrahydrofluoranthene is refluxed with chloranil in *m*-xylene for 24 hrs. → 4-bromofluoranthene. Y = 65%. R. Tobler, T. Holbro, P. Sutter and W. Kern, *Helv. Chim. Acta 24E*, 100 (1941); *C.A. 1942*, 5160.

725.

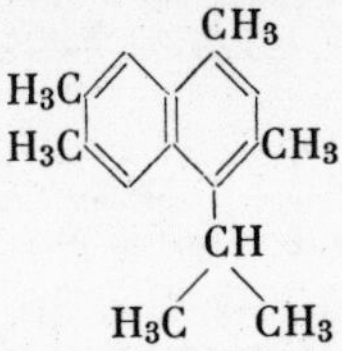

Also: 4-Isopropyl-1,3,6,7-tetramethyl-1,2-dihydronaphthalene → 4-iso-propyl-1,3,6,7-tetramethylnaphthalene. Y = 79%. F.e.s. W. P. Campbell and M. D. Soffer, *J. Am. Chem. Soc.* 64, 417 (1942); *C.A. 1942,* 1922.

N-Bromosuccinimide

726.

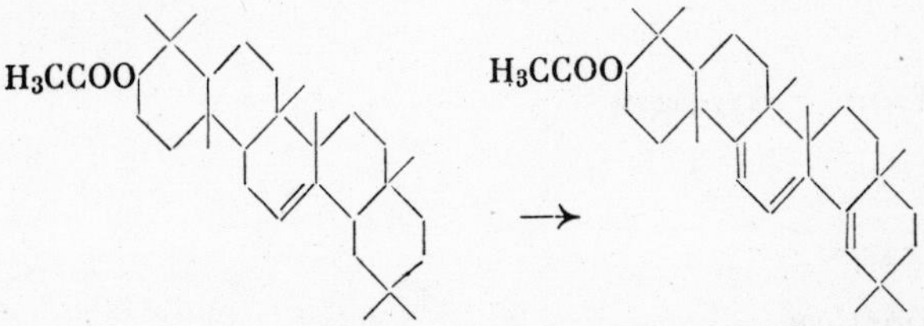

Supplementary double linkages can be introduced in α- and β-amyrin type compounds with N-bromosuccinimide. Ex: 200 mg. β-amyrin acetate is heated for 2 hrs. with $\overline{OC \cdot CH_2 \cdot CH_2 \cdot CO \cdot N}Br$ in CCl₄ → 160–170 mg. β-amyratrionol acetate. F.e.s. L. Ruzicka, O. Jeger and J. Redel, *Helv. Chim. Acta 26,* 1235 (1943); *C.A. 1944,* 1488.

Manganese dioxide   MnO₂

Polyaryl Condensation

727.

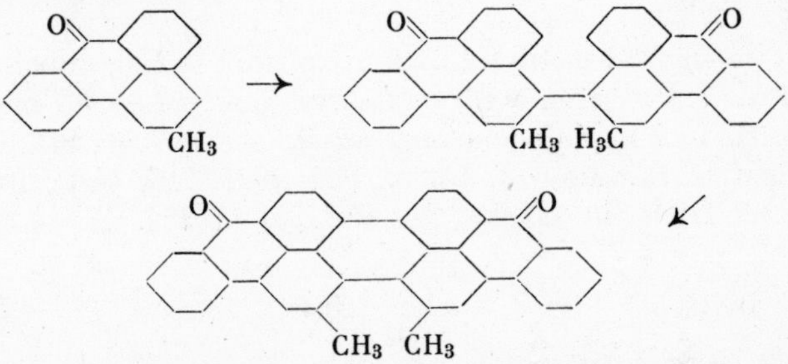

1. 2-Methyl-*meso*-benzanthrone (prepn., see 589) is oxidized at 0–5° with MnO₂ in 80% H₂SO₄ → 2,2'-dimethyl-3,3'-dibenzanthronyl (Y = 78%); 5 g. of this is heated with KOH and EtOH at 120–130° → 4.7 g. crude 16,17-dimethyldibenzanthrone.

2. 2-Methyl-*meso*-benzanthrone (10 g.) (I) is fused with KOH at

230–240° in the presence of glucose → 6 g. 16,17-dimethyldibenzanthrone.

3. (I) is added at 125–130° to a mixture of KAc, MeOH, and KOH and naphthalene; MnO_2 is added over a period of 5–10 min. while the temperature is raised to 215° → 4 g. 16,17-dimethyldibenzanthrone. D. H. Hey, R. J. Nicholls and C. W. Pritchett, *J. Chem. Soc. 1944*, 97; *C.A. 1944*, 3644.

Ferric chloride $FeCl_3$

Aminoacridines from Nitroacridines
    See 23.

Nickel Ni

Pyrroles from Pyrrolines
    See 397.

Mohr's palladium Pd

Dehydrogenation

728. 6,7-Dimethoxy-1-(3,4,5-trimethoxybenzyl)-3,4-dihydroisoquinoline (0.2005 g.) is heated at exactly 200° with Mohr's Pd for 45 min. → 0.1048 g. 6,7-dimethoxy-1-(3,4,5-trimethoxy)benzylisoquinoline, C_{21}-$H_{23}O_5N$. The basis for the technical synthesis of papaverine and the easy preparation of the various real isoquinolines are the dehydrogenations with Mohr's Pd of dihydropapaverine and dihydroisoquinolines. E. Späth and T. Meinhard, *Ber. 75*, 400 (1942); *C.A. 1943*, 3099.

Palladized carbon

729. 6,7-Methylenedioxy-3-methyl-1,2,3,4-tetrahydro-1,2,naphthalenedicarboxylic acid diethyl ester with palladized charcoal → 6,7-methylenedioxy-3-methyl-1,2-naphthalenedicarboxylic acid. Y = 50%. B. J. F. Hudson and R. Robinson, *J. Chem. Soc. 1941*, 715; *C.A. 1942*, 1312. Methods, see Diels and Gädke, *Ber. 58*, 1231 (1925).

730.

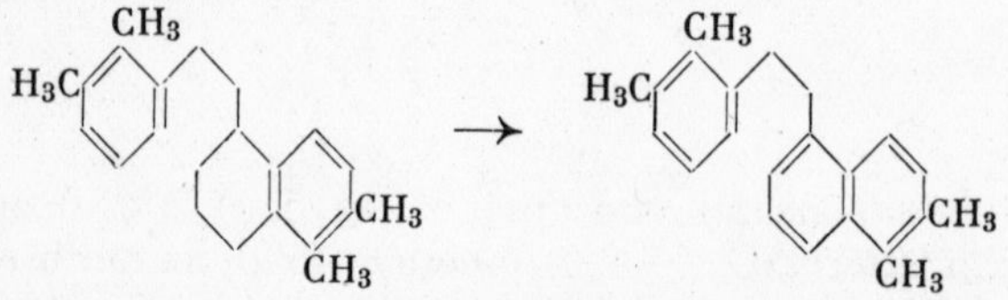

1-(2-Methylphenyl)-2-(1,2-dimethyl-5,6,7,8-tetrahydro-5-naphthyl)-ethane (7.5 g.) is heated at 320° with 4% Pd–charcoal. Approximately 600 cc. H_2 is given off → 5 g. 1-(2-methylphenyl)-2-(1,2-dimethyl-5-

naphthyl)ethane. L. Ruzicka, A. Grob and G. Anner, *Helv. Chim. Acta* 26, 254 (1943); *C.A. 1944*, 345.

731.

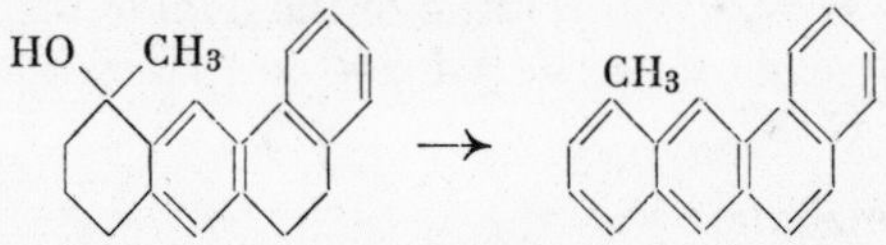

8-Methyl-8-hydroxy-3,4,5,6,7,8-hexahydro-1,2-benzanthracene heated at 300–320° with Pd–charcoal → 8-methyl-1,2-benzanthracene. Y = 84%. F.e.s. W. E. Bachmann and J. M. Chemerda, *J. Org. Chem.* 6, 36 (1941); *C.A. 1941*, 2504.

Platinized carbon   **Pt**

Dehydrogenation and Rearrangement

732.

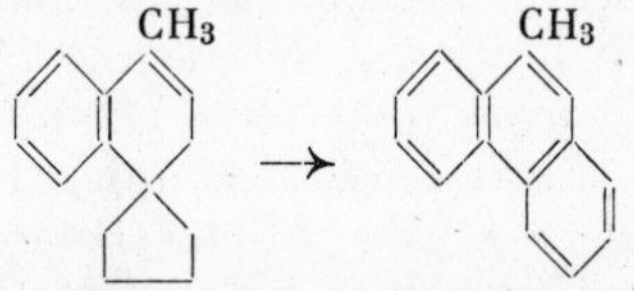

Spiro [cyclopentane-1,1'-4-methyldihydronaphthalene] (3.7 g.) is passed over a Pd–charcoal catalyst for 5 hrs. at 330–340° in an apparatus as described by Levitz and Bogert [*J. Am. Chem. Soc.* 64, 1719 (1942); *C.A. 1942*, 5808] for larger amounts → 2.4 g. 9-methylphenanthrene. M. Levitz and M. T. Bogert, *J. Org. Chem.* 8, 253 (1943); *C.A. 1943*, 5055.

Oxygen ↑   **CC ⇑ O**

Without additional reagents

Thermal Cleavage of Esters of
Fatty Acids   · CH₂CH(OOCR) · → · CH : CH ·
   See 781.

733. Dodecyl palmitate is distilled at 600 mm. pressure → 1-dodecene. Y = 70%. P. Baumgarten, *Ber.* 75, 977 (1942); *C.A. 1943*, 4683.

Dehydration Via Esters of
Fatty Acids   · CH₂CH(OOCR) · → · CH : CH ·

734. A mixture of dodecanols (prepn., see 46) is converted to the stearates with stearoyl chloride; these compounds are heated at 290° and 600 mm. in N₂ → mixture of dodecenes. Y = 95.5%. F. Asinger, *Ber.* 77, 73 (1944); *C.A. 1945*, 906.

735. *n*-Hexadecanol is heated with stearoyl chloride at 100–120° → *n*-hexa-decyl stearate, which is heated at 330–360° and 300 mm. pressure → 1-hexadecene. Y = 69%. No shifting of the double bond occurs during this thermal cleavage. F.e.s. F. Asinger and H. Eckoldt, *Ber.* 76, 585 (1943); *C.A. 1944,* 57.

Cleavage of Benzoates

736.

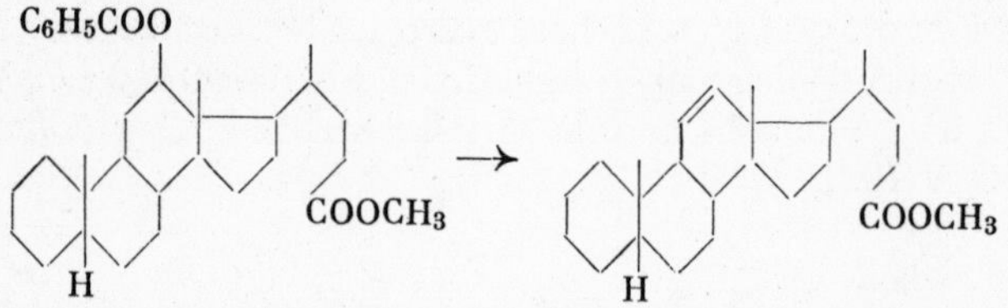

Advantages over the cleavage of acetates: (*1*) the cleavage proceeds more smoothly; and (*2*) the measurable and visible splitting off of the benzoic acid gives an indication of the progress of the reactions. Y, on the basis of recovered starting products = about 50%. Method: Heating for 1–2 hrs. at 12 mm. pressure in CO_2 at approximately 310°. Ex: Me 12(β)-benzoxycholanate → Me 11-cholenate. F.e.s. A. Lardon, P. Grandjean, J. Press, H. Reich and T. Reichstein, *Helv. Chim. Acta* 25, 1444 (1942); *C.A. 1943,* 5981.

Dehydration Via the Xanthates

737.

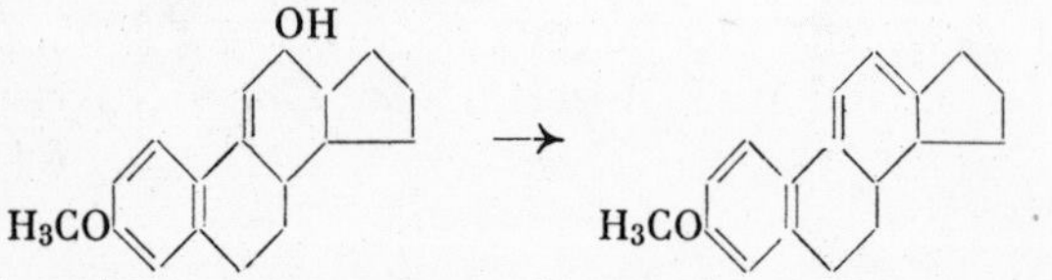

3-Hydroxy-7-methoxy-1,2,3,9,10,11-hexahydro-1,2-cyclopentenophen-anthrene is refluxed with Na, CS_2, and MeI; the resulting methyl xanthate is heated at 180° under reduced pressure → 7-methoxy-1,9,10,11-tetrahydro-1,2-cyclopentenophenanthrene. The yields are small, but $KHSO_4$ treatment caused dehydration as well as dehydro-genation. R. Robinson and S. N. Slater, *J. Chem. Soc. 1941,* 376; *C.A. 1941,* 6964.

Dehydration
Via Anthraquinone-β-Carboxylates $\cdot CH_2CH(OH) \cdot \rightarrow \cdot CH : CH \cdot$

738.

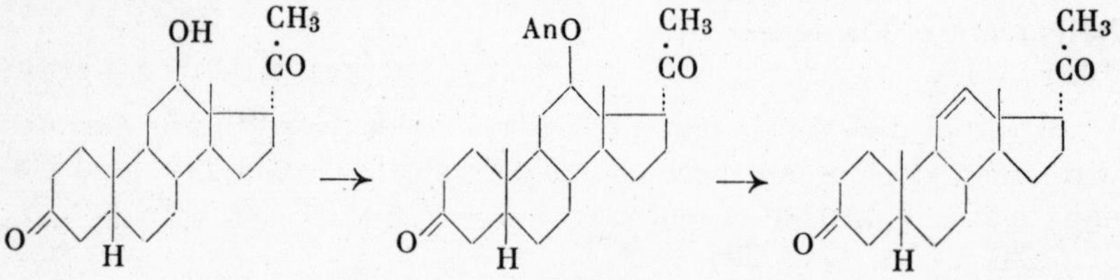

The thermal cleavage of anthraquinone-β-carboxylates proceeds more smoothly than that of the benzoates used earlier [P. Hegner and T. Reichstein, *Helv. Chim. Acta* 26, 721 (1943); *C.A. 1944*, 1518]. 12-(β)-pregnanol-3,20-dione in pyridine is treated with 2-$C_6H_4(CO)_2$-C_6H_3COCl in C_6H_6, boiled shortly, and is worked up in the usual manner after standing for 16 hrs. at 20° → 12-(β)-pregnanol-3,20-dione anthraquinonecarboxylate (Y = 90%). This is heated in a Claisen flask with a sausage-shaped side arm at 0.05 mm. and 295–300° for 2 hrs. → 11-pregnene-3,20-dione (Y = 39.4%). F.e.s. J. v. Euw, A. Lardon and T. Reichstein, *Helv. Chim. Acta* 27, 821 (1944); *C.A. 1945*, 938.

Sodium powder　　　　　　　　　　　　　　　　　　　　　*Na*

Anthracenes

739.

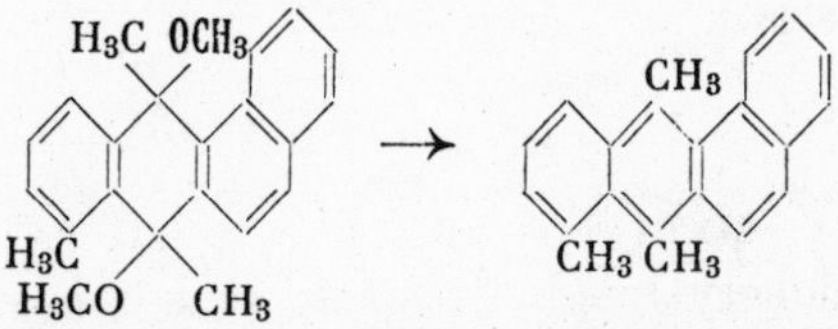

8,9,10-Trimethoxy-9,10-dihydroxy-1,2-benzanthracene with Na powder in a C_6H_6–ether mixture → 8,9,10-trimethyl-1,2-benzanthracene. Y = 82%. W. E. Bachmann and J. M. Chemerda, *J. Org. Chem. 6*, 36 (1941); *C.A. 1941*, 2504.

Alkali alcoholates

Unsaturated Sterids
from Steryl Sulfates　　　　　　　$\cdot CH \cdot C(OSO_3H) \cdot \to \cdot C : C \cdot$

740. The introduction of double bonds into the sterid nucleus is accomplished in good yields by heating the K salts of steryl sulfates in alcohols in the presence of alkali alcoholates at 180°. At lower temperatures no decomposition of the sulfate takes place. Ex: K cholesteryl sulfate is heated at 177° for 1 hr. in a soln. of Na (1 g.) in 200 cc. capryl alcohol (2-octanol) → 3,5-cholestadiene. F.e.s. A. E. Sobel and M. T. Rosen, *J. Am. Chem. Soc. 63*, 3536 (1943).

Potassium hydroxide　　　　　　　　　　　　　　　　　　*KOH*

Splitting Off Acetic Acid　　　　　$\cdot CH_2CH(OOCR) \cdot \to \cdot CH : CH \cdot$

741.

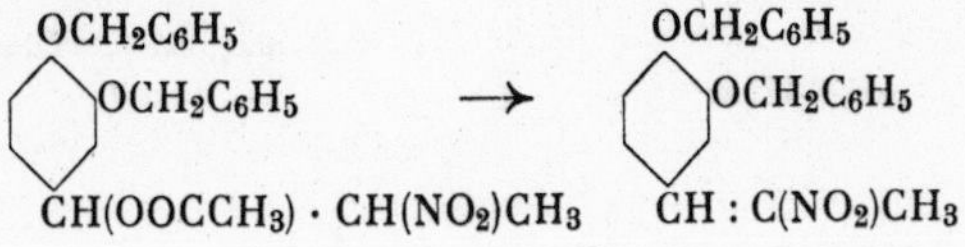

1-(3,4-Dibenzyloxyphenyl)-2-nitropropyl acetate (5 g.) (prepn., see

292) is shaken with lukewarm 8% alc. KOH → 3.5 g. 1-(3,4-dibenzyl-oxyphenyl)-2-nitropropene. G. Bruckner and G. v. Fodor, *Ber.* 76, 466 (1943); *C.A. 1943*, 6656. See also, G. v. Fodor, *Ber.* 76, 1216 (1943); *C.A. 1945, 286.*

Beryllium sulfate $BeSO_4$

Dehydration

742. Cyclohexanol is treated with anhydrous $BeSO_4$ → cyclohexene. Y = nearly quant. F.e.s. R. Pajeau, *Bull. soc. chim. Mém.* [5] 9, 741 (1942); *C.A. 1943, 6531.*

Zinc chloride $ZnCl_2$

Anthrol Synthesis

743.

o-[p-Tolyl-(cyclohexyl)methyl]benzoic acid is heated for 20 min. at 180–190° with $ZnCl_2$ → 2-methyl-10-cyclohexyl-9-anthrone. (s.m. 40). Y = 75%. A. T. Marchevskii and M. I. Urshakov, *J. Gen. Chem. U.S.S.R.* 10, 1369 (1940); *C.A. 1941*, 3626.

Aluminum oxide Al_2O_3

Dehydration   · $CH_2CH(OH)$ · → · $CH : CH$ ·
See 744.

Acetic anhydride $(CH_3CO)_2O$
See 694.

Aluminum alcoholate $Al(OR)_3$
See 44.

Phthalic anhydride

744. Cycloheptanol is added dropwise to boiling $C_4H_6(CO)_2O$ → cyclo-heptene. Y = 98%. Other ethylene derivatives are obtained from the corresponding alcohols with Al_2O_3 at 300–310°. Discussion of this method: J. Boëseken and C. J. A. Hanegraaf, *Rec. trav. Chim.* 61, 69 (1942); *C.A. 1943*, 5012.

Phosphoric acid H_3PO_4

Hydrophenanthrene

745.

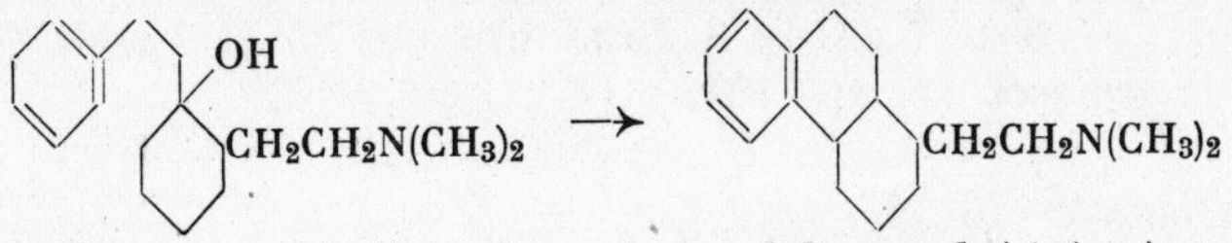

2-(2-Dimethylaminoethyl)-1-phenethylcyclohexanol (4.5 g.) is heated with syrupy H_3PO_4 at 120° → 3 g. 1-(2-dimethyl-aminoethyl)-*asym*-octahydrophenanthrene. R. Grewe, *Ber. 76*, 1072 (1943); *C.A. 1944*, 4935.

Phosphorus oxychloride

Isoquinoline Ring

746.

1-(3-Methoxy-4-benzyloxyphenyl)-1-hydroxy-2-acetamidopropane in $CHCl_3$ is refluxed for 3 hrs. with $POCl_3$ → 1,3-dimethyl-6-methoxy-7-benzyloxyisoquinoline. Y = 69%. G. v. Fodor, *Ber. 76*, 1216 (1943); *C.A. 1945*, 286.

747.

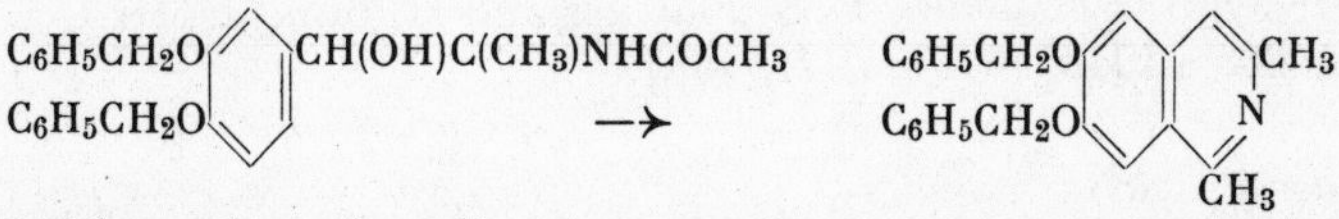

1-(3,4-Dibenzyloxyphenyl)-2-acetamido-1-propanol (0.4 g.) is dissolved in toluene and boiled for 10 min. with $POCl_3$ → 0.2 g. 1,3-dimethyl-6,7-dibenzyloxyisoquinoline · HCl. V. Bruckner and G. v. Fodor, *Ber. 76*, 466 (1943); *C.A. 1943*, 6656.

Cyclic Ketone

748.

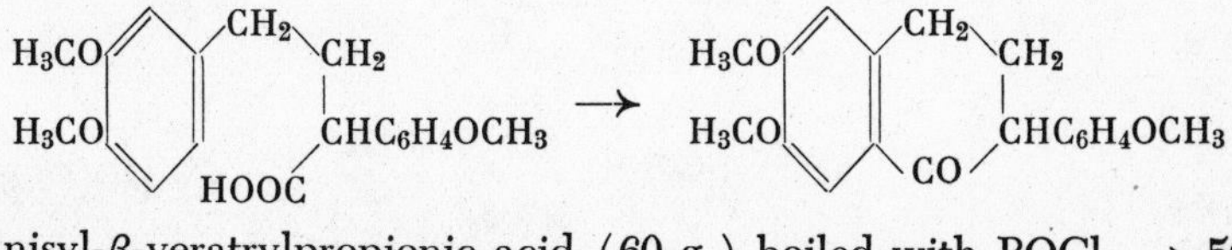

α-Anisyl-β-veratrylpropionic acid (60 g.) boiled with $POCl_3$ → 56 g. 1-keto-6,7-dimethoxy-2-anisyl-1,2,3,4-tetrahydronaphthalene. F.e.s. L. Goldberg and R. Robinson, *J. Chem. Soc. 1941*, 575; *C.A. 1942*, 488.

Acridones

749.

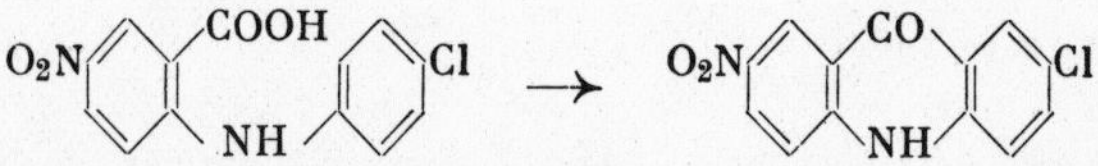

4-Nitro-4'-chlorodiphenylamine-2-carboxylic acid is refluxed in C_6H_6 with PCl_5 or $POCl_3$ until HCl evolution ceases → 3-nitro-7-chloroacridone. Y = 80%. F.e.s. F. R. Bradbury and W. H. Linell, *Quart. J. Pharm. Pharmacol.* 15, 31 (1942); *C.A. 1942*, 5822.

Thionyl chloride   SOCl₂

Dehydration

750.

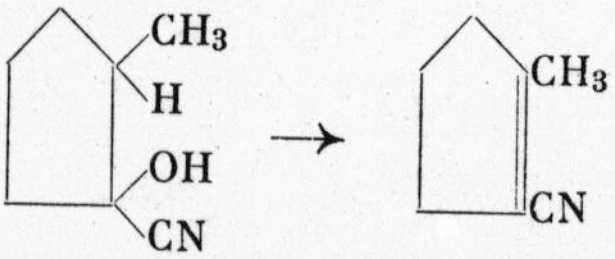

2-Methyl-cyclopentanonecyanohydrin is treated with SOCl₂ in C₅H₅N → 2-methyl-1-cyclopentene-1-carbonitrile. Y = 60%. L. E. King and R. Robinson, *J. Chem. Soc. 1941*, 465; *C.A. 1942*, 462.

Formic acid   HCOOH

751.

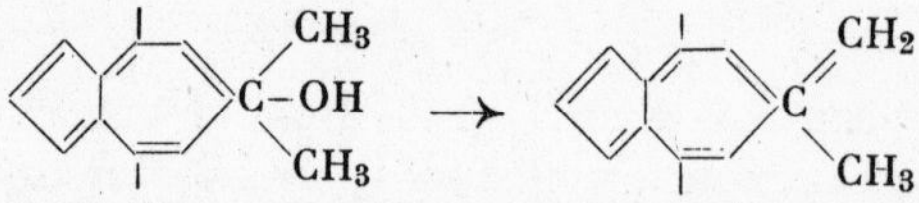

4,8-Dimethyl-6-hydroxy-(isopropyl)azulene (1.53 g.) (prepn., see 682) is heated for 1 hr. on a water bath with HCOOH → 0.99 g. 4,8-dimethyl-6-isopropylazulene. P. A. Plattner and H. Roniger, *Helv. Chim. Acta 26*, 905 (1943); *C.A. 1944*, 1487.

Glacial acetic acid   CH₃COOH

Wieland's Degradation of Bile Acids

752.

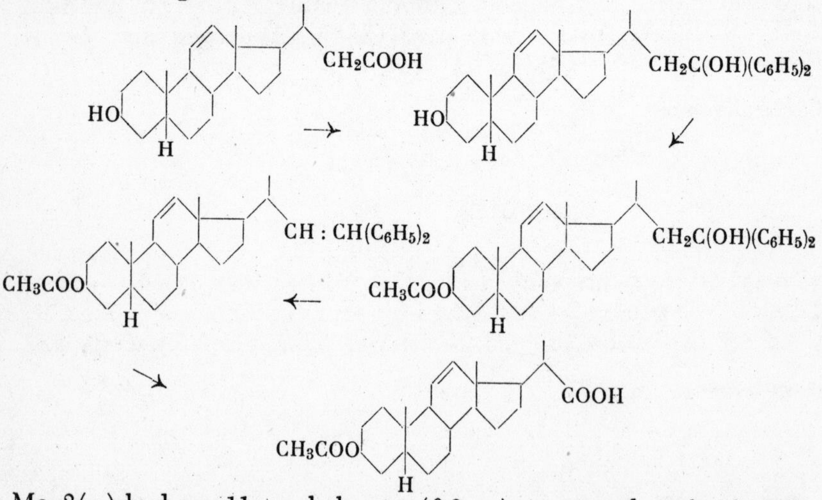

Me 3(α)-hydroxy-11-norcholenate (0.9 g.) is treated with PhMgBr (from Mg, bromobenzene, and ether) → 1.6 g. crude carbinol, which

is treated with Ac_2O in C_5H_5N at room temp. $\to$ 1.6 g. crude acetoxy derivative. This is boiled with glacial AcOH for 2 hrs. $\to$ 0.8 g. of the ethylene derivative, which is treated with CrO_3 in $CHCl_3$–glacial AcOH $\to$ 0.25 g. crude 3(α)-acetoxy-11-bisnorcholenic acid. Also: Me 3(α)-hydroxy-11-cholenate $\to$ 3(α)-acetoxy-11-norcholenic acid. P. Grandjean and T. Reichstein, *Helv. Chim. Acta* 26, 482 (1943), *C.A. 1944*, 1520. Methods: Barbier and Loquin, *Compt. rend.* 156, 1443 (1913); Borwet, *Bull. soc. chim. Mém.* [4]**17**, 202 (1915). For further literature see original.

753.

Me 3(β), 11(α)-dihydroxybisnorcholanate in abs. C_6H_6 and PhMgBr in ether are refluxed for 4 hrs. $\to$ diphenyl-[3(β), 11(α)-dihydroxy-ternorcholanyl]carbinol (crude) which is acetylated with Ac_2O in C_5H_5N $\to$ crude acetate deriv. which is refluxed for 2 hrs. in glacial AcOH $\to$ [3(β)-acetoxy-11(α)-hydroxyetiocholanyl]methyldiphenyl-ethylene (s.m. 414). Y = 61%. J. v. Euw, A. Lardon and T. Reichstein, *Helv. Chim. Acta* 27, 821 (1944); *C.A. 1945*, 938.

Potassium bisulfate $KHSO_4$

Dehydration $\cdot CH_2CH(OH) \cdot \to \cdot CH : CH \cdot$

754. Et cyclohexanol-1-acetate is heated with $KHSO_4$ at 150° $\to$ Et $\Delta^{1,2}$-cyclohexenylacetate. Y = 65–70%. P. Galimberti and S. Ponzini, *Gazz. chim. ital.* 72, 125 (1942); *C.A. 1943*, 2717.

Sulfuric acid H_2SO_4

Acridines   O

755.

2,5-Cl(O_2N)C_6H_3Ac, p-$H_2NC_6H_4NHAc$, and anhyd. K_2CO_3 are heated at 125° for 3 hrs. $\to$ 4-nitro-4'-acetamide-2-acetyldiphenylamine (Y = 72%), which is heated at 125° in glacial AcOH with concd. H_2SO_4 for 2.5 hrs. $\to$ 2-nitro-7-amino-9-methylacridine (Y = 94%). F.e.s. W. Sharp, M. M. J. Sutherland and F. J. Wilson, *J. Chem. Soc. 1943*, 344; *C.A. 1943*, 6666.

756.

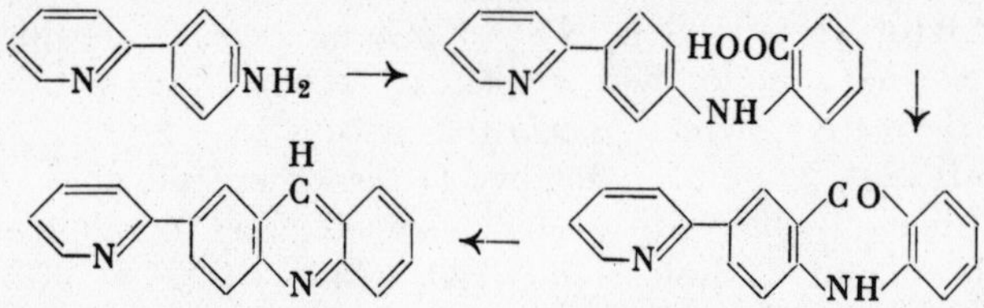

α-(4-Aminophenyl)pyridine (6 g.) is refluxed with o-ClC$_6$H$_4$CO$_2$H and K$_2$CO$_3$ in AmOH → 5.5 g. 4-α-pyridyldiphenylamine-2'-carboxylic acid, 5 g. of which is heated at 100° with concd. H$_2$SO$_4$ → 4.8 g. 4-α-pyridylacridone; 3 g. of the latter is reduced with Al–Hg in 95% EtOH and the reduction product is oxidized with FeCl$_3$ → 0.8 g. 3-α-pyridylacridine. F.e.s. A. H. Cook, I. M. Heilbron and A. Spinks, *J. Chem. Soc. 1943*, 417; *C.A. 1944*, 105.

Iodine I_2

Dehydration $\cdot CH_2CH(OH)\cdot \rightarrow \cdot CH=CH\cdot$

757. Et-2-methyl-3-propyl-3-hexanoate (prepn., see 677) is refluxed with I$_2$ → Et 2-methyl-3-propyl-3-hexanoate (s.m. 696). Y = 83%. F.e.s. J. Colonge and D. Joly, *Ann. Chim.* [11] *18*, 306 (1943); *C.A. 1944*, 5203.

Hydrofluoric acid   *HF*

Cyclization   O

758.

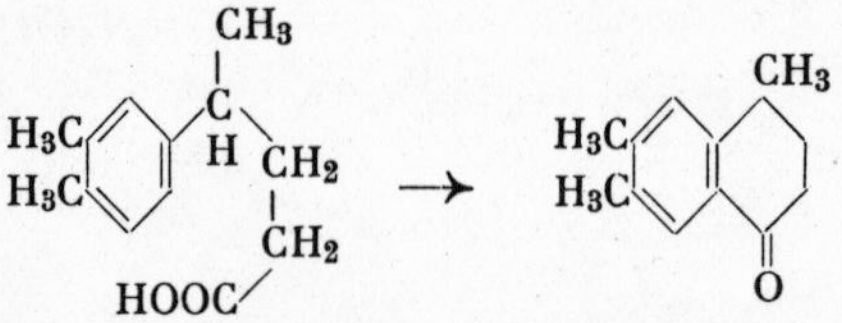

4-(3,4-Dimethylphenyl)pentanoic acid is treated with HF at room temp. (Y = 69%), or with H$_2$SO$_4$ on a steam bath → 4,6,7-trimethyl-1-tetralone (s.m. 784). F.e.s. W. P. Campbell and M. D. Soffer, *J. Am. Chem. Soc. 64*, 417 (1942); *C.A. 1942*, 1922.

759.

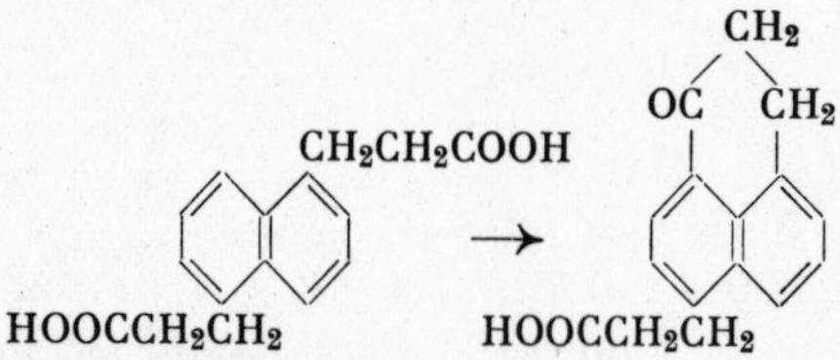

1,5-Naphthalenedipropionic acid is added to cooled HF and slowly heated to room temp. over a period of 15 hrs. → Et 1-perinaphthindanone-7-propionate. $Y = 93\%$. G. Lock and E. Walter, *Ber. 75*, 1158 (1942); *C.A. 1943*, 4720.

760.

2-(*p*-Methylbenzyl)benzoic acid with HF → 2-methyl-9-anthrone. $Y = 84\%$. F.e.s. L. F. Fieser and H. Heymann, *J. Am. Chem. Soc. 64*, 376 (1942); *C.A. 1942*, 1925.

761.

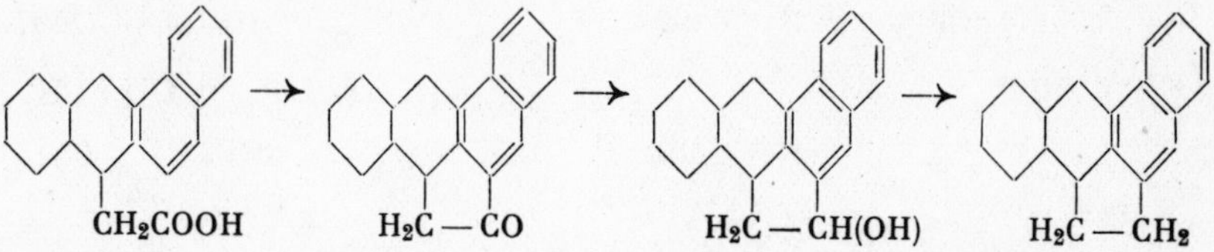

Cyclization of 5,6,7,8,8a,9,10,10a-octahydro-1,2-benzanthracene-10-acetic acid with HF → 4a'-keto-5,6,7,8,8a,9,10,10a-octahydro-4,10-ace-1,2-benzanthrene ($Y = 61\%$), which is reduced with (iso-PrO)$_3$Al in Bz and isopropyl alc. → 4a'-hydroxy-5,6,7,8,8a,9,10,10a-octahydro-4,10-ace-1,2-benzanthracene ($Y = 97\%$). Dehydrogenation with palladized charcoal in 1-C$_{10}$H$_7$Me → 4,10-ace-1,2-benzanthracene ($Y = 60\%$). F.e.s. L. F. Fieser and F. C. Novello, *J. Am. Chem. Soc. 64*, 802 (1942); *C.A. 1942*, 3171.

Hydrochlorides of bases

Indole Ring

762.

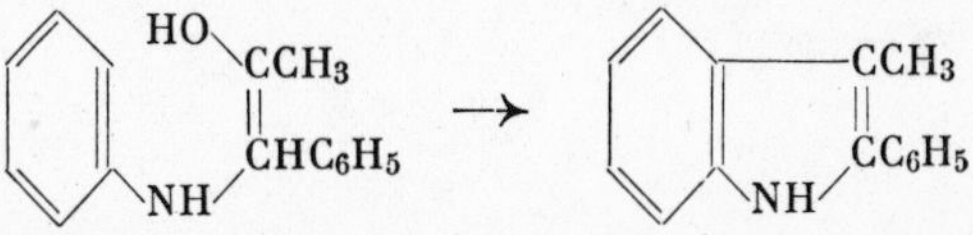

1-Phenyl-1-phenylamino-2-propanone is heated at 160° for 0.5 hr. with an equal amount of aniline · HCl → 2-phenyl-3-methylindole. $Y = 98\%$. F.e.s. P. E. Verkade and E. F. J. Janetzy, *Rec. trav. chim. 62*, 775 (1943); *C.A. 1944*, 6285. See also, *Rec. trav. chim. 62*, 763 (1943).

Quinoline Ring

763.

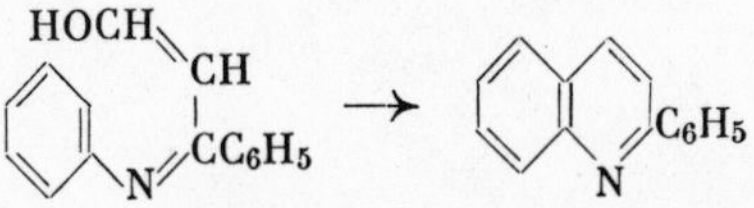

Cyclization of aniline methylene ketones (aniline derivatives of aromatic hydroxymethylene ketones) which does not succeed by ordinary

methods, proceeds smoothly when the Na derivatives of the hydroxymethylene ketones (or their aniline derivs.) are treated with an excess
of aniline and $ZnCl_2$ or aniline · HCl and heated at 180°. Ex: Hydroxy-
methyleneacetophenone → 2-phenylquinoline; Y = 25%. Hydroxy-
methylenebutyrophenone → 2-phenyl-3-ethyl-quinoline; Y = 40%.
M. Montagne and M. Roch, *Compt. rend.* 213, 620 (1941); *C.A. 1944,*
6286.

Hydrochloric acid–glacial acetic acid   HCl–CH₃COOH

Dehydration   · CH₂CH(OH) · → · CH : CH ·

764.

Inactive hydroxyl groups in the 11-position of sterols can be split off
as water with mineral acids. Ex: 11-hydroxyprogesterone is refluxed
for 30 min. with a mixture of glacial AcOH and concd. aq. HCl (4 : 1
by vol.) → 4,11-pregnadiene-3,20-dione. Y = 65%. C. W. Shoppee and
T. Reichstein, *Helv. Chim. Acta 24,* 351 (1941); *C.A. 1942, 2261.* See
also, *Helv. Chim. Acta 26,* 1316 (1943); *C.A. 35,* 2526.

Hydrobromic acid–glacial acetic acid   HBr–CH₃COOH
      See 529.

Palladized charcoal   *Pd*
      See 761.

Via carboxylic acid esters
      See 733–735.

Via sulfates
      See 740.

Via xanthates
      737.

Nitrogen ⅄   CC ⇑ N
Without additional reagents
Pyrimidine Ring from Dihydrotriazine Ring

765.

$$
\begin{array}{ccc}
\underset{\text{C}_6\text{H}_5}{\overset{\text{C}_6\text{H}_5}{\diagdown}}\text{C}\diagup\text{CH}_3 & & \underset{\text{C}_6\text{H}_5}{\diagdown}\text{C} \\
\text{N}\diagup\quad\diagdown\text{NH} & \rightarrow & \text{N}\diagup\quad\diagdown\text{CH} \\
\text{C}_6\text{H}_5\text{C}\diagdown_\text{N}\diagup\text{CC}_6\text{H}_5 & & \text{C}_6\text{H}_5\text{C}\diagdown_\text{N}\diagup\text{CC}_6\text{H}_5
\end{array}
$$

2,4,6-Triphenyl-2-methyl-1,2-dihydro-1,3,5-triazine (prepn., see 285) heated at 300° → 2,4,6-triphenylpyrimidine. F.e.s. R. M. Anker and A. H. Cook, *J. Chem. Soc. 1941*, 323; *C.A. 1941*, 6260.

Potassium hydroxide   KOH
Nitroethylene Compounds
from Pseudo Nitrosites   · CH(NO) · CH(NO$_2$) · → · CH : C(NO$_2$) ·

766.

$$
\begin{array}{ccc}
\overset{\text{OCH}_2\text{C}_6\text{H}_5}{\underset{\text{CH(NO)CH(NO}_2)\text{CH}_3}{\bigcirc\text{OCH}_2\text{C}_6\text{H}_5}} & \rightarrow & \overset{\text{OCH}_2\text{C}_6\text{H}_5}{\underset{\text{CH : C(NO}_2)\text{CH}_3}{\bigcirc\text{OCH}_2\text{C}_6\text{H}_5}}
\end{array}
$$

3,4-Dibenzyloxypropenylbenzene-ψ-nitrosite (prepn., see 292) is shaken with lukewarm, 8% KOH → 1-(3,4-dibenzyloxyphenyl)-2-nitropropene. Y = 90%. G. Bruckner and G. v. Fodor, *Ber. 76*, 466 (1943); *C.A. 1943*, 6656. See also, G. v. Fodor, *Ber. 76*, 1216 (1943); *C.A. 1945*, 286.

Sulfuric acid   H$_2$SO$_4$
α-Substituted Acrylic Acids from Substituted Malonic Acids

767.

$$
\begin{array}{ccccc}
\underset{\text{CH}_3}{\overset{\text{CH}_3}{\diagdown}}\text{CHCH}\diagup^{\text{COOH}}_{\diagdown\text{COOH}} & \rightarrow & \underset{\text{CH}_3}{\overset{\text{CH}_3}{\diagdown}}\text{CH}\cdot\text{C}\cdot\text{CH}_2\cdot\text{N(CH}_3)_2 & \rightarrow & \underset{\text{CH}_3}{\overset{\text{CH}_3}{\diagdown}}\text{CH}\cdot\overset{\cdot}{\text{C}}=\text{CH}_2 \\
& & \diagup^{\text{COOH}}_{\diagdown\text{COOH}}
\end{array}
$$

Isopropylmalonic acid is neutralized with 33.3% (CH$_3$)$_2$NH and, after addition of an equal amount of the acid, the solution is allowed to stand with a 37% HCHO soln. for 3–4 days at 0°. The aminodicarboxylic acid formed is neutralized with NaOH and the soln. boiled for 30 min. while enough H$_2$SO$_4$ is added to keep it acid → α-isopropylacrylic acid (s.m. 457). F. Kögl, J. H. Verbeek, H. Erxleben and W. A. J. Borg, *Z. physiol. Chem. 279*, 121 (1943); *C.A. 1944*, 3978.

Halogen ⚹   CC ⇑ **Hal**

Potassium hydroxide   *KOH*

Polyaryl Condensations

768.

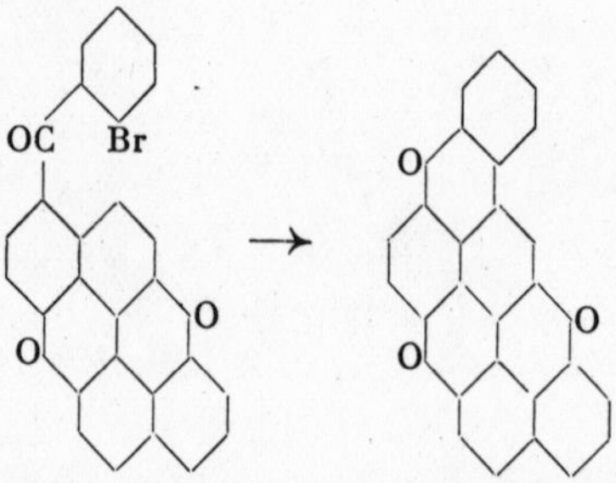

o-Bromobenzoyl-dinaphthalene dioxide (prepn., see 709) is boiled with solid KOH in quinoline → monobenzoylenedinaphthalene dioxide. Crude Y = 79%. F.e.s. R. Pummerer and co-workers, *Ann.* 553, 103 (1942); *C.A. 1943, 5059.*

Potassium alcoholate   *KOR*

New Procedure for Preparation of Polyalkyl Cyclobutanones   O

769. $(C_3H_7)_2CBrCH(CH_3)COCH_2CH_3$ →

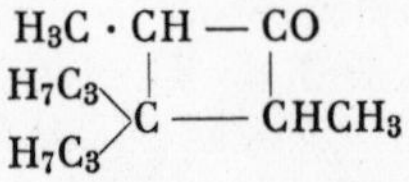

$$H_3C \cdot CH - CO$$
$$H_7C_3 \diagdown C - CHCH_3$$
$$H_7C_3 \diagup$$

β-Bromoketones yield a mixture of the ethylene ketones and the desired cyclobutanones when heated with alcoholic KOH on a water bath. Ex: 4-Methyl-5-propyl-5-bromo-3-octanone → 1,3-dimethyl-2,2-dipropyl-4-cyclobutanone. F.e.s. J. Colonge and D. Joly, *Ann. chim.* [11] *18*, 306 (1943); *C.A. 1944, 5203.*

Potassium carbonate K_2CO_3

Macrocyclic Polymethylene Ketones   O

770.   Three general methods for the synthesis of polymethylene ketones are available:

1. Thermal decomposition of salts of dicarboxylic acids according to L. Ruzicka, M. Stoll and H. Schinz [*Helv. Chim. Acta* 9, 249 (1926); *C.A. 1926, 1792*]. This method is outdated because the others give higher yields.

2. Intermolecular condensation of dinitriles. For a well-tried method, see: K. Ziegler, H. Eberle and H. Ohlinger, *Ann.* 504, 94 (1933); *C.A.*

1934, 117. K. Ziegler and Aurnhammer, *Ann. 513*, 43 (1934); *C.A. 1935*, 746.

3. Cyclization of the metal derivatives of halogen acylacetates with subsequent ketone cleavage.

$$Br(CH_2)_6CH : CH(CH_2)_7COOH \longrightarrow Br(CH_2)_6CH : CH(CH_2)_7COCl \downarrow$$

$$Br(CH_2)_6CH : CH(CH_2)_7COCH_2COOC_2H_5 \longleftarrow \begin{array}{c} Br(CH_2)_6CH : CH(CH_2)_7CO \\ \diagdown \\ CH_3CO \diagup \end{array} CHCOOC_2H_5$$

$$I(CH_2)_6CH : CH(CH_2)_7COCH_2COOC_2H_5 \longrightarrow \begin{array}{c} CH(CH_2)_6CHCOOC_2H_5 \\ \parallel \quad | \\ CH(CH_2)_7CO \end{array} \longrightarrow \begin{array}{c} CH(CH_2)_7 \\ \parallel \qquad \diagdown CO \\ CH(CH_2)_7 \diagup \end{array}$$

Ex: α-16-Bromo-9-hexadecenoic acid (prepn., see 776) is converted to the chloride with $SOCl_2$ and treated with $AcCHNaCO_2Et \rightarrow$ Me α-18-bromo-3-oxo-11-octadecenoate (Y = 60–70%), which with NaI in $Me_2CO \rightarrow$ 18-iodo deriv. K_2CO_3 in methyl ethyl ketone is added over a period of 60 hrs. and the mixture boiled for 24 hrs. $\rightarrow$ Me α-civetone-carboxylate (Y = 86%), with cold MeOH–KOH $\rightarrow$ α-civetone (Y = 86%). H. Hunsdiecker, *Ber. 76*, 142 (1943); *C.A. 1943*, 5403. Methods, see H. Hunsdiecker, *Ber. 75*, 1190 (1942).

771.
$$CH_3OOCCH_2COCH_2CH(CH_3)[CH_2]_{11}Br(I) \longrightarrow \begin{array}{c} CH_3OOCCHCOCH_2CHCH_3 \\ \diagdown [CH_2]_{11} \diagup \end{array}$$

The corresponding iodo derivative of Me 16-bromo-5-methyl-3-oxo-hexadecanoate (prepn., see 649) is added to a mixture of MeEtCO and $K_2CO_3 \rightarrow$ Me *d,l*-muscone-α-carboxylate. Y = 68%. H. Hunsdiecker, *Ber. 75*, 1197 (1942); *C.A. 1943*, 4697.

Copper   *Cu*

Cleavage of Iodine
    See 668.

Copper compounds

Elimination of Bromine and Replacement of Bromine by CN

772.
$$Br\langle \rangle CHBrCHBr\langle \rangle Br \rightarrow Br\langle \rangle CH : CH\langle \rangle Br \rightarrow$$
$$NC\langle \rangle CH : CH\langle \rangle CN$$

1,2-Dibromo-1,2-bis(*p*-bromophenyl)ethane (I) is refluxed for 1 hr. with CuCl in $C_5H_5N \rightarrow$ 4,4'-dibromostilbene (Y = 72%), 8.2 g. of which is refluxed with CuCN and C_5H_5N for 1 hr. in a metal bath at 220° $\rightarrow$ 3.6 g. of 4,4'-dicyanostilbene. Or: (I) is refluxed with 4 moles CuCN and C_5H_5N at a bath temperature of 200–210 for 1.5 hrs. and heated once more after further addition of C_5H_5N → 4,4'-dicyanostilbene (Y = 70%). F.e.s. S. Bance, H. J. Barber and A. M. Woolman, *J. Chem. Soc.* *1943*, 1; *C.A.* *1943*, 2002.

Organic bases

Elimination of HBr　　　　　　　　· CH_2CHBr · → · CH : CH ·
See 645.

773. Monobromoheptene (prepn., see 413) is slowly distilled with quinoline → 2-methyl-2,4-hexadiene. Y = 68%. F.e.s. K. Ziegler and co-workers, *Ann.* *551*, 80 (1942); *C.A.* *1943*, 5032.

774.

trans-2-Decalone (2.78 g.) is treated with Br in glacial AcOH or $CHCl_3$ → 2.85 g. dibromo-*trans*-2-decalone, which is heated with collidine → 0.8 g. *ar*-2-tetralol. 1.2 g. 1-decalone with Br → 2.43 g. dibromo-*trans*-1-decalone, 1.76 g. of which is heated with collidine → 0.51 g. *ar*-1-tetralol. F. Galinovsky, *Ber.* *76*, 230 (1943); *C.A.* *1943*, 5716.

Zinc　　　　　　　　　　　　　　　　　　　　　　　　　　　　Zn

1-Alkylenes from Alkylbromides.
Lengthening Chain by 2 C Atoms

$$CH_3(CH_2)_{12}CH_2MgBr + BrCH_2CHBrOCH_2CH_3 \longrightarrow$$
775.
$$CH_3(CH_2)_{13}CH = CH_2 \longleftarrow CH_3(CH_2)_{13}CH(OC_2H_5)CH_2Br$$

The Grignard compound of tetradecyl bromide is added to CH_2Br-CHBrOEt → 1-tetradecyl-2-bromoethyl Et ether (Y = 60%), which is refluxed with Zn dust → 1-hexadecene (Y = 62.5%). F.e.s. C. Niemann and C. D. Wagner, *J. Org. Chem.* *7*, 227 (1942); *C.A.* *1942*, 5136. Methods, see Boord and co-workers; *C.Z.* *1933*, II, 2253.

Elimination of Bromine　　　　　　· CHBr · CHBr → · CH : CH ·
776. α-θ,6,o-Tribromopalmitic acid is treated with Zn dust in MeOH containing a little glacial AcOH–HBr → α-16-bromo-9-hexadecenoic acid (s.m. 770). Y = 61%. The only terminal Br atom is not eliminated. H. Hunsdiecker, *Ber.* *76*, 142 (1943); *C.A.* *1943*, 5403.

7.

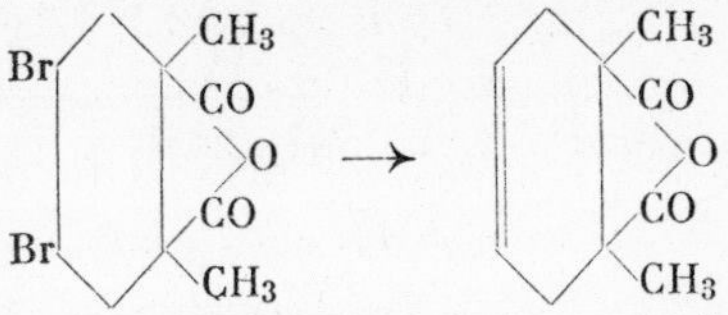

1,2-Dimethyl-4,5-dibromohexahydrophthalic anhydride is boiled with Zn wool in MeOH for 2 hrs. → 1,2-dimethyl-1,2,3,6-tetrahydrophthalic anhydride. Y = 90%. K. Ziegler and co-workers, *Ann. 551*, 1 (1942); *C.A. 1943*, 5376.

Stannic chloride $SnCl_4$

Cyclizations   O

8.

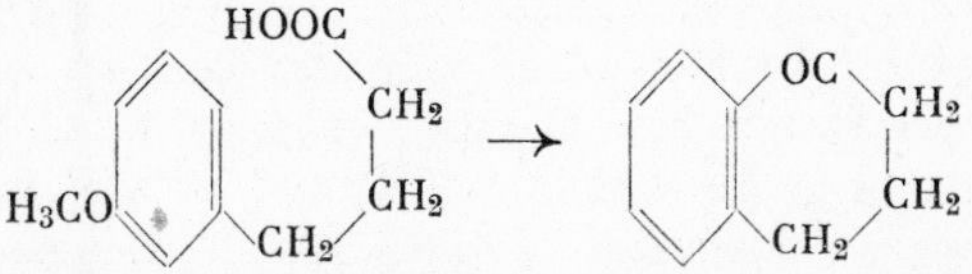

γ-(*m*-Anisyl)butyric acid is treated with PCl_5 in C_6H_6 → α-(*m*-anisyl)butyric acid chloride, which when treated with $SnCl_4$ in the cold → 6-methoxy-1-keto-1,2,3,4-tetrahydronaphthalene. Y = 96%. W. E. Bachmann and D. G. Thomas, *J. Am. Chem. Soc. 64*, 94 (1942); *C.A. 1942*, 5327.

9.

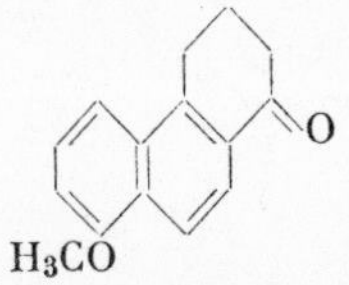

γ-(6-Methoxy-1-naphthyl)butyric acid chloride is treated with $SnCl_4$ in cold benzene → 7-methoxy-1-keto-1,2,3,4-tetrahydrophenanthrene. Y = 90–95%. W. E. Bachmann, Wayne Cole and A. L. Wilds, *J. Am. Chem. Soc. 62*, 824 (1940); *C.A. 1940*, 3757.

30.

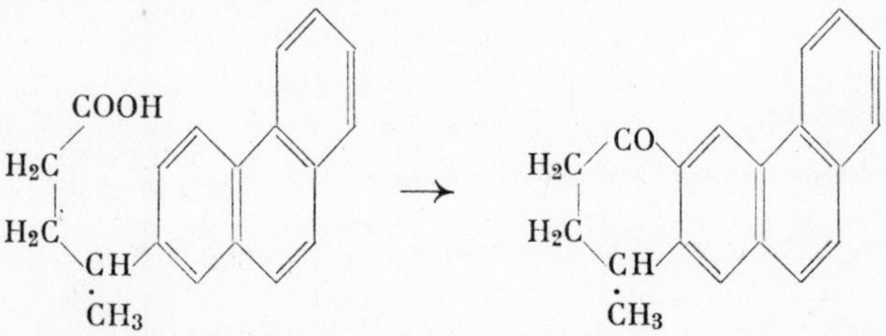

γ-(3-Phenanthryl)valeric acid (prepn., see 629) is treated with PCl_5 in C_6H_6 → γ-(3-phenanthryl)valeric acid chloride. Cyclization in the presence of $SnCl_4$ in C_6H_6 → 5-keto-8-methyl-5,6,7,8-tetrahydro-1,2-benzanthracene. Y = 88%. W. E. Bachmann and J. M. Chemerda, *J. Org. Chem. 6*, 36 (1941); *C.A. 1941*, 2504.

Via intermediate products

Elimination of Hydrobromic Acid from Higher Alkyl Halides without Shifting Double Bond   · CH_2 · $CHBr$ → · $CH : CH$ ·

781. The elimination of halogen acid from alkyl halides of high molecular weight is effected in relatively good yields and, in general, without appreciable migration of the double bond when the halide is treated with Ag stearate or palmitate at 200–250° in C_6H_6. The corresponding fatty acid esters are formed, which split into the fatty acid and olefin at higher temperatures. Ex: Dodecyl bromide in C_6H_6 is heated with a slight excess of Ag stearate for 24 hrs. at 200° in a Ag-coated shaking autoclave → dodecene. Y = 80–83%. F. Asinger, *Ber. 75*, 660 (1942); *C.A. 1942*, 6135–6136. Also, *Ber. 75*, 664, 668 (1942).

Sulfur ⅄   CC ⇑ S

Without additional reagents

Elimination of Sulfur Dioxide
See 615, 713.

Carbon ⅄   CC ⇑ C

Without additional reagents

Carboxylic Acid Esters from α-Keto Esters   · $COCOOR$ → · $COOR$
See 561.

Barium hydroxide $Ba(OH)_2$

Cyclic Ketones from Carboxylic Acids   O

782.
$$HOOC \cdot CH_2CH(CH_2)_2COOH \quad \overset{|}{\underset{CH_3}{}} \quad \rightarrow \quad \begin{array}{c} H_2C - CH_2 \\ | \quad\quad >CO \\ H_3CHC - CH_2 \end{array}$$

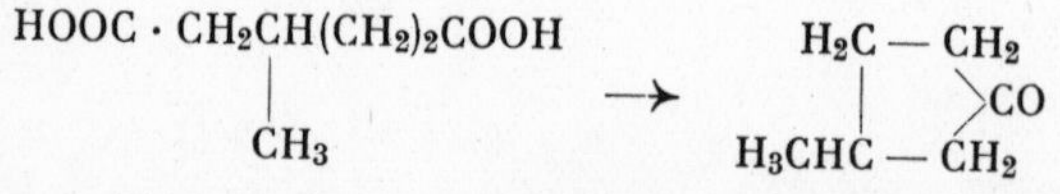

β-Methyladipic acid is heated at 285–295° with $Ba(OH)_2$ → 3-methylcyclopentanone. Y = 70%. C. S. Marvel and L. A. Brooks, *J. Am. Chem. Soc. 63*, 2630 (1941); *C.A. 1942*, 416. Methods: Thorpe and Kon, *Organic Syntheses, Coll. Vol. I*, 187.

Acetic anhydride $(CH_3CO)_2O$

Ring Contraction

3.

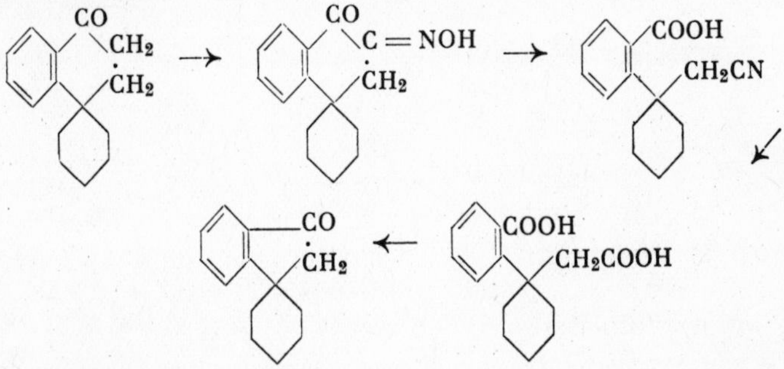

Spiro[cyclohexane-1,1'-tetralin]-4'-one is treated with BuONO and HCl in alcohol–ether at 30–35° → isonitrosospiro[cyclohexane-1,1'-tetralin]-4'-one (Y = 71%). A rearrangement with p-MeC$_6$H$_4$SO$_2$Cl in 10% alc. suspension → 1-o-carboxyphenylcyclohexaneacetonitrile (Y = 90%). Refluxing with 10% aq. NaOH for 12 hrs. on a sand bath → 1-o-carboxyphenylcyclohexaneacetic acid (Y = 84%). When this is slowly heated to 160° with Ac$_2$O according to Blanc → spiro[cyclohexane-1,1'-indan]-3'-one (Y = 85%). M. Levitz, D. Perlman and M. T. Bogert, *J. Org. Chem.* 6, 105 (1941); *C.A. 1941*, 2498.

Powdered glass

Carboxylic Acid Esters from α-Keto Esters   · CO · COOR → · COOR

4.

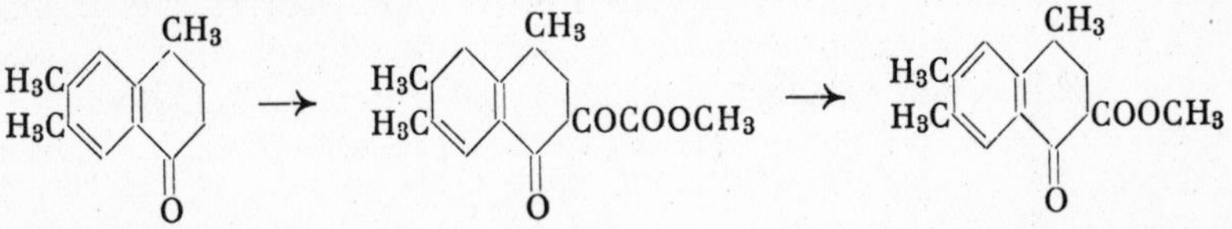

4,6,7-Trimethyl-1-tetralone (prepn., see 758) is treated with Na-(CO$_2$Me)$_2$ in MeOH → Me 4,6,7-trimethyl-1-tetralone-2-glyoxylate (Y = 85%), which is heated with powdered glass at 180° → 4,6,7-trimethyl-2-carbomethoxy-1-tetralone (Y = 83%). W. P. Campbell and M. D. Soffer, *J. Am. Chem. Soc.* 64, 417 (1942); *C.A. 1942*, 1922.

5. Me 7-methoxy-1-keto-1,2,3,4-tetrahydrophenanthrene-2-glyoxalate is stirred with glass powder at 140–150° and heated for 10 min. at 180° → Me 7-methoxy-1-keto-1,2,3,4-tetrahydro-2-phenanthroate. Y = 90–94%. W. E. Bachmann, Wayne Cole and A. L. Wilds, *J. Am. Chem. Soc.* 62, 824 (1940); *C.A. 1940, 3757*.

Heteropolar Bond

Addition

Additon to Nitrogen   Het ⇓ N

Methylammonium Salts

$$R_3N \longrightarrow R_3 \diagdown N^+I^-$$
$$R'\diagup$$

786. Tribenzylamine is heated for 7 hrs. at 80° in a sealed tube with MeI → tribenzylmethylammonium iodide. Y = 80%. L. Birkofer, *Ber. 75*, 429 (1942); *C.A. 1943*, 3067.

Methylacridinium Salts

$$C_5H_5N^+Cl^-$$
$$|$$
$$R$$

787. 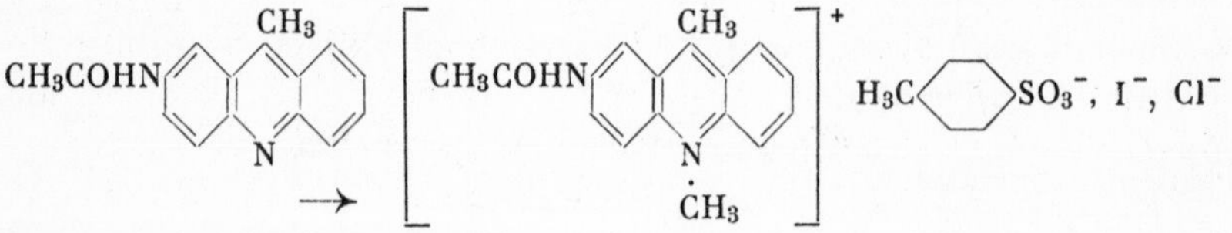
$$\longrightarrow$$
$$H_3C\langle \rangle SO_3^-, \; I^-, \; Cl^-$$

2-Acetimide-9-methylacridine (1 g.) and $p\text{-}MeC_6H_4SO_3Me$ are heated at 145° for 2 hrs. with occasional stirring → 0.7 g. of the methyl-p-toluene sulfonate. 2 g. of this after hydrolysis with HCl is treated with KI → 1 g. methiodide derivative, which is refluxed for 8 hrs. with excess AgCl in aq. MeOH → 0.7 g. 2-amino-9-methylacridinemethyl chloride. F.e.s. W. Sharp, M. M. J. Sutherland and F. J. Wilson, *J. Chem. Soc. 1943*, 344; *C.A. 1943*, 6666.

Soluble Derivatives of Insoluble Azo Dyes

788. By treating the monoazo derivatives of β-naphthols with chloroacetyl chloride or nicotinic acid in the presence of $SOCl_2$, esters are formed which can be converted into water-soluble quarternary salts by treatment with pyridine (or MeI). The starting dye can easily be recovered by treatment with alkali. W. H. Ufimzew, *J. Applied Chem. U.S.S.R. 14*, 600 (1941); *C.A. 1942*, 3361, 4110.

Synthesis Via Pyridinium Salts
α,β-Unsaturated Aldehydes   · CH = CH · CHO
    See 197.

α-Keto Aldehydes from α-Halogen Ketones   · COCH₂Br → · COCHO

See 198–199.

Indole and Pyrrole Carboxylic Acids   · COCH₂Br → · COOH

89.

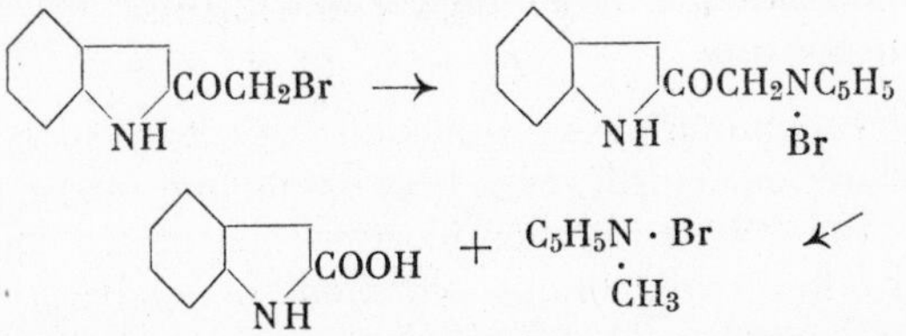

Indacyl- and pyrracylpyridinium bromides are split by alkali similarly to phenacyl derivatives (compare, Kröhnke, *C.Z. 1943*, I, 3196). The yields are quantitative which makes this reaction attractive for the preparation of the indole- and pyrrolecarboxylic acids. Ex: β-Indacyl bromide and pyridine → β-indacylpyridinium bromide (s.m. 199) [*Gazz. chim. ital. 59*, 169, 838 (1929)], which with aq. alc. NaOH → β-indolecarboxylic acid. G. Sanna, *Gazz. chim. ital. 72*, 357 (1942); *C.A. 1943*, 6662.

Addition to Sulfur   Het ⇓ S

Sulfonium Salts

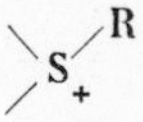

90. Sulfides are allowed to stand for 1–3 days at room temp. with an excess MeI in 1–2 vol. Me₂CO in the dark → Me-sulfonium iodides. Sulfides with an excess of EtI for 2–3 weeks at room temp. in the dark → Et-sulfonium iodides. Sulfides with the equimol. amount Me₂SO₄ in 10% benzene soln. at room temp. → sulfonium methosulfates. Sulfonium halides or methosulfates with Na picrate in H₂O → sulfonium picrates. F.e.s. V. Prelog, V. Hahn, H. Brauchli and H. C. Beyermann, *Helv. Chim. Acta 27*, 1209 (1944); *C.A. 1946*, 848.

Exchange   Het ⇈

p-Bromobenzyl Pseudo Thiuronium Salts

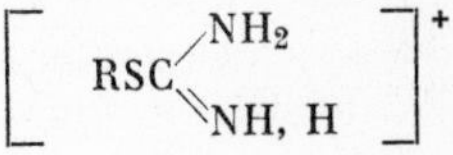

91.

$$BrC_6H_4CH_2SC\diagdown^{NH_2}_{NH} \quad , HBr$$

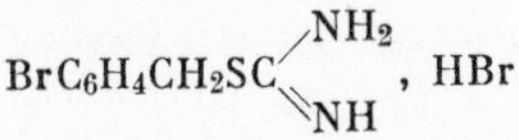

A hot EtOH solution of p-bromobenzyl-ω-thiuronium bromide is added to an aqueous solution of the Na or K salt of a carboxylic acid; if the free acid is used, NaOH or KOH is added for neutralization. The salt precipitates at once in the pure state and may be crystallized from EtOH. Ex: Acetate, butyrate, oxalate, phthalate. F.e.s. B. T. Dewey and H. G. Shasky, *J. Am. Chem. Soc. 63*, 3526 (1941); *C.A. 1942*, 1011.

Benzylthiuronium Salts of Aldehyde and Ketone Bisulfite Compounds

792. As the bisulfite compounds of aldehydes and ketones can only rarely be recrystallized and hardly ever possess definite melting points, they do not lend themselves for identification purposes. Their benzylthiuronium salts, however, can be obtained for analysis; these possess characteristic melting points. Since the excess $NaHSO_3$ interferes with the isolation of the salt, an excess must not be used, or the bisulfite compd. must first be isolated before it is treated with a 10% aq. benzylthiuronium hydrochloride soln., which is slightly acidified with a trace of HCl to avoid hydrolysis. The recovery of the carbonyl compound takes place simply by heating in HCl soln. A. v. Wacek and K. Kratzl, *Ber. 76*, 1209 (1943); *C.A. 1945*, 284.

Diazonium Salts

See 256-259.

Remaining Reactions

Tertiary Amines from Quarternary Ammonium Salts

793.   HOOC⟨⟩N(CH₃)₃Cl $\rightarrow$ HOOC⟨⟩N(CH₃)₂

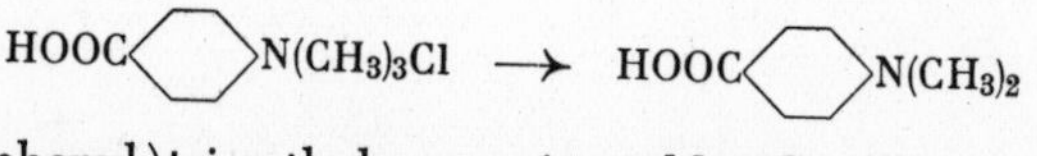

(p-Carboxyphenyl)trimethylammonium chloride (2 g.) is refluxed with Na and abs. EtOH for 3 hrs. $\rightarrow$ 1.5 g. p-$Me_2NC_6H_4CO_2H$. A. Zaki and W. Tadros, *J. Chem. Soc. 1941*, 562; *C.A. 1942*, 420.

SUBJECT INDEX

This index is arranged in a bilateral system. It lists first a specific compound or compound group under the heading *from*, from which starting material it can be synthesized. It lists under *s.m.* the compounds for which the main entry is a starting material. Example: Acridones, *s.m.* acridines—is interpreted as *acridones are the starting material for the synthesis of acridines.*

229

Beckmann rearrangement 153
Benzanthracenes 780
Benzanthrones, substituted 589
Benzene derivatives, see Aryl derivatives
Benzene ring, synthesis of, see Alicyclic compounds
Benzil compounds
— from
 benzoins 156
 carboxylic acid chlorides 684
Benzimidazole derivatives of
 sugars 340
Benzoins
— from
 aldehydes 513
— s.m.
 benzil compounds 156
Benzopyrylium salts 603
Benzoylation, see Acylation
Benzyl cyanides
— s.m.
 diphenylhydroxysuccinic acid
 mononitrile 517
Benzylthiuronium salts
— of bisulfite addition compounds of
 aldehydes and ketones 792
— see also
 p-bromobenzylthiuronium salts
Berrylium sulfate, anhydrous 742
Bicyclooctane ring system 528
Bisaryl ethanes 588
Bisaryls, see Diaryls
Biuret derivatives, substituted
— from
 uretediones 283
Blaise-Guérin, degradation of carboxylic acids 249
Boric acid 621
Borofluoride CC ⇊ O, 177
Bouveault-Blanc reduction 64
Bromacetamide 405
Bromides, see Halogen compounds,
 Replacement
Bromination, see Replacement of
 hydrogen by halogens
Bromine 35
Bromine compounds, see Halogen
 compounds
α-Bromoacetyl compounds, see
 α-Halogen ketones

p-Bromobenzylthiuronium salts 791
α-Bromocarboxylic acids
— from
 carboxylic acids 416, 451
— s.m.
 α-amino alcohols 75
 α-iodocarboxylic acids 451
 mercaptocarboxylic acids 496
Bromo fatty acids, see α-Bromocarboxylic acids
5-Bromo-2-pyrrolecarboxylic acids
— s.m.
 hydroxypyrroles 227
ω-Bromostyrol
— s.m.
 ethinyl alcohols 719
N-Bromosuccinimide as additional
 reagent
— bromination 413
— introduction of the double bond
 CC ⇑ H
Bunte salts, see Alkyl thiosulfates

C

Calcium chloride 518
Calcium hydroxide 33
Calcium oxide 575
Carbamic acid esters, see Urethans
Carbazoles
— from
Carbohydrates
— cleavage 386
— deacetylation HO ⇊ C
— derivatives
 benzimidazoles 340
 quinoxalines 386
 triazoles 614
— hydration 49
— ring opening 134
— see also
 acetobromo sugars
 glycosides
 mercaptals from sugars
 methyl saccharides
 monoses
 polysaccharides, methylated
Carbonates, see Alkyl carbonates
Carbon dioxide, Grignard syntheses
 685–86
Carbon rings, see Alicyclic compounds

Carboxylic acid amides
— *from*
  carboxylic acid esters 306–07
  carboxylic acids 303–05, 352
  — increasing the C chain by 1 C
      atom (subst. amides) 631
  hydrazides (subst. amides) 359
  ketones 151–52, 362
  nitriles 135
  — and carboxylic acids 280
  nitroso compounds 298
— *see also*
  barbituric acid derivatives
— *s.m.*
  aldehydes 72
  amines 72
  nitriles 394–95
Carboxylic acid anhydrides
— *from*
  carboxylic acids 178
  dicarboxylic acids 645
— *s.m.*
  carboxylic acid chlorides 423–24
  dicarboxylic acids, increasing the
    C chain by 2 C atoms 650
Carboxylic acid chlorides
— *from*
  carboxylic acid anhydrides 423–24
  carboxylic acids HalC $\Uparrow$ O
— *s.m.*
  aldehydes 99–102
  benzil compounds 684
  α-diazo ketones CC $\Uparrow$ Hal without
    additional reagents
  α-halogen ketones 623–25
  thiocarboxylic acids 491
Carboxylic acid esters, *see also* Carboxylic acids
— *from*
  alcohols 215–16
  carboxylic acids OC $\Uparrow$ O, 182,
    186–87, 203–04, 306
  α-ketocarboxylic acid esters, 561,
    784–85
— hydrolysis HO $\Uparrow$ C
— *see also*
  acetobromo sugars
  O-acetylhydroxy amino acids
  alkyl carbonates
  α-alkyl α-cyanocarboxylic acid
    esters

arylacetic acid esters
arylglyoxylic acid esters
α-aryl-α-hydroxycarboxylic acid
  esters
α-cyanocarboxylic acid esters
α-halogen dicarboxylic acid esters
β-hydroxycarboxylic acid esters
ketocarboxylic acid esters
lactones
malonic acid ester, disubstituted
— *s.m.*
  barbituric acids 315, 325–26
  carbonyl compounds CC $\Uparrow$ O
  carboxylic acid amides 306–07
  hydrazides 110, 308
  α-ketocarboxylic acids 557
Carboxylic acids, *see also* Carboxylic
  acid esters
— *derivatives*
  p-bromobenzyl thiuronium
    salts 791
— *from*
  acetonitriles, substituted, decreas-
    ing the C chain by 1 C atom
    244
  aldehydes 128–29
  alkyl halides, increasing the C
    chain by 1 C atom, 658,
    685–86
  —, increasing the C chain by 2 C
    atoms, malonic ester syn-
    thesis 640–41
  α-bromo ketones, decreasing the C
    chain by 1 C atom 789
  carboxylic acids, decreasing the C
    chain by 1 C atom 752
  —, increasing the C chain by 1 C
    atom CC $\Uparrow$ Hal without
    additional reagents
  α-ketocarboxylic acids CC $\Uparrow$ C
  hydrocarbons 169–172, 530
  methyl ketones 151
  —, decreasing the C chain by 1 C
    atom 237–38, 243
  nitriles 188–89, 393, 783
— *see also*
  acrylic acids, substituted
  aminocarboxylic acids
  α-bromocarboxylic acids
  5-bromo-2-pyrrolecarboxylic acids
  carboxylic acids, α,β-unsaturation